Mastering

Mathematics for Electrical and Electronic Engineering

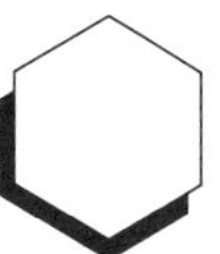

Macmillan Master Series

Accounting
Arabic
Astronomy
Background to Business
Banking
Basic Management
Biology
British Politics
Business Communication
Business Law
Business Microcomputing
C Programming
Catering Science
Catering Theory
Chemistry
COBOL Programming
Commerce
Computer Programming
Computers
Economic and Social History
Economics
Electrical Engineering
Electronics
English as a Foreign Language
English Grammar
English Language
English Literature
French 1
French 2
German 1
German 2
Hairdressing
Human Biology
Italian 1
Italian 2
Japanese
Manufacturing
Marketing
Mathematics
Mathematics for Electrical and Electronic Engineering
Modern British History
Modern European History
Modern World History
Pascal Programming
Philosophy
Physics
Psychology
Restaurant Service
Science
Secretarial Procedures
Social Welfare
Sociology
Spanish 1
Spanish 2
Spreadsheets
Statistics
Study Skills
Word Processing

Mastering

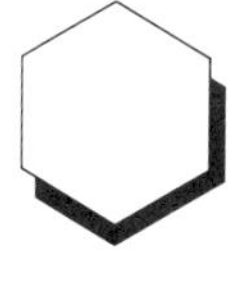

Mathematics for Electrical and Electronic Engineering

Noel M. Morris

MACMILLAN

First published 1994 by
THE MACMILLAN PRESS LTD
Houndmills, Basingstoke, Hampshire RG21 2XS
and London
Companies and representatives
throughout the world

ISBN 0-333-59359-6

A catalogue record for this book is available from the British Library.

Copy-edited and typeset by Povey-Edmondson
Okehampton and Rochdale, England

Printed in China

10 9 8 7 6 5 4 3 2 1
03 02 01 00 99 98 97 96 95 94

To Laura and Alex

Contents

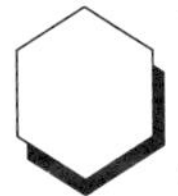

List of figures and tables

Figures

Tables

Preface

Mathematics is an essential tool in the armoury of electrical and electrical technicians and engineers and, in particular, there are certain branches of mathematics which have special relevance to them. This book covers the general background of mathematics, and places special emphasis on the needs of electrical and electronic engineering.

The book attends to the requirements not only of students studying on their own, but also those following BTEC ONC, OND, HNC and HND courses, and will be specially appropriate to A-level students intending to transfer to degree and other courses.

As well as dealing with the essential mathematics of electrical and electronic courses, the book contains a large number of worked examples, which help the reader to explore the subject to greater depth. At the end of each chapter you will find not only many self-test questions (with answers at a later stage), which will help you test your grasp of the subject matter, but also a summary of important facts included in the chapter.

A 'plus' feature of the book is the chapter on SPICE software (Simulation Program with Integrated Circuit Emphasis), which is of special relevance to the solution of all types of circuits. This software is readily available, and a wide range of circuit solutions are described in chapter 16. I am especially indebted to Mr P. Goss, Technical Manager of ARS Microsystems, for his advice and assistance in the matter.

I would like to thank my wife for her support, without which the writing of this book would not have been possible.

NOEL M. MORRIS

How to use this book

Mathematics forms the backbone of Electrical and Electronic Engineering courses, and this book will take the reader through a significant part of his or her education.

The chapters of the book are listed below, together with the type of course for which they are best suited. The symbol **A** designates those suitable for science-based A-level courses, **N** designates those of particular value to BTEC ONC/D courses, and **H** signifies those of interest to BTEC HNC/D courses.

Chapter

1	Fractions, roots and powers – **A**, N
2	Numbers and numbering systems – **A**, **N**, **H**
3	Logarithms, the decibel and the Neper – **A**, **N**, **H**
4	Algebra – **A**, **N**, **H**
5	Simultaneous equations – **A**, N, **H**
6	Trigonometry – **A**, **N**, **H**
7	Further trigonometric skills – **A**, **N**, **H**
8	Mensuration – **A**, N
9	Graphs – **A**, **N**, **H**
10	Vectors and phasors – **A**, **N**, **H**
11	Complex numbers – **A**, **N**, **H**
12	Differentiation – **A**, **N**, **H**
13	Integration – **A**, **N**, **H**
14	Transients in electrical circuits – **A**, **H**
15	Boolean algebra and logic circuits – **A**, **N**, **H**
16	Computer solution of electric circuits – **A**, **N**, **H**

Chapter 16 includes details of one of the most important computer packages for use with electronic and electrical circuit analysis, namely SPICE (Simulation Program with Integrated Circuit Emphasis). There is, however, a wide range of computer packages available for the solution of what otherwise can be very complex problems. For example, DERIVE and MATHCAD are very suitable for the solution of mathematical problems. This type of software is likely to revolutionise the teaching of mathematics.

Most software is available through software houses which advertise in computer magazines. A wide range of very low cost mathematical and scientific software is also available through SHAREWARE suppliers, which are also advertised in computer magazines.

1 Fractions, roots and powers

1.1 Introduction

The word **fraction** means *a part of the whole*, where 'the whole' is the particular size we are dealing with at the time, i.e., it could be the resistance of a resistor, or the current in a conductor, etc.

To fully appreciate the concept of fractions, we also need to appreciate other mathematical features such as prime numbers, factors, lowest common multiple, highest common factor, etc. A knowledge of fractions leads us to the concept of ratios, proportions, percentages, and so on.

By the end of this chapter the reader will be able to

- understand integers, prime numbers and factors,
- manipulate, add, subtract, multiply and divide fractions,
- understand ratios, per cent and per unit values,
- fully appreciate proportions and reciprocals,
- understand the meaning of bases and powers, and work in index notation,
- raise fractions to powers, and deal with fractional powers (roots),
- work in scientific notation.

1.2 Integers, prime numbers, factors and multiples

An **integer** is a **whole number**, i.e., 1, 2, 3, ..., and many integers are the product of two or more other integers. For example $6 = 2 \times 3$, $12 = 6 \times 2 = 3 \times 2 \times 2$, $15 = 3 \times 5$, etc. The integers which are multiplied together to give a higher value are described as **factors** of the higher number. Thus 2 and 3 are factors of 6, 15 has factors of 3 and 5, etc. Reducing a number into its factors is called **factorisation** (see Worked Example 1.1).

Any number which has only the number itself and unity as its factors is known as a **prime number**, e.g. $3 = 1 \times 3$, $5 = 1 \times 5$, etc. The reader should note that *unity is not regarded as a prime number*. Examples of prime numbers include 2, 3, 5, 7, 11, 13, 17, etc.

If we multiply two integers, say $3 \times 7 = 21$, we say that 21 is a **multiple** of 3 and 7, i.e., 3 and 7 are factors of the multiple.

The smallest number that two or more numbers divide into exactly is the **lowest common multiple** (LCM) of the numbers (see Worked Example 1.2).

The largest number which divides exactly into two or more given numbers is the **highest common factor** (HCF) of those numbers (see Worked Example 1.3).

Worked Example 1.1

Determine the prime factors of (a) 44, (b) 178, (c) 495.

Solution

To determine the prime factors of an integer, we divide the number by a prime number (starting with the lowest prime value which will divide into it) as follows

(a) $44 = 2 \times 22 = 2 \times 2 \times 11$
That is, the prime factors of 44 are 2, 2 and 11.
(b) $176 = 2 \times 88 = 2 \times 2 \times 44 = 2 \times 2 \times 2 \times 2 \times 11$
(c) $495 = 3 \times 165 = 3 \times 3 \times 55 = 3 \times 3 \times 5 \times 11$

Worked Example 1.2

What is the LCM of the numbers 50, 66 and 147?

Solution

One of the simplest methods of determining the LCM of the numbers is to reduce each number to its prime numbers as follows

$$\begin{array}{rlllllllll}
50 = & 2 & & \times 5 \times 5 & & = 2 & & \times 5^2 & & \\
66 = & 2 \times 3 & & & \times 11 & = 2 \times 3 & & & & \times 11 \\
147 = & & 3 & \times 7 \times 7 & & = & & & \times 7^2 &
\end{array}$$

The LCM is obtained by multiplying together all the highest power values that occur in the prime number range (powers are fully discussed in sections 1.9–1.11). We see that the highest power of 2 in each number is $2 = 2^1$, the highest power of 3 is $3 = 3^1$, the highest power of 5 is $(5 \times 5) = 5^2$, the highest power of 7 is $(7 \times 7) = 7^2$, and the highest power of 11 is $11 = 11^1$. That is

$$\begin{aligned}
\text{LCM} &= 2 \times 3 \times (5 \times 5) \times (7 \times 7) \times 11 \\
&= 2 \times 3 \times 5^2 \times 7^2 \times 11 = 80\,850
\end{aligned}$$

That is, the *lowest number* that 50, 66 and 147 will divide into exactly is 80 850.

Worked Example 1.3

Determine the HCF of the numbers 36, 168 and 330.

Solution

Once again, we reduce each number to its basic prime factors as follows

$$\begin{aligned} 36 &= 2 \times 2 \quad\quad \times 3 \times 3 \\ 168 &= 2 \times 2 \times 2 \times 3 \quad\quad \times 7 \\ 330 &= 2 \quad\quad \times 3 \quad \times 5 \quad \times 11 \end{aligned}$$

We select the lowest power of each prime number which is common to all three numbers. These are the values 2 and 3, so that

$$\text{HCF} = 2 \times 3 = 6$$

That is, 6 is the *highest integer value* which divides exactly into 36, 168 and 330.

1.3 Fractions

A **fraction** is a part of a unit or of a whole number. If, for example, the number 3 is divided into four equal parts, then the size of each part is $\frac{3}{4}$ or 3/4 of the whole number. The value above the line is the **numerator**, and the value below the line is the **denominator**.

When the value of the numerator is less than the value of the denominator (as it is in the above case), the fraction is known as a **proper fraction**. If the value of the numerator is greater than that of the denominator, the fraction is known as an **improper fraction**; $\frac{4}{3}$ is an improper fraction.

An improper fraction can be expressed as a **mixed number**, where

$$\text{mixed number} = \text{integer} + \text{proper fraction}$$

For example

$$\frac{4}{3} = \frac{3+1}{3} = 1 + \frac{1}{3} = 1\frac{1}{3}$$

Fractions which have the same numerical value are known as **equivalent fractions**. For example, $\frac{6}{8} \equiv \frac{3}{4}$ (where $\equiv$ means 'is equivalent to'). One method of determining the simplest equivalent fraction is to reduce the numerator and the denominator to their prime factors, and the factors which are common to both can be cancelled as follows

$$\frac{42}{180} = \frac{\not{2} \times \not{3} \times 7}{\not{2} \times 2 \times \not{3} \times 3 \times 5} = \frac{7}{2 \times 3 \times 5} = \frac{7}{30}$$

That is, 42/180 is equivalent to 7/30. The process of cancelling numbers which are common to both the numerator and denominator is known as **simplification of fractions**.

A number such as 5.375 is known as a **decimal fraction** (see Chapter 2 for details of decimal numbering systems); 5 is the *integer part* of the number, and 0.375 is the *fractional part*, the two parts being separated by the **decimal point**, which is signified by the '.'.

To convert either a proper fraction or an improper fraction into a decimal fraction, we simply divide the numerator by the denominator as follows

$$6\frac{5}{8} = 6 + \frac{5}{8} = 6 + 0.625 = 6.625$$

Worked Example 1.4

Simplify the following equations: (a) $\frac{132}{252}$, (b) $\frac{225}{450}$, (c) $\frac{130}{520}$.

Solution

Where possible, we should cancel terms in the numerator and denominator which have the same value, as shown below

(a) In this case, we reduce the numerator and denominator to their prime values

$$\frac{132}{252} = \frac{\not{2} \times \not{2} \times \not{3} \times 11}{\not{2} \times \not{2} \times \not{3} \times 3 \times 7} = \frac{11}{21}$$

(b) Since 5 is clearly a common factor to the numerator and denominator, we initially separate 5 out and cancel it as follows

$$\frac{225}{450} = \frac{\not{5} \times 45}{\not{5} \times 90} = \frac{45}{90}$$

Next we reduce the remaining numerator and denominator to their prime values, and cancel wherever possible.

$$\frac{45}{90} = \frac{\not{45}}{2 \times \not{45}} = \frac{1}{2}$$

(c) In this case, 10 is a common factor in both the numerator and denominator, hence

$$\frac{130}{520} = \frac{\not{10} \times 13}{\not{10} \times 52} = \frac{13}{52} = \frac{\not{13}}{4 \times \not{13}} = \frac{1}{4}$$

1.4 Ratios, per cent and per unit values

The **ratio** of one value to another is the number of times one quantity is contained within the other. In the case of a ratio, both the numerator and the denominator have the same dimensions, i.e., they could both be voltage or power values, so that *a ratio is dimensionless*. For example, if a current, I_1, in one branch of a parallel circuit is 8 A, and the total current, I, supplied to the parallel circuit is 24 A, then the ratio of I_1 to I is

$$\frac{I_1}{I} = \frac{6}{24} = \frac{1}{4}$$

or the ratio of I to I_1 is

$$\frac{I}{I_1} = \frac{24}{6} = 4$$

The *current gain* of a transistor amplifier is simply the ratio of the current in the output circuit (the load) to the current in the input circuit (the base circuit). If the current gain is 100, the amplifier causes the current in the load to be 100 times greater than that in the base circuit.

Sometimes a ratio is expressed using a colon (:) to separate the two quantities. For example, we may say that

$$I_1 : I = 1 : 4$$

or

$$I : I_1 = 4 : 1$$

where the colon is thought of as saying 'to'. That is

the ratio of I_1 'to' I is 1 'to' 4

A **per cent** (%) is a fraction which has the number 100 in its denominator; that is, 12 per cent (12%) means 12 out of 100 or $\frac{12}{100}$ *of the total value*. For example, a motor which has an efficiency of 90 per cent means that $\frac{90}{100}$ of total electrical input power is converted into mechanical power, the remaining 10 per cent is 'lost' (usually in heating up the surrounding atmosphere). If we express 20 A as a percentage of 32 A we get

$$\frac{20}{32} \times 100\% = 62.5\%$$

A **per unit** (p.u.) value is simply a *fraction of the whole*, that is

per unit value = per cent value/100

A transformer with an efficiency of 92% also has a 0.92 p.u. efficiency.

Worked Example 1.5

There are twelve direct current motors and 130 alternating current motors in a factory. Express the ratio of the number of d.c. motors (a) to the number of a.c. motors and (b) to the total number of motors in the factory. Also (c) express the proportion of a.c. motors to the total number of motors in the factory as a percentage.

Solution

(a) $$\frac{\text{number of d.c. motors}}{\text{number of a.c. motors}} = \frac{12}{130} = \frac{6}{115}$$

(b) The total number of motors is $12 + 130 = 142$, hence

$$\frac{\text{number of d.c. motors}}{\text{total number of motors}} = \frac{12}{142} = \frac{6}{71}$$

(c) The proportion of a.c. motors to the total number of motors expressed as a percentage is

$$\frac{130}{142} \times 100 = 91.55\%$$

That is, the percentage of d.c. motors is

$$100 - 91.55 = 8.45\%$$

Worked Example 1.6

If a generator requires 110 kW of mechanical power to drive it, and the electrical output power is 95.7 kW, calculate the overall efficiency of the generating plant.

Solution

$$\text{p.u. efficiency} = \frac{\text{electrical output power}}{\text{mechanical input power}}$$

$$= \frac{95.7\,\text{kW}}{110\,\text{kW}} = 0.87\ \text{p.u.}$$

or

$$\%\ \text{efficiency} = \text{p.u. efficiency} \times 100 = 87\%$$

Worked Example 1.7

If the electrical input power to a motor is 32 kW, and the total power loss in the motor is 3.2 kW, determine (a) the mechanical output power from the motor and (b) the overall efficiency of the motor.

Solution

(a) The output power from the motor is

$$\text{output power} = \text{input power} - \text{loss} = 32 - 3.2 = 28.8\,\text{kW}$$

(b) The overall efficiency of the motor is

$$\text{efficiency} = \frac{\text{output power}}{\text{input power}} = \frac{28.8}{32} = 0.9 \text{ p.u.}$$

or 90%

1.5 Direct proportion, inverse proportion and reciprocal

When one quantity changes in exact relationship with another, the two quantities are **directly proportional** to one another. For example, if the voltage applied to a resistor is doubled, then the current in the resistor doubles. If the voltage is reduced by 25%, the current in the resistor reduces by 25%.

We use the symbol $\propto$ to represent 'proportional to'. Since the voltage, V, across a resistor is proportional to the current, I, flowing through it, we may say that

$$V \propto I$$

If k is the *constant of proportionality* between the two, we may say that

$$V = kI$$

Since the constant of proportionality in *Ohm's law* is the resistance, R, we may modify the proportional relationship into an equation by saying

$$V = IR$$

Mathematically, a **reciprocal** relationship is an **inverse relationship**, so that $\frac{1}{4}$ is the reciprocal of 4, $\frac{1}{5}$ is the reciprocal of 5, and so on.

If one quantity doubles when another quantity halves, the two are **inversely proportional** to one another. In a resistive circuit, the current in the circuit and the resistance of the circuit are inversely related to one another.

If, in a circuit which has a constant voltage applied to it, the resistance of the circuit is increased by a factor of three, then the current in the circuit reduces to one-third of its original value.

Experiment has shown that the resistance, R, of a conductor is inversely proportional to the area, a, of the conductor. This is expressed in the form

$$R \propto \frac{1}{a}$$

That is, *doubling the area* of the conductor has the effect of *halving the resistance* of the conductor; *reducing the area of the conductor by a factor of four* has the effect of *increasing the resistance by a factor of four*.

1.6 Addition and subtraction of fractions

Fractions can be added together or subtracted from one another if they have the same denominator. For example

$$\frac{5}{16} + \frac{6}{16} = \frac{5+6}{16} = \frac{11}{16}$$

$$\frac{9}{8} - \frac{4}{8} = \frac{9-4}{8} = \frac{5}{8}$$

If the denominators are not equal, then they should be modified so that they have a **common denominator** (preferably the **lowest common denominator** (LCD), which is the smallest possible value). The simplest method of obtaining a common denominator is by multiplying the denominator values together as follows

$$\frac{4}{30} + \frac{6}{20} = \frac{4 \times 20}{30 \times 20} + \frac{6 \times 30}{20 \times 30} = \frac{80}{600} + \frac{180}{600} = \frac{260}{600}$$

We can determine the LCD by determining the LCM of all the denominators (see section 1.2) as follows

$$30 = 2 \times 15 = 1 \times 3 \times 5$$

$$20 = 2 \times 10 = 2 \times 2 \times 5$$

That is, the LCM of 20 and 30 (the LCD) is

$$2 \times 3 \times 5 = 30$$

hence

$$\frac{4}{30} + \frac{6}{20} = \frac{4}{30} + \frac{6 \times 1.5}{20 \times 1.5} = \frac{4}{30} + \frac{9}{30}$$

$$= \frac{13}{30}$$

Worked Example 1.8

Add the following fractions.

(a) $\frac{1}{10}+\frac{1}{15}$, (b) $\frac{7}{18}+\frac{15}{27}$, (c) $\frac{4}{5}+\frac{7}{12}+\frac{13}{14}$

Solution

(a) To determine the LCM of the denominators (the LCD), we break the values 10 and 15 into their prime factors which are $10 = 5 \times 2$ and $15 = 5 \times 3$. The LCM is therefore $2 \times 3 \times 5 = 30$, hence

$$\frac{1}{10}+\frac{1}{15}=\frac{3}{30}+\frac{2}{30}=\frac{5}{30}=\frac{5}{5\times 6}=\frac{1}{6}$$

(b) Once again, we determine the LCM of the denominators, which are $18 = 2 \times 9$ and $27 = 3 \times 9$, hence the LCD is $2 \times 3 \times 9 = 54$, therefore

$$\frac{7}{18}+\frac{15}{27}=\frac{21}{54}+\frac{30}{54}=\frac{51}{54}$$

(c) In this case we have three denominators, and it is left as an exercise for the reader to show that the LCD is 420, hence

$$\frac{4}{5}+\frac{7}{12}+\frac{13}{14}=\frac{336}{420}+\frac{245}{420}+\frac{390}{420}=\frac{971}{420}=2\frac{131}{420}$$

Worked Example 1.9

Subtract the following fractions. (a) $\frac{3}{5}-\frac{1}{3}$ (b) $\frac{8}{13}-\frac{2}{9}$

Solution

(a) Since both denominators are prime numbers, the LCD is $5 \times 3 = 15$, therefore

$$\frac{3}{5}-\frac{1}{3}=\frac{9}{15}-\frac{5}{15}=\frac{4}{15}$$

(b) In this case the LCD is $13 \times 9 = 117$, and

$$\frac{8}{13}-\frac{2}{9}=\frac{72}{117}-\frac{26}{117}=\frac{46}{117}$$

1.7 Multiplication of fractions

To **multiply** fractions we multiply the numerators together to give a resultant numerator, and multiply the denominators together to give a resultant denominator. If possible, the resulting fraction is simplified. For example, let us determine $\frac{2}{3}$ of $\frac{5}{8}$ as follows (note: 'of' means 'multiply by')

$$\frac{2}{3} \times \frac{5}{8} = \frac{10}{24} = \frac{5 \times \cancel{2}}{12 \times \cancel{2}} = \frac{5}{12}$$

Worked Example 1.10

What is (a) $\frac{5}{8}$ of $1\frac{2}{3}$, (b) 15% of $4\frac{1}{2}$?

Solution

(a) $\frac{5}{8} \times 1\frac{2}{3} = \frac{5}{8} \times \frac{5}{3} = \frac{25}{24}$

(b) $\frac{15}{100} \times 4\frac{1}{2} = \frac{15}{100} \times \frac{9}{2} = \frac{135}{200} = \frac{27}{40}$

1.8 Division of fractions

The basic rule for **division** of fractions is to change the division sign to a multiplication sign and, simultaneously, invert the dividing fraction. For example

$$\frac{2}{3} \div \frac{4}{9} = \frac{2}{3} \times \frac{9}{4} = \frac{18}{12} = \frac{3}{2} = 1\frac{1}{2}$$

Worked Example 1.11

Simplify the following: (a) $\frac{6}{7} \div \frac{3}{14}$, (b) 12% of $\left[\frac{8}{9} \div \frac{4}{3}\right]$, (c) $\frac{5}{8} \times \left[\frac{16}{25} \div \frac{4}{5}\right]$

Solution

(a) $\frac{6}{7} \div \frac{3}{14} = \frac{6}{7} \times \frac{14}{3} = 4$

(b) $12\% \text{ of } \left[\frac{8}{9} \div \frac{4}{3}\right] = 12\% \text{ of } \left[\frac{8}{9} \times \frac{3}{4}\right] = 12\% \text{ of } \frac{2}{3}$

$$= \frac{12}{100} \times \frac{2}{3} = \frac{24}{300} = \frac{2}{25}$$

(c) $\frac{5}{8} \times \left[\frac{16}{25} \div \frac{4}{5}\right] = \frac{5}{8} \times \left[\frac{16}{25} \times \frac{5}{4}\right] = \frac{5}{8} \times \frac{4}{5} = \frac{20}{40}$

$$= \frac{1}{2}$$

1.9 Bases and powers

If we multiply 4 *by itself* three times, it is written in the form

$$4 \times 4 \times 4 = 4^3$$

where 4 is the **base**, and 3 is the **power**, or the **index** or the **exponent** to which the base is raised (note: the plural of index is *indices*).

We describe this number as *4 raised to the power of 3*. Special names are used when the power is either 2 or 3, namely *squared* and *cubed*, respectively; for example 12^2 is *twelve squared*, and 4^3 is *four cubed*. Writing the number in this way is described as **index notation**.

Consider the product

$$4 \times 4 \times 4 \times 4 \times 4 = 4^5$$

This can, alternatively, be written as follows

$$(4 \times 4) \times (4 \times 4 \times 4) = 4^2 \times 4^3$$

That is

$$4^2 \times 4^3 = 4^{(2+3)} = 4^5$$

Hence, when we *multiply numbers with the same base*, we merely *add the powers together*; that is

$$b^n \times b^m = b^{n+m}$$

where b is the base, and n and m are any power, as shown in the following examples

$$5^3 \times 5^4 = 5^7$$

$$6^2 \times 6^{-6} \times 6^3 = 6^{(2-6+3)} = 6^{-1} = 1/6$$

$$(3^2 \times 3^2) + (3^4 \times 3^3) = 3^4 + 3^7$$

An interesting extension to the use of powers is shown below.

$$27^2 = (3 \times 9)^2 = 3^2 \times 9^2 = 9 \times 81 = 729$$

Consider the calculation

$$(2^2)^3 = (2 \times 2)^3 = (2 \times 2) \times (2 \times 2) \times (2 \times 2)$$
$$= 2^6$$

From this we conclude that **when a base raised to a power is raised to a further power, the two powers are multiplied**. For example

$$(5^3)^4 = 5^{(3\times4)} = 5^{12}$$

and

$$(10^4)^2 = 10^{(4x2)} = 10^8$$

Let us look at the division of numbers using the index notation using the following example.

$$2^5/2^2 = (2 \times 2 \times 2 \times 2 \times 2)/(2 \times 2) = 32/4 = 16$$
$$= 2^3 = 8$$

Also

$$2^{(5-2)} = 2^3 = 8$$

That is *when we divide numbers with the same base*, we *subtract the power of the denominator from the power of the numerator*, or

$$b^n/b^m = b^{(n-m)}$$

For example

$$5^5/5^3 = 5^{5-3} = 5^2$$

and

$$6^7/6^{10} = 6^{7-10} = 6^{-3}$$

The following calculation produces an interesting result.

$$3^2/3^2 = 3^{(2-2)} = 3^0$$

Using numerical values

$$3^2/3^2 = 9/9 = 1$$

That is $3^0 = 1$!

In fact, **any number raised to the power zero has the value of unity**. That is $2^0 = 1$, $50^0 = 1$, $121^0 = 1$, etc.

It also follows that

$$1/3^2 = 3^0/3^2 = 3^{(0-2)} = 3^{-2}$$

that is **the power of a reciprocal is the negative of the power of the denominator**. For example

$$\frac{1}{5} = 5^{-1}$$

$$3^{-3} = \frac{1}{3^3} = \frac{1}{27}$$

$$5 \times 6^{-2} = \frac{5}{6^2} = \frac{5}{36}$$

$$4^2 \times 3^{-3} = \frac{4^2}{3^3} = \frac{16}{27}$$

$$7^2 \times 7^{-4} = 7^{(2-4)} = 7^{-2} = \frac{1}{7^2} = \frac{1}{49}$$

Worked Example 1.12

Determine the value of (a) $5^2 \times 5^3$, (b) $4^3 \times 4^0$, (c) $6^4 \times 6^{-5}$, (d) $2^2 + 3^4$, (e) $4^2 + 2^{-1}$, (f) $3(2^2) - 5(3^2)$.

Solution

We write out the solution in full here but, in practice, this is not always necessary.

(a) $5^2 \times 5^3 = (5 \times 5) \times (5 \times 5 \times 5) = 25 \times 125 = 3125$
(b) $4^3 \times 4^0 = (4 \times 4 \times 4) \times 1 = 64$
(c) $6^4 \times 6^{-5} = 6^{(4-5)} = 6^{-1} = 1/6 = 0.16667$
(d) $2^2 + 3^4 = (2 \times 2) + (3 \times 3 \times 3 \times 3) = 4 + 81 = 85$
(e) $4^2 + 2^{-1} = (4 \times 4) + 1/2 = 16.5$
(f) $3(2^2) - 5(3^2) = 3(2 \times 2) - 5(3 \times 3) = 12 - 45 = -33$

1.10 Raising a fraction to a power

The rules described for integers also apply to fractions. For example

$$\left[\frac{2}{3}\right]^2 = \frac{2^2}{3^2} = \frac{4}{9}$$

$$\left[\frac{5}{8}\right]^3 = \frac{5^3}{8^3} = \frac{125}{512}$$

$$\left[\frac{3}{4}\right]^3 \times \left[\frac{5}{8}\right]^2 = \frac{3^3}{4^3} \times \frac{5^2}{8^2} = \frac{675}{4096}$$

$$\left[\frac{3}{4}\right]^3 \div \left[\frac{7}{8}\right]^2 = \frac{3^3}{4^3} \div \frac{7^2}{8^2} = \frac{3^3}{4^3} \times \frac{8^2}{7^2} = \frac{27}{49}$$

It also follows that

$$\left[\frac{3}{4}\right]^{-2} = \frac{1}{\left[\frac{3}{4}\right]^{2}}$$

but

$$\left[\frac{3}{4}\right]^{-2} = \frac{3^{-2}}{4^{-2}} = \frac{1}{3^{2} \times 4^{-2}} = \frac{4^{2}}{3^{2}}$$

That is to say

$$\left[\frac{b}{a}\right]^{-n} = \left[\frac{a}{b}\right]^{n}$$

Worked Example 1.13

What is the value of (a) $\left[\frac{7}{8}\right] \times \left[\frac{7}{8}\right]^{2}$, (b) $\left[\frac{4}{5}\right]^{2} - \left[\frac{4}{5}\right]^{0}$,

(c) $\left[\frac{3}{4}\right]^{2} \times \left[\frac{3}{4}\right]^{-1}$, (d) $\left[\frac{5}{8}\right]^{2} \div \left[\frac{5}{8}\right]^{3}$.

Solution

(a) $$\left[\frac{7}{8}\right] \times \left[\frac{7}{8}\right]^{2} = \left[\frac{7}{8}\right]^{(1+2)} = \left[\frac{7}{8}\right]^{3} = \frac{7^{3}}{8^{3}} \approx 0.67$$

Note: $\approx$ means 'approximately equal to'.

(b) $$\left[\frac{4}{5}\right]^{2} - \left[\frac{4}{5}\right]^{0} = \left[\frac{4}{5}\right]^{2} - 1 = \frac{-9}{25} = -0.36$$

Remember, any number raised to the power zero has unity value.

(c) $$\left[\frac{3}{4}\right]^{3} \times \left[\frac{3}{4}\right]^{-1} = \left[\frac{3}{4}\right]^{(3-1)} = \left[\frac{3}{4}\right]^{2} = \frac{9}{16} = 0.5625$$

(d) $$\left[\frac{5}{8}\right]^{2} \div \left[\frac{5}{8}\right]^{3} = \left[\frac{5}{8}\right]^{(2-3)} = \left[\frac{5}{8}\right]^{-1} = \frac{8}{5} = 1.6$$

Worked Example 1.14

Evaluate (a) $\left[\frac{5}{8}\right]^2 \times \left[\frac{3}{4}\right]^{-1}$, (b) $\left[\frac{5}{8}\right] \div \left[\frac{3}{4}\right]^{-1}$.

Solution

(a) $\left[\frac{5}{8}\right]^2 \times \left[\frac{3}{4}\right]^{-1} = \left[\frac{5}{8}\right]^2 \times \frac{4}{3} = \frac{5^2}{8^2} \times \frac{4}{3} = \frac{100}{192}$

(b) $\left[\frac{5}{8}\right]^2 \div \left[\frac{3}{4}\right]^{-1} = \frac{5^2}{8^2} \times \frac{3}{4} = \frac{75}{256}$

1.11 Fractional powers

We say that $5 \times 5 = 5^2$, which is described as *five squared*. It follows that the **square root** of 25 (or 5^2) is 5. That is

$$\sqrt{25} = 5$$

where $\sqrt{}$ is the symbol for the square root. Similarly, we may say

$$\sqrt{64} = 8$$

Strictly speaking, we should say

$$\sqrt{64} = \pm 8$$

because $(+8)^2 = 64$ and $(-8)^2 = 64$. That is, **the square root of a number may either have a positive sign or a negative sign**. In many cases the answer has a positive sign, but there are some cases where we must consider the possibility of the answer having either mathematical sign.

We can also show that we are evaluating the root of a number by giving it a **fractional power**. In the case of a square root, we can say that

$$\sqrt{25} = 25^{1/2} = 5$$

$$\sqrt{16} = 16^{1/2} = 4$$

Also, since

$$3^3 = 3 \times 3 \times 3 = 27$$

we may say that

$$27^{1/3} = \sqrt[3]{27} = 3$$

That is, the **cube root** of 27 is 3. The **fourth root** of a number is one, when multiplied by itself four times gives the original number. The **fifth root** of a number is one, when multiplied by itself five times gives the original number, etc.

The rules for *multiplication and division of fractional roots* follow the same pattern as those for powers. For example

$$15^{1/3} \times 15^{1/3} = 15^{(1/3+1/3)} = 15^{2/3}$$
$$16^{1/4} \times 16^{1/2} = 16^{(1/4+1/2)} = 16^{3/4}$$
$$12^{1/2} \div 12^{3/4} = 12^{(1/2-3/4)} = 15^{-1/4}$$
$$9^{1/2} \div 9^{1/3} = 9^{(1/2-1/3)} = 9^{1/6}$$

The answers to the first two of the above examples are fairly complex because the numerator of the resulting fractional power is not unity. This can best be understood from the following. Consider the number $16^{3/4}$, whose value can be determined as follows

$$16^{3/4} = (16^{1/4})^3 = (2)^3 = 8$$

Let us look at the following more complex calculation

$$\frac{25^{2/3} \times 14^{1/3} \times 18^{2/5}}{14^{1/2} \times 18^{5/6} \times 25^{1/3}}$$

This can be written in the form

$$25^{(2/3-1/3)} \times 14^{(1/3-1/2)} \times 18^{(2/5-5/6)}$$
$$= 25^{1/3} \times 14^{-1/6} \times 18^{-13/30}$$
$$= 25^{1/3}/(14^{1/6} \times 18^{13/30})$$

We will not evaluate this at this stage. Where a calculation involves several numbers with a different base as occurs, for example, in the above calculation, the value of each term must be worked out separately using either a calculator or logarithms.

It is worth pointing out here that the value of many roots are **irrational numbers**, i.e., they are not whole numbers and are non-recurring. For example

$$\sqrt{2} = 1.41421\ldots$$
$$\sqrt{6} = 2.44948\ldots$$

Worked Example 1.15

Simplify the following and determine their value.

(a) $\left[\dfrac{125}{27}\right]^{1/3}$, (b) $625^{1/4} \times 5^2$,

(c) $125^{2/3} \times 27^{2/3} \times 16^{-1/2}/(16^2 \times 27^{-1/3} \times 125^{1/3})$.

Solution

(a) $\left[\dfrac{125}{27}\right]^{1/3} = \dfrac{125^{1/3}}{27^{1/3}} = \dfrac{5}{3} = 1\dfrac{2}{3}$

(b) $625^{1/4} \times 5^2 = 5 \times 5^2 = 5^3 = 125$

(c) $\dfrac{125^{2/3} \times 27^{2/3} \times 16^{-1/2}}{16^2 \times 27^{-1/3} \times 125^{1/3}}$

$= 125^{(2/3-1/3)} \times 27^{(2/3-(-1/3))} \times 16^{(-1/2-2))}$

$= 125^{1/3} \times 27^1 \times 16^{-5/2} = \dfrac{125^{1/3} \times 27}{16^{5/2}}$

$= \dfrac{5 \times 27}{1024} = \dfrac{135}{1024} \approx 0.132$

1.12 Scientific notation

Engineers frequently need to use both very large and very small values, which are both difficult to write down and manipulate. Fortunately, **scientific notation** or **standard form** (also known as *standard index form*) make the values more manageable.

For example, the number 692 500 is written in scientific notation as 6.925×10^5. That is, we write the number with one digit to the left of the decimal point; this number is known as the **mantissa**. The mantissa is multiplied by 10 raised to some power; the power is known as the **exponent**. In the above case, the mantissa is 6.925, and the exponent is 5. A list of powers of 10 in common use and their international abbreviation is given in Table 1.1.

For example, a voltage of 2 780 000 V is represented as 2.78 MV, a resistance of 1700 Ω as 1.7 kΩ, a current of 0.0256 A as 25.6 mA, etc.

TABLE 1.1 SI multiplier values

Multiplier	*Prefix*	*Abbreviation*
10^{12}	tera-	T
10^{9}	giga-	G
10^{6}	mega-	M
10^{3}	kilo-	k
10^{-2}	centi-	c
10^{-3}	milli-	m
10^{-6}	micro-	μ
10^{-9}	nano-	n
10^{-12}	pico-	p

Numbers can easily be multiplied and divided in the scientific notation; consider the following calculation.

$$\frac{(7.6 \times 10^3) \times (2.375 \times 10-4)}{(89.76 \times 10^6) \times (72 \times 10^{-9})}$$
$$= \frac{7.6 \times 2.375 \times 10^{(3-4)}}{89.76 \times 72 \times 10^{(6-9)}} = \frac{18.05 \times 10^{-1}}{6462.72 \times 10^{-3}}$$
$$= 0.00279 \times 10^{(-1+3)} = 0.00279 \times 10^2 = 0.279$$

In fact, using scientific notation, we can quickly estimate the result of a calculation as follows. If we 'round' all the values in the above calculation to the nearest whole number, we get an 'approximate' solution as follows

$$\frac{8 \times 2 \times 10^{(3-4)}}{90 \times 72 \times 10^{(6-9)}} = \frac{16}{6480} \times 10^{(-1-(-3))}$$
$$\approx 0.0025 \times 10^2 = 0.25$$

To *add* or *subtract* numbers in the scientific notation, we must expand them into normal form as follows

$$5.6 \times 10^4 + 2.3 \times 10^5 - 4 \times 10^3$$
$$= 56\,000 + 230\,000 - 4000 = 282\,000$$
$$= 2.82 \times 10^5 \text{ or } 0.282 \times 10^6$$

Worked Example 1.16

Express the following in scientific notation.
(a) 5 870 000, (b) 3100, (c) 0.000392.

Solution

(a) $5\,870\,000 = 5.87 \times 10^6$
(b) $3100 = 3.1 \times 10^3$

(c) $0.000392 = 3.92 \times 10^{-4}$
The reader should note that 10^{-4} is not one of the values listed in Table 1.1 and, in engineering circles, it is usually better to show 3.92×10^{-4} as 0.392×10^{-3} or as 392×10^{-6}.

Self-test questions

1.1 What are the prime factors of (a) 324, (b) 2695, (c) 1170?

1.2 What is the LCM of the numbers 21, 50 and 60?

1.3 Determine the HCF of the numbers 140, 210 and 330.

1.4 Simplify the following fractions (a) $\frac{186}{310}$, (b) $\frac{54}{432}$, (c) $\frac{180}{576}$

1.5 Add the following fractions (a) $\frac{5}{6}+\frac{7}{8}$, (b) $\frac{9}{10}+\frac{8}{30}$,
(c) $2\frac{7}{8}+3\frac{4}{10}$.

1.6 Subtract the following (a) $\frac{5}{6}-\frac{7}{8}$, (b) $\frac{9}{10}-\frac{8}{30}$,
(c) $2\frac{7}{8}-3\frac{4}{10}$

1.7 If 5 per cent of the current in a circuit is 2.3 A, what current flows in the circuit?

1.8 If the current gain of a transistor is 122, and the input current (the base region current) is 20 μA, what is the collector current? Note: current gain = collector current/base current.

1.9 Evaluate the following (a) $\frac{5}{6}\times\frac{2}{3}$, (b) $\frac{5}{6}\div\frac{2}{3}$,
(c) 15% of $(1\frac{2}{3}\times\frac{5}{6})$, (d) $\frac{1}{5}\times\frac{2}{3}\div\frac{1}{2}$.

1.10 Determine the value of the following. (a) $\left[\frac{5}{8}\right]^2$, (b) $\left[\frac{1}{2}\right]^2\times\frac{2}{3}$,
(c) $\left[\frac{4}{5}\right]^{-1}\div\left[\frac{5}{8}\right]^{-2}$, (d) $\left[\frac{2}{3}\right]^2+\left[\frac{1}{2}\right]^3$.

1.11 Express the following in scientific notation (a) 101 010, (b) 0.0010101, (c) 101.01.

1.12 Write down the following values using the abbreviations in Table 1.1 (a) 2 560 000, (b) 6.7×10^{11}, (c) 10.3×10^{-4}, (d) 7.9×10^{-11}.

1.13 Evaluate the following (a) $(9.3 \times 10^5) \times (7.6 \times 10^4)/5 \times 10^8$, (b) $(1.7 \times 10^4 - 15 \times 10^3)/7 \times 10^2$.

Summary of important facts

An **integer** is a **whole number**, and a **prime number** is one which cannot be divided exactly by another whole number (except unity); examples of prime numbers include 2, 3, 5, 7, 11, 13, 17. The smallest number that two or more other numbers divide into exactly is the **lowest common multiple** (LCM) of the numbers, and the largest number which divides exactly into two or more given numbers is the **highest common factor** (HCF) of those numbers.

A **fraction** is part of a whole quantity; the value above the line in the fraction is the **numerator**, and the value below the line is the **denominator**. In a **proper fraction**, the numerator is less than the denominator, and in an **improper fraction** the numerator is greater than the denominator. An improper fraction can be expressed as a **mixed number**, i.e., as an integer in association with a proper fraction. Fractions which have the same numerical value, i.e., 1/2 and 2/4 are **equivalent fractions**. Some fractions can be **simplified** by cancelling out prime factors in the numerator and denominator. A **decimal fraction** comprises an *integer part* and a *fractional part*, the two parts being separated by a *decimal point*.

A **ratio** is a fraction in which the numerator and the denominator have the same dimensions, i.e., it is *dimensionless*.

Per cent (%) means *per hundred*, and a per cent value means a fraction out of 100 units. **Per unit** (p.u.) means a fraction out of the whole, and the per cent value is 100 times greater than the per unit value.

When one item is **directly proportional** to another, the two quantities increase in relation to one another, i.e., when one doubles, both double in value. Two items are **inversely proportional** to one another if, for example, doubling the value of one results in the other halving in value. A **reciprocal** relationship is an inverse relationship.

When *adding* or *subtracting* fractions, they must have a **common denominator**. The **lowest common denominator** (LCD) is the LCM of the denominators. To **multiply fractions**, the numerators are multiplied to give a resultant numerator, and the denominators are multiplied to give a resultant denominator. If possible, the fraction should be simplified. To **divide fractions**, the division sign is changed to a multiplication sign, and the dividing fraction is inverted.

When a value is written as 3^5, the number 3 is the **base** and 5 is the **index** or **power**. When *multiplying* numbers having the same base, the *indices are added*. When dividing numbers having the same base, *the index of the denominator is subtracted from the numerator index*. When a base which is raised to a power is raised to a further power, the *indices are multiplied*. When a number is raised to the power zero (0), *its value is 1*. A base raised to a negative power is the *reciprocal of the base raised to the corresponding positive power*. When a number is raised to a fractional power, *the denominator of the fraction is the root of the number, and the numerator is the power*.

A number written in **scientific notation** or **standard form** has one digit to the left of the decimal point, and the remainder to the right of it; this part is known as the **mantissa**. The mantissa is multiplied by 10 raised to a power; the power of 10 is known as the exponent. The most important engineering exponents are listed in Table 1.1.

2 Numbers and numbering systems

2.1 Introduction

Numbers are at the heart of all arithmetic processes, and there are many numbering systems in use, each having its own particular advantage. The most popular is the **decimal** or **denary system**, which is widely used by man.

Perhaps the next most important in engineering terms is the **binary system**, which is used in all computer systems; many versions of the binary system are in use including the *octal system*, the *hexadecimal system*, and a range of *binary-coded decimal* (BCD) *systems*. Many versions of binary numbering system are used in data transmission systems, several of which have built-in *redundancy* in the code which allow them to be used for error-detection and correction of the transmitted data.

Many binary numbering systems are designed for special purposes such as the reliable measurement of the position of an object such as the arm of a robot, etc. Since these systems are designed with a special purpose in mind, many of the normal mathematical processes such as addition, subtraction, multiplication and division may not be very easy with them.

At the end of this chapter the reader will be able to

- understand the terminology of number and numbering systems,
- work with decimal, hexadecimal, octal and binary numbers,
- convert one numbering system to another,
- fully appreciate binary-coded decimal systems (BCD),
- add, subtract, multiply and divide binary numbers.

2.2 Terminology

The number of digits used in a numbering system is known as the **base** or **radix** of the system. For example

the binary system has a radix of 2
the octal system has a radix of 8
the decimal or denary system has a radix of 10
the hexadecimal system has a radix of 16

The value of each term in a number is equal to one of the radix values multiplied by a power (which depends on the 'position' within the number).

For example

$$\text{decimal } 985 = (9 \times 10^2) + (8 \times 10^1) + (5 \times 10^0)$$

We have already looked at powers in chapter 1, where we saw that any number raised to the power zero is equal to 1. That is, $10^0 = 1$, $8^0 = 1$, $2^0 = 1$, etc. Also, the spaces both to the right and left of any number are assumed to be filled with *non-significant zeros*. That is

$$986 = 000986.000$$

The *maximum value* for any digit in a numbering system is

$$\text{maximum value} = \text{radix} - 1$$

For example, the largest value that may be written down *in any position* in the decimal number is $(10 - 1) = 9$, in the octal system it is $(8 - 1) = 7$, in the binary system it is $(2 - 1) = 1$, etc. It follows that the largest number a 3-digit decimal system can store is 999, in a 3-digit octal system it is 777, and in a 3-digit binary system it is 111.

To differentiate between numbering systems, the radix is written down as a suffix as follows

binary 1011 is written down as 1011_2
octal 1011 is written down as 1011_8
decimal 1011 is written down as 1011_{10}
hexadecimal 1011 is written down as 1011_{16}

The most significant character in a decimal number is known as the **most significant digit** (msd), and the least significant digit character is the **least significant digit** (lsd). A **BI**nary digi**T** is known as a **bit**, and the most significant character in a binary number is known as the **most significant bit** (msb), and the least significant character is the **least significant bit** (lsb).

2.3 The basis of numbering systems

The integer part and fractional part of a number are separated by the **radix point**. That is, the radix point is in the position where the power to which the radix is raised becomes negative. For example, the decimal number 26.58 can be written

$$26.58 = (2 \times 10^1) + (6 \times 10^0) + (5 \times 10^{-1}) + (8 \times 10^{-2})$$

In the case of a decimal number, the radix point is known as the *decimal point*, and in the case of a binary system it is known as the *binary point*.

A **polynomial** is an expression involving powers of the radix which are written in descending order from the left. If the radix of a numbering system is r, then an expression for a number can be written as follows

$$(v_3 \times r^3) + (v_2 \times r^2) + (v_1 \times r^1) + (v_0 \times r^0) + (v_{-1} \times r^{-1}) + (v_{-2} \times r^{-2}), \text{ etc}$$

where v represents the value of the digit within the range zero to (radix − 1).

Thus the decimal number 3406.78 is written in the above format, where

$$v_3 = 3,\ v_2 = 4,\ v_1 = 0,\ v_0 = 6,\ v_{-1} = 7,\ v_{-2} = 8$$

The first twenty-four numbers in the binary, octal, decimal and hexadecimal systems are listed in Table 2.1. We will look in detail at some of them below.

TABLE 2.1 The first 24 numbers in the binary, octal, decimal and hexadecimal systems

System	*binary*	*octal*	*decimal*	*hexadecimal*
Radix	2	8	10	16
	00000	00	00	00
	00001	01	01	01
	00010	02	02	02
	00011	03	03	03
	00100	04	04	04
	00101	05	05	05
	00110	06	06	06
	00111	07	07	07
	01000	10	08	08
	01001	11	09	09
	01010	12	10	0a
	01011	13	11	0b
	01100	14	12	0c
	01101	15	13	0d
	01110	16	14	0e
	01111	17	15	0f
	10000	20	16	10
	10001	21	17	11
	10010	22	18	12
	10011	23	19	13
	10100	24	20	14
	10101	25	21	15
	10110	26	22	16
	10111	27	23	17
	11000	30	24	18

As mentioned earlier, in the binary system the largest number that may be written down in any position is 1, so the decimal number 2 is written

$$2_{10} = (1 \times 2^1) + (0 \times 2^0) = 10_2$$

and the decimal number 3 is written

$$3_{10} = (1 \times 2^1) + (1 \times 2^0) = 11_2$$

Looking at one of the larger binary numbers in Table 2.1, we see that

$$01101_2 = (0 \times 2^4) + (1 \times 2^3) + (1 \times 2^2) + (0 \times 2^1) + (1 \times 2^0)$$

That is, binary 01101 is equivalent to decimal 13.

The 'length' of the largest number a computer can handle is known as the **word length** of the computer. In the early days of computing this was typically eight bits or one **byte** (half a byte was formerly known as a nibble!); today a word length of four bytes (32 bits) or greater is used in many systems.

When the value of the number reaches the radix of the system (or an integer multiple of the radix), the next higher-order digit is introduced. Thus in the octal system the 8th value is

$$7_8 + 1_8 = 10_8 = (1 \times 8^1) + (0 \times 8^0)$$

The above number should be stated as 'one, zero in octal' and NOT as 'ten octal', simply because the use of 'ten' is restricted to the decimal system. The next higher octal value is 11_8, and the sixteenth number is $20_8 = (2 \times 8^1) + (0 \times 8^0)$.

In every numbering system, we must assign a character to each value. Thus, in the hexadecimal system, we assign the character 'a' to the 10th value, 'b' to the 11th value, and so on up to the 15th which is 'f'. The 16th value in the code then becomes

$$10_{16} = (1 \times 16^1) + (0 \times 16^0)$$

the 17th value is

$$11_{16} = (1 \times 16^1) + (1 \times 16^0)$$

and so on. Clearly

$$ac3_{16} = (10_{10} \times 16^2) + (12_{10} \times 16^1) + (3_{10} \times 16^0)$$

which is equivalent to 2755_{10}. The hexadecimal system may seem a little complex at this stage but, with experience, it becomes as easy to use as the pure binary system.

Each of the codes in Table 2.1 is described as a **weighted code** because each character in the code can be given a numerical value or 'weight'. In the case of the decimal code the 'weight' of each column is ten times that of the column to its right; in the binary code the weight of each column increases by a factor of 2, and in the hexadecimal code it increases by a factor of 16, and so on.

2.4 Converting an integer of any radix into decimal

To convert a number of any radix into decimal, we merely have to **expand the number as a polynomial in powers of the radix**, and add the terms, as shown below

$$\begin{aligned} 1011_2 &= (1 \times 2^3) + (0 \times 2^2) + (1 \times 2^1) + (1 \times 2^0) \\ &= (8 + 0 + 2 + 1)_{10} = 11_{10} \end{aligned}$$

$$\begin{aligned}2abc_{16} &= (2 \times 16^3) + (a \times 16^2) + (b \times 16^1) + (c \times 16^0)\\ &= (2_{10} \times 16^3) + (10_{10} \times 16^2) + (11_{10} \times 16^1) + (12_{10} \times 16^0)\\ &= (8192 + 2560 + 176 + 12)_{10} = 10940_{10}\end{aligned}$$

2.5 Converting a decimal integer into another radix

To convert a decimal integer to another radix, we **divide the integer repeatedly by the radix: successive remainders give the required number**.

When converting a non-decimal number to another non-decimal number, it is often convenient to convert the first non-decimal into decimal, and then convert the decimal value into the second non-decimal number using the methods outlined in sections 2.4 and 2.5.

Worked Example 2.1

Convert 386_{10} into octal.

Solution

The procedure is as follows

```
8)386
 8)48   remainder 2 (this is the lsd)
  8)6   remainder 0
    0   remainder 6 (this is the msd)
```

That is $386_{10} = 602_8$

Worked Example 2.2

Convert 492_{10} into hexadecimal.

Solution

In this case we have to divide the number repeatedly by 16, as follows

```
16)492
 16)30   remainder 12₁₀ or c₁₆  (lsd)
  16)1   remainder 14₁₀ or e₁₆
     0   remainder 1            (msd)
```

or $492_{10} = 1ec_{16}$

2.6 Converting a binary integer into an octal integer

The procedure is fairly straightforward, because we simply **divide the binary value into groups of three bits** (adding, where necessary, non-significant zeros). **Each group is then written down as its octal equivalent value.**

For example, we convert the binary value 1101011 into octal as follows

$$1\ 101\ 011_2 = 001\ 101\ 011_2 = 153_8$$

2.7 Converting a binary integer into a hexadecimal integer

In this case, we simply **divide the binary number into groups of four bits** (adding any necessary non-significant zeros). **Each group is then written down as its hexadecimal equivalent**. For example

$$111001101_2 = 0001\ 1100\ 1101_2 = 1cd_{16}$$

2.8 Dealing with a number having a fractional part

In many cases a number has both an integer and a fractional part, e.g., 25.86_{10}, 1011.001_2, $3abe.f4_{16}$, etc.

When converting a *non-decimal value into a decimal number*, we deal with it in the manner outlined in section 2.4, an example being given in Worked Example 2.3.

When converting a *decimal number into any other radix*, the integer part and the fractional part are dealt with separately. The integer part is dealt with as described in section 2.5. The fractional part is dealt with by multiplying it repeatedly by the radix, the resulting integral part giving the required value; the fractional part after each multiplication is passed on to the next multiplication stage, as shown in Worked Example 2.4.

The reader is asked to note that certain exact decimal fractions, such as 0.1_{10}, are represented by recurring binary fractions. The reader should verify that 10.1_{10} converts to give a recurring binary fractional part.

Worked Example 2.3

Convert the octal number 756.34_8 into decimal.

Solution

$$\begin{aligned} 756.34_8 &= (7 \times 8^2) + (5 \times 8^1) + (6 \times 8^0) + (3 \times 8^{-1}) + (4 \times 8^{-2}) \\ &= [(7 \times 64) + (5 \times 8) + (6 \times 1) + (3/8) + (4/64)]_{10} \\ &= [448 + 40 + 6 + 0.375 + 0.0625]_{10} \\ &= 494.4375_{10} \end{aligned}$$

Worked Example 2.4

Convert the decimal number 38.375 into binary.

Solution

In this case we deal with the integer and fractional parts separately in the manner described above

Integer part		*Decimal part*
2)38		
2)19	remainder 0	$0.375 \times 2 = 0$ .75
2)9	remainder 1	$0.75 \times 2 = 1$ .5
2)4	remainder 1	$0.5 \times 2 = 1$ (lsb)
2)2	remainder 0	
2)1	remainder 0	
0	remainder 1 (msb)	

The integer part (38) is repeatedly divided by 2 to give the integer part of the solution, and the fractional part of the number (0.375) is multiplied by 2, the integer part of this calculation giving the required value. The number is read from the msb to the lsb as follows

$$38.375_{10} = 100110.011_2$$

2.9 Binary coded decimal codes

Whilst electronic systems deal most easily with binary numbers, mankind prefers decimal codes. By *coding* decimal numbers in binary form, suitable numbering systems can be devised which are acceptable to both man and machine alike. Such coding systems are known as **binary-coded decimal codes** (BCD codes).

The reader will note that the *pure binary code* in Table 2.1 uses four bits to convey the ten decimal digits 0–9. There are, in fact, more than 29 000 million possible 4-bit codes we can use. Of these, 70 have weighted codes, 17 of them have *positive weights*, and others have *negative weights*.

Three examples of BCD code are given in Table 2.2, the first two having positive weights, the third having a negative weight for one of the columns. The value of a '1' in any column is multiplied by the 'weight' associated with that column (note: the 'weight' is a decimal value). Consider for example decimal 5; in the 8421 code its value is

$$0101_{8421} = (0 \times 8)_{10} + (1 \times 4)_{10} + (0 \times 2)_{10} + (1 \times 1)_{10} = 5_{10}$$

TABLE 2.2 4-bit binary-decimal codes

Decimal	*Weighting of BCD code*											
number	*8*	*4*	*2*	*1*	*2*	*4*	*2*	*1*	*6*	*4*	*2*	*(−3)*
0	0	0	0	0	0	0	0	0	0	0	0	0
1	0	0	0	1	0	0	0	1	0	1	0	1
2	0	0	1	0	0	0	1	0	0	0	1	0
3	0	0	1	1	0	0	1	1	1	0	0	1
4	0	1	0	0	0	1	0	0	0	1	0	0
5	0	1	0	1	1	0	1	1	1	0	1	1
6	0	1	1	0	1	1	0	0	0	1	1	0
7	0	1	1	1	1	1	0	1	1	1	0	1
8	1	0	0	0	1	1	1	0	1	0	1	0
9	1	0	0	1	1	1	1	1	1	1	1	1

In the 2421 code its value is

$$1011_{2421} = (1 \times 2)_{10} + (0 \times 4)_{10} + (1 \times 2)_{10} + (1 \times 1)_{10} = 5_{10}$$

and in the 642(−3) code its value is

$$1011_{642(-3)} = (1 \times 6)_{10} + (0 \times 4)_{10} + (1 \times 2)_{10} + (1 \times (-3))_{10} = 5_{10}$$

When the value of the number exceeds decimal 9, the weight associated with each column is increased by a factor of 10, as shown in Table 2.3.

TABLE 2.3 Binary-decimal codes for higher values

Decimal	*8421 BCD value*								*2421 BCD value*							
number	*80*	*40*	*20*	*10*	*8*	*4*	*2*	*1*	*20*	*40*	*20*	*10*	*2*	*4*	*2*	*1*
9	0	0	0	0	1	0	0	1	0	0	0	0	1	1	1	1
10	0	0	0	1	0	0	0	0	0	0	0	1	0	0	0	0
.																
.																
79	0	1	1	1	1	0	0	1	1	1	0	1	1	1	1	1
80	1	0	0	0	0	0	0	0	1	1	1	0	0	0	0	0
.																

2.10 Addition of numbers

For the sum

$$x + y = z$$

x is called the **augend**, y the **addend** and z the **sum**. If the sum exceeds the value of the radix, a **carry** is produced. For example

$$3_{10} + 6_{10} = \text{sum of } 9_{10} \text{ and no carry}$$

$$3_{10} + 9_{10} = \text{sum of 2 and a carry of 1}$$

When two digits are added, the carry never exceeds 1. The carry mentioned above is the **carry-out** from the sum, and this becomes the **carry-in** of the next higher addition. Let us look at this in the following examples

	decimal				*octal*				*hexadecimal*		
augend		7	7	7		7	7	7	7	7	7
addend		6	5	0		6	5	0	6	5	0
carry-in	1	1	0		1	1	0		0	0	
	↖	↖	↖		↖	↖	↖		↖	↖	
carry-out		1	1	0		1	1	0		0	0
sum	1	4	2	7	1	6	4	7	d	c	7

Generally speaking, addition in some codes (such as a BCD code) usually requires special rules to account for the fact that it is not a natural binary code.

(a) Addition in pure binary

The addition of binary numbers has a special place in electrical and electronic engineering, and we will take a detailed look at it here. When we add two binary digits, there are four possible combinations for the sum and carry, which are as follows

$0 + 0 =$ sum of 0 and a carry of 0

$0 + 1 =$ sum of 1 and a carry of 0

$1 + 0 =$ sum of 1 and a carry of 0

$1 + 1 =$ sum of 0 and a carry of 1

An electronic circuit which performs this type of addition is known as a **half-adder** (see also Chapter 15) because it does not deal with the *carry-in* from a previous addition stage.

A **full-adder** is a circuit which handles not only the addend and the augend of the present addition, but also any carry-in from the previous stage of addition. The operation of a full-adder is summarised as follows (see also Table 2.4).

If all inputs are '0', the SUM = '0' and CARRY-OUT = '0'
If one input is '1', the SUM = '1' and CARRY-OUT = '0'
If two inputs are '1', the SUM = '0' and CARRY-OUT = '1'
If all inputs are '1', the SUM = '1' and CARRY-OUT = '1'

We will illustrate the above by means of the following example.

TABLE 2.4 Truth table of a binary full-adder

Inputs			*Outputs*	
AUGEND	*ADDEND*	*CARRY-IN*	*SUM*	*CARRY-OUT*
0	0	0	0	0
0	0	1	1	0
0	1	0	1	0
0	1	1	0	1
1	0	0	1	0
1	0	1	0	1
1	1	0	0	1
1	1	1	1	1

Worked Example 2.5

Add the following 4-bit binary values: (a) 1101 and 1010, (b) 1011 and 1110.

Solution

(a) This example corresponds to $13_{10} + 10_{10} = 23_{10}$, and the final sum is the sum of the augend, the addend and the carry-in

augend		1	1	0	1
addend		1	0	1	0
carry-in	1	0	0	0	
	↖	↖	↖	↖	
carry-out		1	0	0	0
sum	1	0	1	1	1

As with the following example, we see that the addition of two 4-bit numbers results in a number whose length is 5 bits. In fact, *it is generally the case that when we add two n-bit values together, the sum may be (n+1) bits long*. All calculators and computers are designed to deal with this fact.

(b) In this case the sum is equivalent to $11_{10} + 14_{10} = 25_{10}$

augend		1	0	1	1
addend		1	1	1	0
carry-in	1	1	1	0	
	↖	↖	↖	↖	
carry-out		1	1	1	0
sum	1	1	0	0	1

2.11 Unsigned and signed binary numbers

Up to this point, we have assumed that all binary values are positive, that is they are **unsigned numbers**. The negative sign is a man-made concept which cannot be understood by computers and electronic circuits. In the following discussion, we will restrict our attention to 8-bit (one byte) numbers; when dealing with the 8-bit unsigned number $1000\,0000_2$, it has the decimal value $+128_{10}$, and the number $1111\,1111_2$ has the decimal value $+255_{10}$.

A method universally adopted in electronic systems is to assign the *most significant bit* (msb) of a **signed binary number** as a **sign bit**. If the value of the sign bit is '0', then we are dealing with a positive value; that is, the *largest positive value* that an 8-bit signed binary word can store is $0111\ 1111_2$ or $+127_{10}$. If the sign bit is '1', then we are dealing with a negative number; negative numbers are stored in what is known as *binary complement form*. There are two forms of complement representation, which are explained in section 2.12.

From the above we therefore see that, when dealing with signed numbers, 0101 0101 is a *positive value*, and 1010 1010 is a *negative value* which is stored in binary complement form.

2.12 Negative binary values

As mentioned above, there are two forms of binary complement notation, and they are the **1's complement** and **2's complement** (or **true complement**), respectively.

The *1's complement* representation of a binary number is obtained as follows

Change the 0's into 1's, and the 1's into 0's throughout the number.

The *2's complement* representation of a binary number is obtained by either of the following methods

1. **Form the 1's complement of the number, and add '1' to the least significant bit of the number so formed.**
2. **Copy the number (commencing at the lsb) up to and including the least significant '1'; thereafter, change all the 1's into 0's and 0's into 1's.**

Examples of 8-bit binary numbers and their complement form are given in Table 2.5.

TABLE 2.5 Binary numbers and their complements

Example	*Binary number*	*1's complement*	*2's complement*
(i)	0000 0000	1111 1111	0000 0000
(ii)	0000 0001	1111 1110	1111 1111
(iii)	0101 0101	1010 1010	1010 1011
(iv)	1000 0001	0111 1110	0111 1111
(v)	1111 1111	0000 0000	0000 0001

Example (i) is interesting in that we see that the 2's complement of binary zero has the same binary form as the number itself, i.e. $0 = \pm 0$! The reader will note that the 1's complement of zero is quite different, the '1' in the msb position indicating that -0 has a negative value.

The binary number in Examples (ii) and (iii) both have a '0' in the msb position, indicating that the original number has a positive value. Both of the complement forms have a '1' in the msb position, indicating that they are negative values, and are stored in *complement notation*.

The binary numbers in Examples (iv) and (v) are negative values (indicated by the '1' in the msb position), and the complement forms have a '0' in the same position, indicating that they are positive values. It is interesting to observe that the binary number in Example (v) corresponds to -1, and the 'negative' of this (or $-(-1)$) is shown as 0000 0000 in the 1's complement notation; caution is therefore necessary when dealing with signed binary numbers.

The use of binary complement notation is illustrated in section 2.13.

2.13 Binary subtraction

If $b - c = d$, b is the **minuend**, c the **subtrahend** and d the **difference**. To subtract c from b, we must form the 'negative' of the subtrahend (i.e. form the complement of the number), and add it to b; that is

$$b - c = b + (-c) = d$$

The rule for the subtraction process depends on whether we are using the 2's complement or the 1's complement; both rules are described below.

(a) Subtraction using the signed 2's complement

The 2's complement of the subtrahend is added to the minuend. If the sign bit of the result is '0', then the result is the true difference; if the sign bit is '1', the result is the 2's complement of the difference. Any overflow (NOT the sign bit) produced by the calculation is 'lost'.

(b) Subtraction using the signed 1's complement

The 1's complement of the subtrahend is added to the minuend, the sum being known as the *uncorrected sum*. Any overflow (NOT the sign bit) from the calculation is added to the least significant bit of the uncorrected sum (known as the *end-around carry*) to give the *corrected sum*. If the sign bit of the corrected sum is '0', the result is the true difference; if the sign bit of the corrected sum is '1', the result is the 1's complement of the difference.

The use of these rules is illustrated in Worked Example 2.6.

Worked Example 2.6

Convert the following numbers into pure binary, and calculate the result using both 2's complement and 1's complement notation; (a) $7.75_{10} - 5.25_{10}$, (b) $5.25_{10} - 7.75_{10}$.

Solution

Initially we will convert the values 7.75_{10} and 5.25_{10} into their 8-bit binary equivalents using the method outlined in section 2.8

$$+7.75_{10} \equiv 0111.1100_2$$
$$+5.25_{10} \equiv 0101.0100_2$$

2's complement solution

Using the method described in section 2.12 we get

$$-7.75_{10} \equiv 1000.0100_2 \quad \text{(2's complement form)}$$
$$-5.25_{10} \equiv 1010.1100_2 \quad \text{(2's complement form)}$$

(a)

$$\begin{array}{lr} +7.75_{10} \equiv & 0111.1100_2 \\ -5.25_{10} \equiv & 1010.1100_2 \\ \hline \text{sum} & (1)0010.1000_2 \equiv +2.5_{10} \end{array}$$

(1) → overflow (lost)

(b)

$$\begin{array}{lr} +5.25_{10} \equiv & 0101.0100_2 \\ -7.75_{10} \equiv & 1000.0100_2 \\ \hline \text{sum} & 1101.1000_2 \end{array} \quad \text{negative solution}$$

Since the answer is negative, the 'true' difference is obtained by taking the 2's complement of the answer, and giving it a negative sign. That is

$$\text{difference} = -(0010.1000_2) \equiv -2.5_{10}$$

1's complement solution

In this case

$$-7.75_{10} \equiv 1000.0011_2 \quad \text{(1's complement form)}$$
$$-5.25_{10} \equiv 1010.1011_2 \quad \text{(1's complement form)}$$

(a)

$$\begin{array}{lr} +7.75_{10} \equiv & 0111.1100_2 \\ -5.25_{10} \equiv & 1010.1011_2 \\ \hline \text{uncorrected sum} & (1)0010.0111_2 \\ \text{'end around carry'} & \to 1 \\ \hline \text{corrected sum} & 0010.1000_2 \equiv +2.5_{10} \end{array}$$

(b)

$$
\begin{array}{rr}
+5.25_{10} \equiv & 0101.0100_2 \\
-7.75_{10} \equiv & 1000.0011_2 \\
\hline
& (0)1101.0111_2 \\
\text{'end around carry'} & \rightarrow 0 \\
\hline
\text{corrected sum} & 1101.0111_2 \quad \text{negative solution}
\end{array}
$$

Since the answer is negative, the 'true' difference is obtained by taking the 1's complement of the answer and giving it a negative sign as follows

$$\text{difference} = -(0010.1000_2) \equiv -2.5_{10}$$

2.14 Binary multiplication

Given that $A \times B = C$, A is the **multiplicand**, B the **multiplier** and C the **product**. The operations in *hand multiplication* of binary numbers is generally similar to hand multiplication of decimal numbers, with the exception that we only need multiply by '1' or by '0', as illustrated in Worked Example 2.7.

The process of multiplication in calculators and computers is much the same, other than that the various computer 'words' are stored in *registers* inside the machine, and the product is stored in a special 'double length' register (because the product is 'longer' than the multiplicand or the multiplier).

Worked Example 2.7

Multiply 1001.1_2 (9.5_{10}) by 101.1_2 (5.5_{10}).

Solution

Initially we 'remove' the binary points, and proceed as follows

$$
\begin{array}{lrl}
\text{multiplicand} & 10011 & \\
\text{multiplier} & 1011 & \\
\hline
 & 10011 & \text{multiplier bit} = 1 \\
\text{partial products} & 10011 & \text{multiplier bit} = 1 \\
 & 00000 & \text{multiplier bit} = 0 \\
 & 10011 & \text{multiplier bit} = 1 \\
\hline
\text{sum of partial products} & 11010001 &
\end{array}
$$

Since the multiplier has a length of 4 bits, there are four partial products (as shown above, the position of the binary point is ignored at this stage). These are added to give the overall product. The position of the binary point is fixed by counting the total number of fractional points in the multiplicand and in the multiplier, which is $(1 + 1) = 2$. That is

$$1001.1_2 \times 101.1_2 = 110100.01_2 = 52.25_{10}$$

2.15 Binary division

If $A/B = C$, A is the **dividend**, B the **divisor** and C the **quotient**. The process of division by hand is generally similar to that for decimal numbers but, in this case, we perform the subtraction process by adding the 2's complement of the divisor, as illustrated in Worked Example 2.8.

In a calculator or in a computer, the dividend and the quotient is stored in a register and, generally, the maximum length of the quotient depends on the length of the register (or number of registers) in which it is stored.

Worked Example 2.8

Divide 1011.01_2 (11.25_{10}) by 100.1_2 (4.5_{10}).

Solution

To overcome any problems which may occur due to the decimal point, we convert the ratio into an 'integer' ratio as follows

$$\frac{1011.01}{100.1} = \frac{1011.01 \times 2^2}{100.1 \times 2^2} = \frac{101101}{10010}$$

That is, we 'move' both binary points two places to the right, and the overall value of the ratio is unchanged

	10.1	quotient
divisor	10010)101101	dividend
	01110	2's complement of divisor
(1) is lost ⟵	(1)00100	ADD, record '1' in quotient
	1001	'Bring down' next bit
		Division not possible
	10010	'Bring down' a 0 and record '0' in quotient.
	01110	2's complement of divisor
(1) is lost ⟵	(1)00000	ADD, record '1' in quotient

That is

$$\frac{1011.01_2}{100.1_2} = 10.1_2 \equiv 2.5_{10}$$

Each time we can divide by the divisor we record a '1' in the quotient line, and add the 2's complement of the divisor.

If, after 'bringing down' the next bit after the divisor has been subtracted, the difference is too small for division, a '0' is recorded in the quotient, and we bring down the next bit (or a '0' if we have moved beyond the length of the dividend), and proceed as normal.

Self-test questions

2.1 Convert the following into their decimal equivalents (a) 7852_9, (b) 2734_8, (c) 253_6, (d) 421_5, (e) $95c_{16}$, (f) 93.1_{14}, (g) 1011.01_2, (h) $73.f_{16}$.

2.2 Translate the following decimal numbers into their pure binary equivalents (a) 5268, (b) 23.75, (c) 0.0125.

2.3 Translate the decimal numbers in question 2.2 into hexadecimal.

2.4 Convert the following fractions into pure binary numbers (a) $\frac{1}{16}$, (b) $\frac{7}{8}$, (c) $\frac{2}{3}$, (d) $\frac{17}{32}$.

2.5 Convert the following decimal numbers into values with the radix indicated (a) 989 into radix 8, (b) 732 into radix 6, (c) 876 into radix 5, (d) 932 into radix 3.

2.6 Convert the following numbers into the system with the radix indicated (a) 857_9 into radix 6, (b) 576_8 into radix 9, (c) 222_5 into radix 3.

2.7 Write down the 2421 BCD value for decimal 896.

2.8 Convert the following decimal numbers into pure binary and add them together using binary arithmetic (a) $4 + 7$, (b) $16 + 20$, (c) $17.5 + 12.75$, (d) $5\frac{5}{16} + 2\frac{3}{8}$, (e) $7.5 + 5.3 + 5\frac{7}{8}$.

2.9 Convert the following decimal numbers into pure binary and subtract them using binary arithmetic: (a) $5 - 2$, (b) $20 - 10$, (c) $4 - 5$, (d) $6.25 - 4.25$, (e) $7 - 2.5 - 3\frac{3}{4}$.

2.10 Convert the following decimal numbers into pure binary and multiply them using binary arithmetic (a) 6×3, (b) 7.5×3.75, (c) 0.25×4.25, (d) $0.5 \times 4 \times 0.3$, (e) -2×6.

2.11 Divide the following using binary arithmetic (a) 6/3, (b) 7.5/2.5, (c) 1.125/6, (d) 24.375/3.75.

Summary of important facts

The **decimal** or **denary** numbering system, having a base or **radix** of 10, is most convenient to man, but computers and electronic systems use **binary** systems. The **pure binary system** has a radix of two (i.e., the numbers '0' and '1' are used), the **octal system** has a radix of 8 (0 to 7), the **hexadecimal system** has a radix of 16 (0 to 15), etc. Hexadecimal numbers are 'numbered' 0, 1, 2, 3, 4, 5, 6, 7, 8, 9, a, b, c, d, e, and f.

There are a range of **binary-coded decimal** (BCD) systems which are used as an intermediate code between the binary and decimal codes. Some BCD codes are **weighted codes** in which each character has its own value or 'weight' (some of them being *negatively weighted*), and other codes (the majority of BCD codes) are *unweighted*. Some of the latter have special use in engineering.

The **radix point** serves to separate the integer part of a number from the fractional part (in the decimal system we call it the *decimal point*, and in a binary system it is the *binary point*).

A **binary digit** is described as a **bit**, and a group of eight consecutive bits as a **byte**. The **word length** of a computer or a calculator is usually an integral number of bytes, i.e., 8 bits, 16 bits, 32 bits, etc.

The process of converting a number of one radix to a number of another radix is fairly straightforward, and is explained in sections 2.4–2.7.

In **addition**, $x + y = z$, where x is the **augend**, y the **addend** and z the **sum**. If the sum of *two digits* exceeds the radix of the system, a **carry-out** is produced; this becomes the **carry-in** for the addition of the next higher pair of digits. An electronic **half-adder** adds two bits together, but does not deal with the carry-in from a lower-order addition. A **full-adder** adds two bits together with the carry-in from the previous stage.

The **negative sign** is a man-made concept and in an **unsigned binary number**, the value of the number is always positive. In a **signed binary number**, the **most significant bit** (msb) is the **sign bit**. If the msb is '0', then the number is stored as a true binary number. If the msb is '1', the number is negative and is stored in a **binary complement form**. The two types of binary complement notation are the **one's complement** and the **two's complement** (or **true complement**) form. Full details are given in section 2.12.

In **subtraction**, $b - c = d$, where b is the **minuend**, c the **subtrahend**, and d the **difference**. To subtract c from b, we *add* the 2's complement of c to b. If the resulting sign bit is '0', the result is the true difference. If the sign bit is '1', the result is negative and is stored in binary complement form. Any 'overflow' from the calculation is 'lost'.

Binary **multiplication** *by hand* is carried out in much the same way as decimal multiplication by hand. Also binary **division** *by hand* is carried out in much the same way as decimal division by hand, but any subtraction is performed using binary complement addition.

3 Logarithms, the decibel and the Neper

3.1 Introduction

An early aid to calculation was the use of logarithms, which simplified the process of multiplication and division. Many variables both in life and in engineering have a logarithmic relationship between them; these include transients in circuits, and frequency response of electronic amplifiers and transmission lines. All students of engineering need not only to understand the basic properties of logarithms, but also how to apply them in practice.

By the end of this chapter the reader will be able to

- understand the principle of logarithms,
- multiply, divide and determine the value of roots and powers using logarithms,
- perform calculations using decibels (dB) and nepers,
- perform calculations using natural or naperian logarithms,
- convert a logarithm of one base into a logarithm of another base.

3.2 The principle of logarithms

Consider the calculation 100×1000. Although we can perform this mentally, we will use it as a simple illustration of the way in which the logarithm of a number is formed, and how multiplication is carried out using logarithms.

Using a base of 10, we can see that

$$100 = 10^2 \text{ and } 1000 = 10^3$$

and

$$100 \times 1000 = 10^2 \times 10^3 = 10^{(2+3)} = 10^5 = 100\,000$$

If we describe the power to which the base is raised to give the number as the **logarithm of the number**, then

$$2 = \text{logarithm of 100 to base 10}$$
$$3 = \text{logarithm of 1000 to base 10}$$
$$5 = \text{logarithm of 100 000 to base 10}$$

We can see from the above example that **the logarithm of the product is the sum of the logarithms of the numbers which are multiplied together**.

Next we will look at the division process 100 000/100 in the following.

$$\frac{100\,000}{100} = 10^{(5-2)} = 10^3 = 1000$$

Once again we see that

5 = logarithm of 100 000 to base 10
2 = logarithm of 100 to base 10
3 = logarithm of 1000 to base 10

That is, **the logarithm of a quotient is obtained by subtracting the logarithm of the divisor from the logarithm of the dividend**.

From the above examples we see that we can define a logarithm as follows

> **The logarithm of a number is the power to which the base must be raised in order to give the number**.

If y is a *number*, b is the *base of the logarithm system*, and x is the *logarithm*, then

$$y = b^x$$

Although we cannot prove the following statement, the logarithm x is given by

$$x = \log_b y$$

The right-hand side of this equation is read as 'the logarithm of y to base b'.

It was shown in Chapter 1 that

$$b^0 = 1$$

where b is *any base value*, i.e. it could be 2, 10, 15, etc. That is

$$\log_b 1 = 0$$

that is, **the logarithm of 1 to any base is zero**. This clearly implies that *the logarithm of a number greater than 1 has a positive value, and the logarithm of a number less than 1 has a negative value.*

Also from the above we see that

$$1000 = 10^3 \text{ or } \log_{10} 1000 = 3$$

and

$$1000^2 = (10^3)^2 = 10^{(2x3)} = 10^6 = 1\,000\,000$$

That is

$$\log_{10} 1000^2 = \log_{10} 1\,000\,000 = 6$$

or

$$\log_{10} 1000^2 = 2 \times \log_{10} 1000 = 2 \times 3 = 6$$

This means that

> **the logarithm of a number which is raised to a power is equal to the product of the power and the logarithm of the number.**

We can express this as follows.

$$\log_b x^m = m \log_b x$$

for example

$$\log_{10} 2^3 = 3 \log_{10} 2$$

Also, since $b^1 = b$ then

$$\log_b b = 1$$

that is

$$\log_{10} 10 = 1$$
$$\log_2 2 = 1, \text{ etc.}$$

That is, **the logarithm of a number to its own base is unity.**

Additionally, the reader is asked to note that a negative number does not have a real logarithm. That is, **logarithms only exist for positive numbers.**

Worked Example 3.1

What is the logarithm of (a) 25 to base 5, (b) 27 to base 3?

Solution

The reader will recall that

number = base raised to the power of the logarithm

(a) Since $25 = 5^2$, then

logarithm of 25 to base 5 = 2

or

$$\log_5 25 = 2$$

(b) Here $27 = 3^3$, so that

logarithm of 27 to base 3 = 3

or

$$\log_3 27 = 3$$

3.3 Common logarithms or logarithms to base 10

A **common logarithm** has a base of 10, and the logarithm of a number x to base 10 is written as $\mathbf{lg}\, x$, $\mathbf{log}\, x$ or as $\mathbf{log_{10}}\, x$, where x is a decimal number.

We can evaluate the common logarithm of a number by working out the power to which 10 must be raised to give the number. If 10 is raised to 0.699, the results is 5, that is

$$5 = 10^{0.699}$$

hence

$$\log 5 = 0.699$$

That is, the logarithm of 5 to base 10 is 0.699. It also follows that the common logarithm of 500 can be determined as follows.

$$500 = 5 \times 100 = 10^{0.699} \times 10^2 = 10^{(2+0.699)}$$

or

$$\log 500 = 2.699$$

The integer part (2) of the logarithm is known as the **characteristic**, and the fractional part (0.699) is the **mantissa**. The reader should note that *the mantissa always has a positive value* (see below).

The logarithm of 0.5 is determined as follows.

$$0.5 = 5 \times 10^{-1} = 10^{0.699} \times 10^{-1}$$
$$= 10^{(-1+0.699)} = 10^{-0.301}$$

That is

$$\log 0.5 = -0.301$$

This is, in fact, the value which would be given by a calculator. Since the whole logarithm is negative, then *the characteristic of the logarithm (as defined above) is not 0, and 0.301 is not the mantissa.* When performing calculations by hand (or by tables of logarithms) we say that

$$\log 0.5 = -0.301 = -1 + 0.699 = \bar{1}.699$$

This value is described as 'bar one point six, nine, nine', and the characteristic has a value of -1 or $\bar{1}$, and the mantissa is $+0.699$. In tables of common (and other) logarithms, *only the mantissae values are listed.*

The logarithm of 0.0005 is determined as follows.

$$0.0005 = 5 \times 10^{-4} = 10^{0.699} \times 10^{-4} = 10^{(-4+0.699)}$$

hence

$$\log 0.0005 = -4 + 0.699 = -3.301$$

or, alternatively

$$\log 0.0005 = \bar{4}.699 \text{ (bar 4 point six, nine, nine)}$$

Also

$$0 = \frac{1}{\infty} = \frac{1}{10^{\infty}} = 10^{-\infty}$$

That is

$$\lg 0 = -\infty$$

That is, **the logarithm of zero is minus infinity** (this is also the case for the logarithm of zero to any base!)

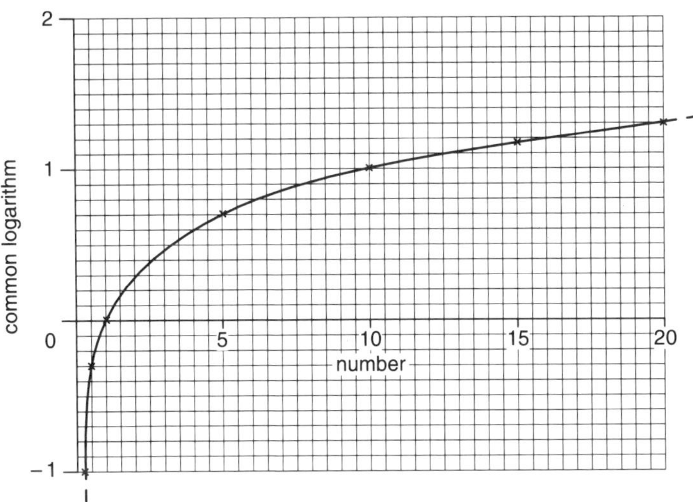

Figure 3.1 Graph showing the value of the common logarithm of a range of numbers

A graph showing how the common logarithm of a number in the range from about 0.1 to 20 changes is shown in Figure 3.1.

Worked Example 3.2

Given that $7.01 = 10^{0.8457}$, determine the common logarithm of (a) 701, (b) 70.1, (c) 7.01, (d) 0.701, (e) 0.00701.

Solution

(a) $701 = 100 \times 7.01 = 10^2 \times 10^{0.8457} = 10^{(2+0.8457)}$
$= 10^{2.8457}$

That is $\log 701 = 2.8457$

(b) $70.1 = 10 \times 7.01 = 10^1 \times 10^{0.8457} = 10^{(1+0.8457)}$
$= 10^{1.8457}$

That is $\log 70.1 = 1.8457$

(c) $7.01 = 10^{0.8457}$

That is $\log 7.01 = 0.8457$

(d) $0.701 = 0.1 \times 7.01 = 10^{-1} \times 10^{0.8457}$

$= 10^{(-1+0.8457)} = 10^{-0.1543}$

That is $\log 70.1 = -0.1553$ or $\bar{1}.8457$

(e) $0.00701 = 10^{-3} \times 7.01 = 10^{-3} \times 10^{0.8457}$

$= 10^{(-3+0.8457)} = 10^{-2.1543}$

That is $\log 0.00701 = -2.1543$ or $\bar{3}.8457$

3.4 Antilogarithms – the reverse of logarithms

In section 3.2 we saw that

$$\text{number} = \text{base}^{\text{logarithm}}$$

That is, the value of a number is equal to the base raised to the logarithm of the number. If, for example, the logarithm of a number raised to base 10 is 1.699 then, using a calculator, we can show that

$$\text{number} = 10^{1.699} = 50$$

The process of determining the value of a number from its logarithm is known as taking the **antilogarithm** of the logarithm. If the value of a logarithm is $\bar{1}.78$ (or $[-1 + 0.78] = -0.22$), then the value of the number is

$$\text{number} = 10^{-0.22} = 1/10^{0.22} = 1/1.696 = 0.6026$$

3.5 Multiplication using common logarithms

Multiplication is carried out by **adding the logarithms of the numbers, and taking the antilogarithm of the answer**.

For example the product of 28.2 and 54.3 is obtained as follows.

Number	*Logarithm*
28.2	1.4502
54.3	1.7348
ADD	3.1850

We determine the antilogarithm of the product either by using a calculator or a set of antilogarithm tables as follows. Using a *calculator*, the answer is determined as follows

$$\text{product} = 10^{3.185} = 1531$$

Alternatively, we use the mantissa (0.1850) in association with a set of *antilogarithm tables* as follows

$$\text{antilog}\, 0.1850 = 1.531$$

and the characteristic (3) of the product tells us that this value is multiplied by 10^3. That is, the product is

$$1.531 \times 10^3 = 1.531 \times 1000 = 1531$$

Let us now consider the product 3.6×0.0005. There are two ways of doing this, as shown below

Number	*Logarithm*	
3.6	0.5563	0.5563
0.0005	$\bar{4}.6990$	−3.3010
	$\bar{3}.2553$	−2.7447

The left-hand set of logarithms shown above assumes that we are using a set of common logarithm tables, whilst the right-hand solution assumes that we are using a calculator.

When dealing with the left-hand set of logarithms, we simply add the mantissae as normal positive values, and the carry of 1 from the fractional part simply cancels 1 from the sum of the 'bar' values, making $\bar{4}$ into $\bar{3}$ in the solution. In the case of the right-hand set of results, it is simply a matter of adding (−3.3010) to +0.5563.

The solution can be obtained from the left-hand calculation using a set of antilogarithms as follows

$$\begin{aligned}\text{solution} &= 10^{-3} \times \text{antilog}\, 0.2553 = 10^{-3} \times 1.8 \\ &= 0.0018\end{aligned}$$

Using a calculator, the result is

$$\text{result} = 10^{-2.7447} = 0.0018$$

3.6 Division using common logarithms

Division is performed by **subtracting the logarithm of the divisor from the logarithm of the dividend**. Consider the calculation 263/5.8, which is performed below

Number	*Logarithm*
263	2.4200
5.8	0.7634
SUBTRACT	1.6566

Using a calculator the solution is evaluated directly as follows

$$263/5.8 = 10^{1.6566} = 45.35$$

Alternatively, using a set of antilogarithm tables, the mantissa (0.6566) and the characteristic (1) can be used to determine the solution as follows.

$$\begin{aligned}\text{solution} &= 10^1 \times \text{antilog}\, 0.6566 \\ &= 10 \times 4.535 = 45.35\end{aligned}$$

In the above calculation we have used 4-figure logarithms, and it is of interest to note that there is an error of only about −0.01 per cent in the calculation due to the restriction of the number length to four figures.

Next we will consider the calculation 2.6/372, as follows.

Number	*Logarithm*	
Dividend	2.6	0.4150
Divisor	372	2.5705
	SUBTRACT	$-2.1555 \equiv \bar{3}.8445$

The answer can be determined either by means of a calculator or a set of antilogarithm tables as follows. Using a calculator, we get

$$\text{answer} = 10^{-2.1555} = 0.00699$$

From the tables we obtain

$$\text{answer} = 10^{-3} \times \text{antilog}\, 0.8445 = 10^{-3} \times 7 = 0.007$$

Worked Example 3.3

Evaluate the following using logarithms: (a) 45.8 × 26.35, (b) 4.58/26.35, (c) 4.58 × 2.635/37.5.

Solution

(a)

Number	*Logarithm*
45.8	1.6609
26.35	1.4208
ADD	3.0816

That is $48.5 \times 26.35 = \text{antilog}\, 3.0816 = 10^{3.0816} = 1206.8.$

(b)

Number	*Logarithm*
4.58	0.6609
26.35	1.4208
SUBTRACT	$-0.7599 \equiv \bar{1}.2402$

That is $4.85/26.35 = \text{antilog}\, \bar{1}.2402 = 10^{-0.7599} = 0.1738.$

(c)

Number	*Logarithm*
4.58	0.6609
2.635	0.4208
ADD	1.0817
37.5	1.5740
SUBTRACT	$-0.4923 = \bar{1}.5077$

Hence $4.58 \times 2.635/37.5 = \text{antilog}\,\bar{1}.5077 = 10^{-0.4923}$
$= 0.3219.$

3.7 Calculation of roots and powers using logarithms

To determine the value of a number raised to a power, multiply the logarithm of the number by the power, and evaluate the antilogarithm.

The reader will recall, of course, that a root of a number is the fractional power, i.e., the cube root of a number implies that the number is raised to the power 1/3.

Worked Example 3.4

Evaluate (a) $\sqrt{(2.53 \times 4.9)}$, (b) $(5.6 \times 0.15)^{1/3}$, (c) 4^{-2}, (d) $0.167^{-1.6}$.

Solution

(a) Initially we will complete the calculation under the square root sign, after which we evaluate the square root of the logarithm.

Number	*Logarithm*
2.53	0.4031
4.9	0.6902
ADD	1.0933

$$\sqrt{(2.53 \times 4.9)} = \text{antilog}\,(1.0933/2)$$
$$= \text{antilog}\,0.5467 = 10^{0.5467} = 3.5209$$

(b)

Number	*Logarithm*		
5.6	0.7482		0.7482
0.15	−0.8239	or	$\bar{1}.1761$
ADD	−0.0757	or	$\bar{1}.9243$

Using the left-hand result in association with a calculator gives

$$(5.6 \times 0.15)^{1/3} = \text{antilog}\,(-0.0737/3)$$
$$= \text{antilog}\,(-0.0252) = 10^{-0.0252} = 0.9436$$

The above method is to be preferred when evaluating the solution, because a little more care is needed when we use the right-hand result. In this case, we must make the characteristic of the logarithm exactly divisible by 3, as follows

$$\bar{1}.9243 = -1 + 0.9243 = (-1 - 2) + (2 + 0.9243)$$
$$= -3 + 2.9243$$

and

$$(5.6 \times 0.15)^{1/3} = \text{antilog}\,((-3 + 2.9243)/3)$$
$$= \text{antilog}\,(-1 + 0.9748) = \text{antilog}\,(\bar{1}.9748)$$
$$= 0.9436$$

(c) In this case $\lg 4 = 0.6021$
hence

$$4^{-2} = \text{antilog}\,(0.6021 \times (-2)) = \text{antilog}\,(-1.2041)$$
$$= 10^{-1.2041} = 0.0625$$

Note: $4^{-2} = 1/4^2 = 1/16 = 0.0625$

(d) $\log 0.167 = -0.7773$ or $\bar{1}.2227$
therefore

$$0.167^{-1.6} = \text{antilog}\,(-0.7773 \times (-1.6))$$
$$= \text{antilog}\,1.2437 = 17.52$$

Note: $0.167^{-1.6} = 1/0.167^{1.6} = 1/0.0571 = 17.52$

3.8 The decibel

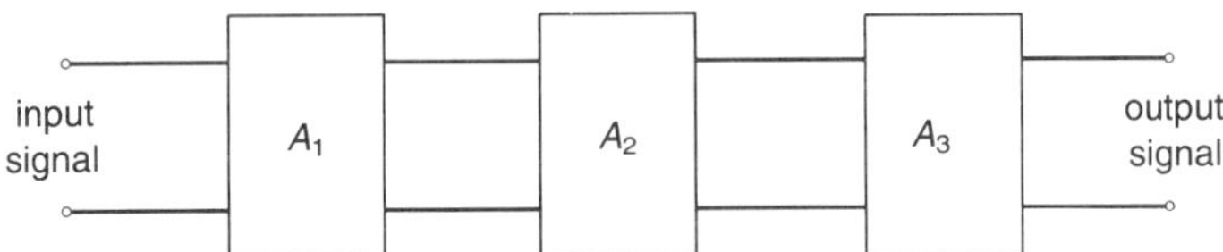

Figure 3.2 Cascaded electronic units

Many electronic systems contain cascaded units (see Figure 3.2), so that the signal applied to the input terminals is initially 'multiplied' or increased in magnitude by the 'gain' A_1 of the first stage; the magnitude of the signal applied to the second stage is therefore ($A_1 \times$ input signal).

The second stage of the amplifier increases the gain by A_2, and the third stage increases the gain by A_3. The overall gain between the input terminals and the output is therefore ($A_1 \times A_2 \times A_3$). If each of these values is a power gain (do not confuse this with the *voltage gain* or the *current gain* of the stages, for the reason described later), then the overall **power gain**, A_P, of the circuit is

$$A_P = A_1 \times A_2 \times A_3$$

Clearly, there is some advantage to be gained by calculating the logarithmic gain of an amplifier, because *we merely need to add the logarithmic gains together in order to determine the overall logarithmic gain.*

If the *input power* applied to the amplifier is P_{in}, and the *output power* from the amplifier is P_{out}, then

$$A_P = \frac{P_{out}}{P_{in}}$$

The common logarithmic gain of the amplifier is given by

$$\log \frac{P_{out}}{P_{in}}$$

The unit for this gain is the **Bel** (B) (named after Alexander Graham Bell, who patented the telephone). If, for example $P_{out} = 2\,\text{W}$ and $P_{in} = 0.1\,\text{W}$, then the logarithmic power gain is

$$\log \frac{2}{0.1} = \log 20 = 1.301\,\text{B}$$

Unfortunately, the Bel is much too large a unit to be used in practice, and the usual unit is the **decibel** (dB), where

$$1\,\text{B} = 10\,\text{dB}$$

so that we express the power gain in dB in the form

$$10 \log \frac{P_{out}}{P_{in}}$$

Using the above values we get

$$10 \log \frac{2}{0.1} = 10 \log 20 = 13.01\,\text{dB}$$

Some items of equipment, such as potentiometers, reduce or **attenuate** the magnitude of the signal. For example, if the power applied to an attenuator is 0.5 W, and the output power is 0.1 W, then the ‘power gain’ *in* is

$$\log \frac{0.1}{0.5} = \log 0.2 = -0.699\,\text{B}$$

or

$$10 \log \frac{0.1}{0.5} = 10 \log 0.2 = -6.99\,\text{dB}$$

This is described as ‘an attenuation of 6.99 dB’. The reader should note that when we are dealing with attenuators, we use negative logarithmic values (not ‘bar’ logarithmic values, i.e. we do not describe the above attenuation as $\bar{7}.01$).

Worked Example 3.5

The power 'gain' of each stage of a 3-stage electronic amplifier are, respectively, 6.5 dB, 3.6 dB and −5 dB. Calculate the overall power gain (a) in dB, (b) numerically. If the input power is 0.1 mW, what is the output power?

Solution

(a) The overall power gain in dB is

$$A_P = 6.5 + 3.6 - 5 = 5.1\,\text{dB}$$

(b) Since

$$\text{dB power gain} = 10\log\frac{P_{out}}{P_{in}}$$

then, using our knowledge of logarithms, it follows that

$$\log\frac{P_{out}}{P_{in}} = \frac{\text{dB power gain}}{10}$$

or

$$\frac{P_{out}}{P_{in}} = 10^{(\text{dB powergain}/10)} = 10^{5.1/10} = 10^{0.51} = 3.24$$

That is, the amplifier provides a power amplification of 3.24, hence

$$\text{output power} = 3.24 \times 0.1\,\text{mW} = 0.324\,\text{mW}.$$

3.9 Voltage and current ratios in decibels

The power consumed in a resistor is I^2R, so that if power values of P_1 and P_2 are consumed in resistor R when currents I_1 and I_2, respectively, flow in it, then the *numerical power ratio* P_2/P_1 is

$$\frac{P_2}{P_1} = \frac{I_2{}^2R}{I_1{}^2R} = \frac{I_2{}^2}{I_1{}^2} = \left[\frac{I_2}{I_1}\right]^2$$

hence the **current power ratio** in dB is

$$10\log\frac{P_2}{P_1} = 10\log\left[\frac{I_2}{I_1}\right]^2 = 10 \times 2\log\left[\frac{I_2}{I_1}\right] = 20\log\left[\frac{I_2}{I_1}\right] = 20\log A_I$$

where A_I is the **numerical current amplification** or **current gain**. Similarly, the power P_2 consumed in R can be expressed in the form $V_2{}^2/R$, and the power P_1 consumed in R can be expressed in the form $V_1{}^2/R$, where V_2 and V_1 are the respective voltages across R when P_2 and P_1 are consumed. The **voltage power ratio** in dB is therefore

$$10\log\frac{P_2}{P_1} = 10\log\frac{V_2^2/R}{V_1^2/R} = 10\log\left[\frac{V_2}{V_1}\right]^2$$

$$= 20\log\left[\frac{V_2}{V_1}\right] = 20\log A_V$$

where A_V is the **numerical voltage amplification** or **voltage gain** of the amplifier.

In the above equations we have assumed that both P_1 and P_2 are developed in the same value of resistance. In practice, P_1 may be the input resistance of an amplifier (which usually has a high value), and P_2 may be developed in a load such as a loudspeaker (which may have a low resistance). This difference in resistance value is conveniently overlooked by engineers, and it is assumed that the two values of resistance are equal to one another! The reader should refer to Worked Example 3.6 for a typical case.

Worked Example 3.6

A 100 mV alternating signal is applied to the input of an amplifier whose input impedance is 10 kΩ. If the amplifier supplies a power of 10 W to a loudspeaker of resistance 8 Ω, calculate the power gain and the voltage gain of the amplifier in dB.

Solution

The input power to the amplifier is

$$P_1 = \frac{(\text{input voltage})^2}{\text{input resistance}} = \frac{(100 \times 10^{-3})^2}{10\,000} = 1 \times 10^{-6}\,\text{W or } 1\,\mu\text{W}$$

Since the output power is 10 W, the power gain in dB is

$$\text{dB power gain} = 10\log\frac{\text{output power}}{\text{input power}} = 10\log\frac{10}{10^{-6}}$$

$$= 10\log 10^7 = 10 \times 7 = 70\,\text{dB}$$

The output voltage is

$$V_{out} = \sqrt{(\text{output power} \times \text{output resistance})}$$

$$= \sqrt{(10 \times 8)} = 8.94\,V$$

Even though the input power is developed in the 10 kΩ input resistance, and the output power is developed in an 8 Ω loudspeaker, we ignore the relative values of resistance, and say that

$$\text{voltage gain} = 20\log\frac{\text{output voltage}}{\text{input voltage}} = 20\log\frac{8.94}{0.1}$$

$$= 20 \times 1.951 = 39.02\,\text{dB}$$

3.10 Natural logarithms (Naperian or hyperbolic logarithms)

In 1614 a Scottish farmer-mathematician named John Napier published a paper entitled 'Description of the Marvellous Rule of Logarithms', which included the first tables of logarithms, called **natural logarithms**, for aiding calculations. These logarithms, which use the base e (= 2.71828 ...), are also called **Naperian logarithms** in his honour and, in fact, there was an early calculator known as *Napier's bones*. The value of e can be calculated from

$$e = 1 + \frac{1}{1} + \frac{1}{1 \times 2} + \frac{1}{1 \times 2 \times 3} + \frac{1}{1 \times 2 \times 3 \times 4} + \ldots \textit{ad infinitum}$$

Naperian logarithms are also called **hyperbolic logarithms**. The reader will find that naperian logarithms enter very largely into any work associated with engineering and physical science, and a knowledge and understanding of them is important.

The Naperian logarithm of a number x is written as $\mathbf{log}_e\,\boldsymbol{x}$ or $\mathbf{ln}\,\boldsymbol{x}$; we shall use the latter. The general rules applying to common logarithms also apply to natural logarithms. For example

$$\mathbf{log}_e \boldsymbol{e} = \mathbf{ln}\,\boldsymbol{e} = 1$$
$$\mathbf{log}_e\,1 = \mathbf{ln}\,1 = 0$$

The Naperian logarithm of a number greater than unity has a positive value, and the Naperian logarithm of a number less than unity has a negative value. Also

$$\ln(A \times B) = \ln A + \ln B$$
$$\ln(A/B) = \ln A - \ln B$$
$$\ln A^n = n \ln A$$

Using either a calculator or Naperian logarithm tables, we find that

$$\ln 3 = 1.0986$$

that is

$$2.71828^{1.0986} = 3$$

hence

$$\ln 30 = \ln(3 \times 10) = \ln 3 + \ln 10 = 1.0986 + 2.3026$$
$$= 3.4012$$

and

$$\ln 0.3 = \ln(3 \times 0.1) = \ln 3 + \ln 0.1$$
$$= 1.0986 - 2.3026 = -1.204 = -2 + 0.796$$
$$= \bar{2}.796$$

From the above equations

$$\ln(0.3 \times 30) = \ln 0.3 + \ln 30 = -1.204 + 3.4012$$
$$= 2.1972 = \ln 9$$

and

$$\ln(30/0.3) = \ln 30 - \ln 0.3 = 3.4012 - (-1.204) = 4.6052 = \ln 100$$

Also

$$\ln 100 = \ln 10^2 = 2 \ln 10 = 2 \times 2.3026 = 4.6052$$

Worked Example 3.7

A resistor and a capacitor are connected in series to a 10 V d.c. supply, and the voltage across the capacitor t seconds after the supply is connected is given by

$$v_C = 10(1 - e^{-0.2t})\ \text{V}$$

Calculate the voltage across the capacitor when $t = 3.5$ s. Determine also the time that has elapsed after the circuit is complete when v_C reaches 7.5 V.

Solution

Using a calculator we get, for $t = 3.5$ s

$$e^{-0.2t} = e^{-0.2 \times 3.5} = e^{-0.7} \approx 0.5$$

The voltage across the capacitor when $t = 3.5$ s is therefore

$$v_C = 10(1 - 0.5) = 10 \times 0.5 = 5\ \text{V}$$

From the question we know that

$$v_C = 10(1 - e^{-0.2t})$$

hence

$$\frac{v_C}{10} = 1 - e^{-0.2t}$$

or

$$e^{-0.2t} = 1 - \frac{v_C}{10}$$

Taking Naperian logarithms of both sides of the equation gives:

$$\text{LHS} = -0.2t \ln e = -0.2t$$

$$\text{RHS} = \ln\left[1 - \frac{v_C}{10}\right]$$

That is

$$-0.2t = \ln\left[1 - \frac{v_C}{10}\right]$$

or

$$t = \frac{1}{-0.2}\ln\left[1 - \frac{v_C}{10}\right] = -5\ln\left[1 - \frac{v_C}{10}\right]$$

Substituting the value of $v_C = 7.5\,\text{V}$, we get

$$t = -5\ln\left[1 - \frac{7.5}{10}\right] = -5\ln 0.25 = -5 \times (-1.3863)$$

$$= 6.9315\,\text{s}$$

3.11 The Neper

The **Neper** (N) is based on a current or voltage ratio (which should be compared with the Bel, which is based on a power ratio), and uses Naperian logarithms; it is mostly used in association with telecommunications systems.

If the current at one point in a circuit is I_1, and the current at another point is I_2, then

$$\text{current ratio in nepers} = \ln\frac{I_2}{I_1}\ \text{N}$$

If, for example, the current at the transmitting end of a transmission line (I_1) is 0.1 A, and it reduces (due to line leakage) to a value of 0.05 A further along the line, then the loss in nepers is

$$\ln\frac{0.05}{0.1} = \ln 0.5 = -0.6931\ \text{N}$$

If we calculate the *loss in decibels* we get

$$20\log\frac{0.05}{0.1} = 20\log 0.5 = 20 \times (-0.301) = -6.02\,\text{dB}$$

That is, a ratio of 1 dB is equivalent to

$$(-6.02/-0.6931) = 8.68\ \text{N}$$

3.12 Converting a logarithm of one base to another base

We saw in section 3.2 that if x is the logarithm of a number to base a, then

$$y = a^x \text{ and } x = \log_a y$$

If b is the base of another set of logarithms then

$$\log_b y = \log_b(a^x) = x \log_b a$$
$$= \log_a y \times \log_b a$$

or

$$\log_a y = \frac{\log_b y}{\log_b a}$$

Suppose that $b = 10$ (i.e. common logarithms), then the logarithm of y to some new base a is

$$\log_a y = \frac{\log_b y}{\log_b a} = \frac{\log_{10} y}{\log_{10} a} = \frac{\log y}{\log a}$$

At this stage we have manipulated the equation without fully explaining how we have done it; the reader should refer to Chapter 4 (Equations) for a full explanation of the method of manipulation.

Suppose that we wish to convert the common logarithm of 3 into its Naperian logarithm equivalent. In this case $a = 10$, $y = 3$ and b $(= e) = 2.718$, so that

$$\log_e 3 = \ln 3 = \frac{\log 0.3}{\log e} = \frac{0.4771}{0.4343} = 1.0985$$

If we wish to convert the logarithm to base 10 of 0.3 into base e, then $a = 10$, $y = 0.1$ and $b = 2.718$, and

$$\log_e 0.3 = \ln 0.3 = \frac{\log 0.3}{\log e} = \frac{-0.5229}{0.4343} = -1.204$$
$$= -2 + 0.796 = \bar{2}.796$$

Worked Example 3.8

Evaluate the following. (a) $\log_2 10$, (b) $\log_3 9$, (c) $\log_{2.5} 5.6$, (d) $\log_6 0.7$.

Solution

(a) $\log_2 10 = \dfrac{\log_{10} 10}{\log_{10} 2} = \dfrac{1}{0.3010} = 3.3219$

We can check this answer using a calculator which can handle powers as follows

$$\text{number} = \text{base}^{\text{logarithm}} = 2^{3.3219} = 10$$

(b) $\log_3 9 = \dfrac{\log_{10} 9}{\log_{10} 3} = \dfrac{0.9542}{0.4771} = 2$

(c) $\log_{2.5} 5.6 = \dfrac{\log_{10} 5.6}{\log_{10} 2.5} = \dfrac{0.7482}{0.3979} = 1.8802$

(d) $\log_6 0.7 = \dfrac{\log_{10} 0.7}{\log_{10} 6} = \dfrac{-0.1549}{0.7782} = -0.1991 = -1 + 0.8009 = \bar{1}.8009$

Self-test questions

3.1 Determine the common logarithm of (a) 5.72, (b) 73.7, (c) 909.2, (d) 0.572, (e) 0.00123.

3.2 For the following common logarithms, determine the antilogarithm of (a) 0.789, (b) 1.456, (c) 6.32, (d) $\bar{2}.76$.

3.3 Determine the Naperian logarithm of the numbers in question 3.1.

3.4 Determine the antilogarithm of the following Naperian logarithms (a) 0.79, (b) 2.36, (c) $\bar{2}.36$, (d) 5.8, (e) −1.2.

3.5 Using logarithms where possible, determine the common logarithm of (a) 7.6×5.4, (b) $7.6/5.4$, (c) $26.3 \times 5.7/(0.1 \times 10.9)$, (d) $((93.2 \times 6.2)/(9.7 + 7.2))^{-1}$, (e) $\sqrt{(59.2/(7.3 - 5.4))}$.

3.6 The voltage appearing across a component t seconds after a d.c. supply is connected is given by $v = 100(1 - e^{-t/50})$, where t is the time in seconds. Calculate the voltage when (a) $t = 35$ s and (b) $t = 50$ s after the supply is connected. How long does it take the voltage to rise to 80 V?

3.7 The current flowing in a circuit t seconds after a d.c. supply is connected is given by $i = 10(1 - e^{-t/0.1})$. Determine the time when the current is (a) 5 A, (b) 8.5 A.

3.8 In an electronic amplifier circuit the input current is 0.1 mA, and the output current is 0.008 A. Calculate the current gain (a) in dB, (b) in nepers.

3.9 Determine the value of (a) $\log_5 6$, (b) $\log_4 0.2$, (c) $\log_9 4$.

Summary of important facts

The **logarithm** of a number is the **power to which the base must be raised in order to give the number**. If y is the number, b is the base and x the logarithm, then

$$y = b^x$$

or

$$x = \log_b y$$

and x is the **logarithm of y to base b. A logarithm is only real for a positive number**.

An **antilogarithm** (or 'antilog') is the reverse of a logarithm. That is if $\log_b y = x$ then

$$\text{antilog}_b x = y = b^x$$

Common logarithms have a base of 10, and the common logarithm of y is written $\mathbf{\log_{10} y}$ or $\mathbf{\lg y}$. That is $y = 10^x$, and $x = \log_{10} y = \log y$.

Naperian logarithms, **natural logarithms** or **hyperbolic logarithms** use base e (= 2.71828...), and the Naperian logarithm of y is written $\mathbf{\log_e y}$ or $\mathbf{\ln y}$. That is $y = e^x$, and $x = \log_e y = \ln y$.

The laws of logarithms (to any base) include the following.

$$\mathbf{\log (A \times B) = \log A + \log B}$$

$$\mathbf{\log (A/B) = \log A / \log B}$$

$$\mathbf{\log A^n = n \log A}$$

$$\mathbf{\log 1 = 0}$$

The **change of base rule** for logarithms is

$$\mathbf{\log_a y = \frac{\log_b y}{\log_b a}}$$

If $b = 10$, i.e., we are using common logarithms, then

$$\mathbf{\log_a y = \frac{\log_{10} y}{\log_{10} a}}$$

Also

$$\mathbf{\log_e n = 2.3026 \log_{10} n}$$

$$\mathbf{\log_{10} n = 0.4343 \log_e n}$$

The **decibel** (dB) is equal to **ten times the common logarithm of the ratio of two power levels**, or *twenty times the common logarithm of the ratio of two voltage or current levels*. Strictly speaking, the latter is only correct if the two voltages are across the same value of resistance, or the two currents flow in the same resistance.

$$\text{dB ratio} = 10 \log \frac{P_2}{P_2} = 20 \log \frac{V_2}{V_2} = 20 \log \frac{I_2}{I_2}$$

where P represents a power, V a voltage, and I a current.

The dB value is positive if the ratio is greater than unity, it is zero if the ratio is unity, and is negative if the ratio is less than unity.

The **neper** (N), is the Naperian logarithm of the ratio of two values of current.

$$\text{neper value} = \log_e \frac{I_2}{I_1} = \ln \frac{I_2}{I_1}$$

and 1 neper = 8.686 dB or 1 dB = 0.1151 N

4 Algebra

4.1 Introduction

Algebra is the branch of mathematics in which we use *symbols* to represent variables. For example, if v is a velocity, t is time, and the distance covered in time t is represented by d, then $d = v \times t$.

In this chapter we will be meeting algebraic expressions, equations and identities. An **algebraic expression** is any mathematical form which can be represented by symbols; for example $(8 - 3I)$ is an example of an expression, where I may be the current in a circuit. An **equation** contains an equals sign, and is only true for certain values of the variables. For example, $2 = 8 - 3I$ is an equation, and is only true for $I = 2$. An **identity** is a relationship *which is true for all values of the variable* and, strictly speaking, the two sides of the identity should be related by an 'identity' sign ($\equiv$). For example, $6I = 16I - 10I$ is an identity which is satisfied by any value of I. In many cases the identity sign is dropped, and is replaced by an equals sign.

Additionally, we shall be looking at more complex equations such as quadratic equations, cubic equations, etc. A **quadratic equation** is an expression of the **second degree**, in which the variable is raised to the power of 2; for example $ax^2 + bx + c = 0$ is a quadratic equation. In a **cubic equation**, the variable is raised to the power of 3; $ax^3 + bx^2 + cx + d = 0$ is a cubic equation.

We will also learn to **solve equations**, that is we will determine the value of the unknown in the equation; this value is a **root of the equation** (there may be several of these).

A set of **simultaneous equations** is a special case where two or more equations simultaneously apply to a problem. We frequently meet with this situation in electrical and electronic circuits, and so important are they that chapter 5 is devoted to their solution.

By the end of this chapter, the reader will be able to

- add, subtract, multiply and divide algebraic quantities,
- understand the basic laws of algebra,
- understand the laws of indices (powers),
- understand methods of transposing and manipulating formulae,
- understand how to factorise expressions,
- understand how to solve quadratic equations.

4.2 Basic considerations

When writing equations, we use the first letters in the alphabet, e.g., a, b, c, etc., to represent constants, and the last letters in the alphabet, e.g., x, y, z, to represent 'unknowns' or 'variables'. Thus, in the equation $ax^2 + bx + c = 0$, the letters a, b, and c are constants, and x is the unknown.

The expression $2y$ means

$$2y = 2 \times y = y + y$$

and $3y^2$ means

$$3y^2 = 3 \times y^2 = 3 \times y \times y$$

The value which precedes the variable y is called the **coefficient** of the variable. That is $2y$ has a coefficient of 2, and $3y^2$ has a coefficient of 3. The coefficient can have a negative value or a fractional value as follows.

$$-3.7y^2 = (-3.7) \times y^2 = (-3.7) \times y \times y$$

When a factor is common to two or more terms in an algebraic expression, the factor can be shown outside a bracket which contains the terms it is common to. For example

$$ax + ay = a(x + y)$$

this is known as **factorisation**.

4.3 Introduction to algebraic manipulation

As with normal arithmetic, basic algebraic methods include addition, subtraction, multiplication and division. Also, as will be seen later, these are combined to give more complex methods of manipulation.

(a) Addition

When algebraic quantities *of the same kind* are added together, the coefficients of that quantity are added. For example

$$x + 5x + 7x = (1 + 5 + 7)x = 13x$$

If an expression contains different kinds of algebraic quantity, then only coefficients of the same kind may be added, as shown below

$$\begin{aligned} 2x + 4z + 3y + 10x + 2y + 3z &= (2 + 10)x + (3 + 2)y + (4 + 3)z \\ &= 12x + 5y + 7z \end{aligned}$$

(b) Subtraction

The rule of algebraic subtraction is identical to arithmetic subtraction, subject to the fact that the quantities being subtracted are of the same kind. That is we cannot subtract $3x$ from $2y$, or $6y$ from $9z$. Simple examples are given below.

$$7x - 4x = (7 - 4)x = 3x$$
$$10x - (-2x) = 10x + 2x = (10 + 2)x = 12x$$

The reader will note that we use brackets around the $(-2x)$ to clarify the equation (which, strictly speaking, is an identity). Also

$$\begin{aligned}&(8x + 7y - 3z) - (10x + 4y - 5z)\\&\quad = (8x - 10x) + (7y - 4y) + (-3z - 5z)\\&\quad = -2x + 3y - 8z\end{aligned}$$

(c) Multiplication

Algebraic multiplication follows the normal rules of arithmetic, but due regard should be made to the sign of the quantities being multiplied, and the rule is

products with like signs give a positive result
products with unlike signs give a negative result.

For example

$$4x \times 5y = 20xy$$
$$(-2x) \times (-3y) = 6xy$$
$$(-3x) \times 8y = -24xy$$
$$7x \times (-6y) = -42xy$$

Brackets are often used to make an expression more readable. When brackets are used, the inner brackets are simplified first, and we gradually work to the outer brackets, as shown below.

$$\begin{aligned}2x[8xy - 2x(2x - 3y)] &= 2x[8xy - 4x^2 + 6xy] = 2x[14xy - 4x^2]\\&= 28x^2y - 8x^3\end{aligned}$$

This can be simplified further, because we see that 4 is a common factor of 28 and 8, and x^2 is a common factor of x^2y and x^3. That is, we can simplify the above by taking $4x^2$ outside a set of brackets as follows

$$28x^2y - 8x^3 = 4x^2(7y - 2x)$$

If we wish to multiply $(x - 3)$ by $(y + 2)$, we can proceed in either of two ways. The first method follows the general rules of multiplication and is

$$\begin{array}{llll} & x - 3 & & \\ & y + 2 & & \\ \hline & xy - 3y & & y \times (x - 3) \\ & & 2x - 6 & 2 \times (x - 3) \\ \hline \text{ADD} & xy - 3y + & 2x - 6 & \end{array}$$

The second method is

$$\begin{aligned}(x-3)(y+2) &= x(y+2)-3(y+2)\\ &= xy+2x-3y-6\end{aligned}$$

A more complex example is the product of $(3x-2y-4)$ and $(-x+4y-3)$ as follows

$$\begin{aligned}&(3x-2y-4)(-x+4y-3)\\ &\quad = 3x(-x+4y-3)-2y(-x+4y-3)-4(-x+4y-3)\\ &\quad = (-3x^2+12xy-9x)+(2xy-8y^2+6y)+(4x-16y+12)\\ &\quad = -3x^2+(12+2)xy+(-9+4)x+(6-16)y-8y^2+12\\ &\quad = -3x^2+14xy-5x-10y-8y^2+12\end{aligned}$$

A note on the multiplication of negative numbers

A negative sign simply implies 'the reverse of' or 'in the opposite direction to' a positive value. Thus a value of $+4$ implies an increase in the positive direction, and -4 implies 4 'in the opposite direction'. Hence

$$-4 = (-1)\times(+4)$$

We may therefore say that

$$(-1)\times(-4) = -(-4)$$

That is $-(-4)$ is a value of 4 'in the opposite direction' to -4, i.e., 4 in a positive direction, or

$$(-1)\times(-4) = -(-4) = +4$$

Also

$$(-1)\times(-1) = -(-1) = +1$$

and

$$(-3)\times(-6) = -(3\times(-6)) = -(-18) = +18, \text{ etc.}$$

(d) Division

When dividing one algebraic value by another, the variables are written in fractional form, i.e., $2x/3y$, $(2x-3)/(4x+5)$, etc. Where possible, simplification is carried out by cancelling the coefficients in the numerator and denominator. For example

$$\frac{2x^2+4x}{4x^2+12x} = \frac{2x(x+2)}{4x(x+3)} = \frac{x+2}{2(x+3)}$$

In the above case, $2x$ is a common factor both in the numerator and in the denominator, and can be cancelled.

Also, the rule for mathematical signs must be obeyed, and is

When like signs are divided, the result is positive.
When unlike signs are divided, the result is negative.

For example

$$\frac{9x}{3x^2} = \frac{3x}{x^2} = \frac{3}{x}$$

$$\frac{-3x^2}{-9x^2} = \frac{x^2}{3x} = \frac{x}{3}$$

$$\frac{-9x^2}{3x} = \frac{-3x^2}{x} = -3x$$

$$\frac{3x}{-9x^2} = \frac{x}{-3x^2} = -\frac{1}{3x}$$

To illustrate some of the general principles, we will divide $(24x - 6y + 18xy)$ by $6xy$ as follows

$$\frac{24x - 6y + 18xy}{6xy} = \frac{24x}{6xy} - \frac{6y}{6xy} + \frac{18xy}{6xy}$$

We simplify each term by cancelling common coefficients and variables as follows

$$\frac{4x}{xy} - \frac{y}{xy} + \frac{3xy}{xy} = \frac{4}{y} - \frac{1}{x} + 3$$

Worked Example 4.1

Simplify
(a) $10x + 3y - 7x + 8y - x - 15y$,
(b) $-2x + 3(y - x) + 6y(1 - 2x)$,
(c) $5(w - z) - 3(z - w) + 2z$,
(d) $(a + b)(a + b)$,
(e) $(x + y)(x - y)$,
(f) $(x^2 + y^2 + xy + 2xy + y^2)/(x + y)$,
(g) $(6mn + 7gh + gh - mn + n)/ghmn$.

Solution

(a) First, we group the variables in x and y as follows

$$\begin{aligned} &10x + 3y - 7x + 8y - x - 15y \\ &\quad = (10 - 7 - 1)x + (3 + 8 - 15)y = 2x - 4y \end{aligned}$$

(b) Initially we will simplify the expression by expanding the bracketed terms as follows.

$$-2x + 3(y - x) + 6y(1 - 2x) = -2x + 3y - 3x + 6y - 12xy$$

and then we group similar variables together

$$(-2 - 3)x + (3 + 6)y - 12xy = -5x + 9y + 12xy$$

Further simplification is possible by grouping either the x and the xy terms together, or the y and the xy terms together. Both alternatives are left as an exercise for the reader to complete.

(c) Once again, we expand the brackets, and group the variables as shown below.

$$\begin{aligned} &5(w - z) - 3(z - w) + 2z \\ &\quad = 5w - 5z - 3z + 3w + 2z \\ &\quad = (5 + 3)w + (-5 - 3 + 2)z = 8w - 6z \end{aligned}$$

(d) This is a useful example which shows how the expansion of $(a + b)^2$ is obtained.

$$\begin{aligned} (a + b)(a + b) &= a(a + b) + b(a + b) \\ &= a^2 + ab + ba + b^2 \\ &= a^2 + 2ab + b^2 \end{aligned}$$

Note: $ab \equiv ba$ (see also section 4.4).

(e) $$\begin{aligned} (x + y)(x - y) &= x(x + y) + y(x - y) \\ &= x^2 + xy + yx - y^2 \\ &= x^2 + 2xy - y^2 \end{aligned}$$

(f) $$\begin{aligned} &\frac{x^2 + y^2 + xy + 2xy + y^2}{x + y} \\ &\quad = \frac{x^2 + (1 + 2)xy + (1 + 1)y^2}{x + y} \\ &\quad = \frac{x^2 + 3xy + 2y^2}{x + y} \end{aligned}$$

(g) $$\begin{aligned} &\frac{6mn + 7gh + gh - mn + n}{ghmn} \\ &\quad = \frac{(6 - 1)mn + (7 + 1)gh + n}{ghmn} = \frac{7mn + 8gh + n}{ghmn} \\ &\quad = \frac{7mn}{ghmn} + \frac{8gh}{ghmn} + \frac{n}{ghmn} = \frac{7}{gh} + \frac{8}{mn} + \frac{1}{ghm} \end{aligned}$$

4.4 Basic laws of algebra

The following basic laws are used to manipulate algebraic expressions

Associative law

$$a + (b + c) = (a + b) + c$$

Example: $2 + (3 + 4) = (2 + 3) + 4$

$$a(bc) = (ab)c$$

Example: $2 \times (3 \times 4) = (2 \times 3) \times 4$

Commutative law

$$a + b = b + a$$

Example: $2 + 3 = 3 + 2$

$$ab = ba$$

Example: $2 \times 3 = 3 \times 2$

Distributive law

$$a(b + c) = ab + ac$$

Example: $2(3 + 4) = (2 \times 3) + (2 \times 4)$

4.5 Algebraic laws of indices (powers)

These follow the general laws for the powers of numbers (see also chapter 1), and are

$$x^m \times x^n = x^{m+n}$$

$$\frac{x^m}{x^n} = x^{m-n}$$

$$(x^m)^n = x^{mn}$$

$$x^{1/n} = \sqrt[n]{x}$$

$$x^{m/n} = \sqrt[n]{x^m}$$

$$x^{-n} = 1/x^n$$

$$x^0 = 1$$

4.6 Transposition and manipulation of formulae

When we are presented by an equation such as Ohm's law, i.e.,

$$E = I \times R$$

the term on the left-hand side of the equation is known as the **subject** of the equation. If we wish to change the subject of the formulae to, say, the current I, we must re-arrange or **transpose** the formulae. The general rule which *must be followed during transposition* is

always make the same changes to both sides of the equation.

That is, if we multiply one side of the equation by a number or a variable, we must also multiply the other side by the same factor or variable. The same applies to division, addition, subtraction, raising to a power, etc.

Let us look at a method of making I the subject of Ohm's law. Initially, *we divide both sides of the equation* by R as follows

$$\frac{E}{R} = \frac{I \times R}{R} = I$$

This eliminates the variable R from the right-hand side of the original equation, so that

$$I = \frac{E}{R}$$

Consider the following equation for the resistance of a conductor

$$R_\theta = R_0(1 + \alpha_0\theta)$$

where

R_θ = resistance of the conductor at temperature θ

R_0 = resistance of the conductor at zero degrees celsius

α_0 = linear resistance-temperature coefficient referred to 0°C

θ = temperature in degrees celsius.

To make θ the subject of the equation we can proceed as follows.

1. Divide both sides by R_0

$$\frac{R_\theta}{R_0} = \frac{R_0}{R_0}(1 + \alpha_0\theta) = 1 + \alpha_0\theta$$

2. Subtract unity from both sides

$$\frac{R_\theta}{R_0} - 1 = 1 + \alpha_0\theta - 1 = \alpha_0\theta$$

3. Divide both sides by α_0

$$\theta = \frac{1}{\alpha_0}\left[\frac{R_\theta}{R_0} - 1\right] = \frac{\alpha_0\theta}{\alpha_0} = \theta$$

That is

$$\theta = \frac{1}{\alpha_0}\left[\frac{R_\theta}{R_0} - 1\right]$$

If necessary, we can proceed a little further by re-arranging the items inside the brackets on a common denominator of R_0 as follows

$$\frac{R_\theta}{R_0} - 1 = \frac{R_\theta}{R_0} - \frac{R_0}{R_0} = \frac{R_\theta - R_0}{R_0}$$

so that the equation may be re-written in the form

$$\theta = \frac{R_\theta - R_0}{\alpha_0 R_0}$$

Next we will consider the equation for the power consumed in a resistor, which is

$$P = I^2 R$$

If we wish to make I the subject of the formulae, we can proceed as follows

1. Divide both sides by R

$$\frac{P}{R} = \frac{I^2 R}{R} = I^2$$

2. Take the square root of both sides

$$\sqrt{\left[\frac{P}{R}\right]} = \sqrt{I^2} = I$$

or

$$I = \sqrt{(P/R)}$$

Worked Example 4.2

Transpose the following equations so that the variable listed is the subject of the equation: (a) a in $S = l/\mu a$, (b) S_2 in $\Phi = F/(S_1 + S_2)$, (c) H in $\mu_0\mu_r = B/H$, (d) R_2 in $R_T = R_1 R_2/(R_1 + R_2)$, (e) Q in $Z = R_D/(1 + 2Q\delta)$, (f) τ in $i = E(1 - e^{(-t/\tau)/R})$, (g) C in $w_O = 1/\sqrt{(LC)}$.

Solution

All the equations are taken from electrical and electronic theory in the real world.

(a) To eliminate l and μ from the right-hand side of the equation, we multiply *both sides* by μ and divide by l as follows

$$S \times \frac{\mu}{l} = \frac{l}{\mu a} \times \frac{\mu}{l} = \frac{1}{a}$$

That is

$$\frac{S\mu}{l} = \frac{1}{a}$$

Cross-multiplying gives

$$aS\mu = l$$

or

$$a = \frac{l}{S\mu}$$

(b) Multiplying both sides of the equation by $(S_1 + S_2)$ gives

$$\Phi(S_1 + S_2) = \frac{F}{(S_1 + S_2)} \times (S_1 + S_2) = F$$

Dividing both sides by Φ results in

$$\frac{\Phi(S_1 + S_2)}{\Phi} = \frac{F}{\Phi}$$

or

$$S_1 + S_2 = F/\Phi$$

Subtracting S_1 from both sides of the equation yields

$$S_1 + S_2 - S_1 = S_2 = \frac{F}{\Phi} - S_1$$

(c) We multiply both sides of the equation by H in order to eliminate H from the right-hand side and, simultaneously, divide both sides by the product $\mu_0\mu_r$ as follows

$$\frac{H}{\mu_0\mu_r} \times \mu_0\mu_r = \frac{B}{H} \times \frac{H}{\mu_0\mu_r} = \frac{B}{\mu_0\mu_r}$$

or

$$H = \frac{B}{\mu_0\mu_r}$$

(d) Initially, we multiply both sides by $(R_1 + R_2)$ as follows

$$R_T(R_1 + R_2) = \frac{R_1R_2}{(R_1 + R_2)} \times (R_1 + R_2) = R_1R_2$$

that is

$$R_TR_1 + R_TR_2 = R_1R_2$$

Subtracting R_TR_2 from both sides of the equation, and simplifying the right-hand side of the resulting equation gives

$$R_TR_1 + R_TR_2 - R_TR_2 = R_1R_2 - R_TR_2 = R_2(R_1 - R_T)$$

That is

$$R_T R_1 = R_2(R_1 - R_T)$$

Finally, dividing both sides of the equation by $(R_1 - R_T)$ yields

$$R_2 = R_T R_1/(R_1 - R_T)$$

(e) In this case we multiply both sides of the equation by $(1 + 2Q\delta)$ and divide both sides by Z as follows

$$Z \times \frac{(1+2Q\delta)}{Z} = \frac{R_D}{(1+2Q\delta)} \times \frac{(1+2Q\delta)}{Z} = \frac{R_D}{Z}$$

That is

$$1 + 2Q\delta = \frac{R_D}{Z}$$

Next, we subtract unity from both sides of the equation to give

$$1 + 2Q\delta - 1 = 2Q\delta = \frac{R_D}{Z} - 1$$

and finally we divide both sides of the equation by 2δ as follows

$$\frac{2Q\delta}{2\delta} = Q = \frac{\left[\frac{R_D}{Z} - 1\right]}{2\delta}$$

(f) This is an equation relating to a transient in an electrical circuit (see chapter 14 for details), and the equation is

$$i = \frac{E}{R}(1 - e^{-t/\tau})$$

Initially we multiply both sides of the equation by R and divide by E, as shown below

$$i \times \frac{R}{E} = \frac{E}{R}(1 - e^{-t/\tau}) \times \frac{R}{E} = 1 - e^{-t/\tau}$$

Next, we subtract unity from both sides

$$\frac{iR}{E} - 1 = 1 - e^{-t/\tau} - 1 = -e^{-t/\tau}$$

To eliminate the negative sign from $-e^{-t/\tau}$, we multiply both sides by -1 as follows

$$\text{RHS} = (-1) \times \left[\frac{iR}{E} - 1\right] = -\frac{iR}{E} + 1 = 1 - \frac{iR}{E}$$

$$\text{LHS} = (-1) \times (-e^{-t/\tau}) = e^{-t/\tau}$$

so that

$$1-\frac{iR}{E}=e^{-t/\tau}$$

or

$$e^{-t/\tau}=1-\frac{iR}{E}$$

The right-hand side of this equation can alternatively be written in the form

$$1-\frac{iR}{E}=\frac{E}{E}-\frac{iR}{E}=\frac{E-iR}{E}$$

giving

$$e^{-t/\tau}=\frac{E-iR}{E}$$

Taking Naperian logarithms of both sides of the equation to base e (see Chapter 3 for details) results in the following

$$\text{LHS}=-\frac{t}{\tau}\log_e e=-\frac{t}{\tau}\times 1=-\frac{t}{\tau}$$

$$\text{RHS}=log_e\left[\frac{E-iR}{E}\right]=\ln\left[\frac{E-iR}{E}\right]$$

That is

$$-\frac{t}{\tau}=\ln\left[\frac{E-iR}{E}\right]$$

Dividing both sides of the equation by $-t$ gives

$$\text{LHS}=-\frac{t}{\tau}\times\frac{1}{-t}=\frac{1}{\tau}$$

$$\text{RHS}=\frac{\ln[(E-iR)/E]}{-t}$$

that is

$$\frac{1}{\tau}=\frac{\ln[(E-iR)/E]}{-t}$$

Finally, inverting both sides of the equation gives

$$\tau=\frac{-t}{\ln[(E-iR)/E]}$$

Since, in practice, τ is a positive value, the equation implies that the logarithm of the denominator must have a negative value. That is, the ratio $(E-iR)/E$ has a value which is less than unity!

(g) The equation is

$$w_O = \frac{1}{\sqrt{(LC)}}$$

To remove the square root sign from the right-hand side of the equation, we 'square' both sides as follows

$$w_O^2 = \left[\frac{1}{\sqrt{(LC)}}\right]^2 = \frac{1}{LC}$$

Next, we multiply both sides by C and divide by w_O^2 as follows

$$\text{LHS} = w_O^2 \times \frac{C}{w_O^2} = C$$

$$\text{RHS} = \frac{1}{LC} \times \frac{C}{w_O^2} = \frac{1}{Lw_O^2}$$

or

$$C = \frac{1}{Lw_O^2}$$

4.7 Factorising

When a factor is common to several terms in an expression, we can extract the factor (which may either be a number or a variable or a combination of the two) from the expression, and leave the remainder of the expression inside a set of brackets. This process is known as **factorisation**.

For example, the number $3x$ is a common factor in the expression $(3x + 9x^2)$, which is factorised as follows

$$3x + 9x^2 = 3x(1 + 3x)$$

The reader is always advised to check the answer by **multiplying out the final expression** (which should give the original expression), because it is always possible to make a simple error.

The expression $x^2 + 2x$ can be factorised as follows

$$x^2 + 2x = x(x + 2)$$

and the following expression may be factorised as shown

$$9xy + 27x^2y + 18xy^2 = 9xy(1 + 3x + 2y)$$

In some cases it may be necessary to split the expression into several groups, and factorise each group. Consider the expression

$$wy + xy - wz - xz$$

This may be factorised as follows

$$wy + xy - wz - xz = y(w + x) - z(w + x)$$
$$= yA - zA = A(y - z)$$

where $A = (w + x)$. The final form of the expression is, therefore

$$(w + x)(y - z)$$

Worked Example 4.3

If possible, factorise the following

(a) $2z + 8q$,
(b) $5ax + 10bx^3$,
(c) $42a - 14ax^2$,
(d) $v^2 + v^4$,
(e) $3v^2 + i^2$,
(f) $2vR - 2vjX + 3iR - 3ijX$,
(g) $xy - xy^2 + x^2y - x^2y^2$.

Solution

(a) Since the only common factor in this expression is 2, it follows that

$$2z + 8q = 2(z + 4q)$$

(b) In this case the common factor is $5x$, so that

$$5ax + 10bx^3 = 5x(a + 2bx^2)$$

(c) Here $14a$ is the common term, therefore

$$42a - 14ax^2 = 14a(3 - x^2)$$

(d) v^2 is the common factor, hence

$$v^2 + v^4 = v^2(1 + v^2)$$

(e) There is no common factor in this expression, and it cannot be factorised.

(f) Here we need to factorise the expression in several steps, as follows

$$2vR - 2vjX + 3iR - 3ijX$$
$$= 2v(R - jX) + 3i(R - jX) = (R - jX)(2v + 3i)$$

(g) Once again, we factorise in several steps as follows

$$xy - xy^2 + x^2y - x^2y^2$$
$$= x(y - y^2) + x^2(y - y^2) = (y - y^2)(x + x^2)$$

4.8 Methods of solving a quadratic equation

A **quadratic equation** is one in which the highest power to which the unknown quantity is raised is 2, e.g., $6x^2 + 11x - 10 = 0$, and such equations frequently occur in engineering.

The general form of a quadratic equation is

$$ax^2 + bx + c = 0$$

where a, b and c are constants, and x is the unknown. There are four general methods of solving quadratic equations:

1. By factorisation (where possible),
2. By 'completing the square',
3. By the use of the 'quadratic formulae',
4. Graphically (see Chapter 8).

In the type of quadratic we consider, there are (generally) two possible solutions for the unknown value, as will be illustrated below.

(a) Solution of a quadratic equation by factorisation

In a number of cases, solution of a quadratic equation by factorisation is fairly simple, and is obtained by extracting the factors of the equation. Initially we must write down the equation so that **it is equated to zero**. Consider the case of the equation

$$x^2 + x = 6$$

This is re-written in the form

$$x^2 + x - 6 = 0 \tag{4.1}$$

At this stage it is not obvious that the factors of the equation are $(x - 2)$ and $(x + 3)$, and we will look at a method of obtaining the correct factors.

In a simple case of this kind, the equation can be re-written in the form

$$(x + m)(x + n) = 0$$

where m and n are the factors we need. If we multiply the above equation out we get

$$x^2 + x(m + n) + mn = 0$$

Comparing this form of the equation with (4.1), we see that if the two equations are equivalent, then the coefficient of x in (4.1) is equal to $(m + n)$, and the numerical coefficient in (4.1) is equal to mn.

To solve (4.1), we need to determine two values whose sum, i.e., $(m + n)$, is unity, and whose product, i.e., mn, is -6. Initially, we will write down the factors of -6, which are $(1, -6)$, $(-6, 1)$, $(3, -2)$ and $(2, -3)$; all four of these combinations satisfy the requirement that their product is -6.

However, only the pair $(3, -2)$ satisfy the requirement that their sum is unity, hence

$$x^2 + x - 6 = (x + 3)(x - 2) = 0$$

Since the equation is equal to zero, either of the two bracketed terms can be zero, so that either

$$x + 3 = 0 \quad \text{or} \quad x - 2 = 0$$

that is

$$x = -3 \quad \text{or} \quad x = 2.$$

If either of these values is inserted into (4.1), we will find that the value of the equation is zero.

We therefore say that the **roots of the equation** are $x = -3$ and $x = 2$.

Let us consider the following equation, which is somewhat more complex

$$2x^2 - 11x - 6 = 0$$

Initially we consider the factors of the coefficient of x^2, i.e., the factors of 2, which are 2 and 1, respectively. That is, $2x^2$ simply comprises the product of $2x$ and x. Next we consider the factors of -6; as before, these are $(3, -2)$, $(2, -3)$, $(-6, 1)$ and $(1, -6)$. Having done this, we look at a tabular method of determining the roots of the equation $2x^2 - 11x - 6 = 0$ as follows:

Table 4.1 Simple tabular method of determining the roots of the equation $2x^2 - 11x - 6 = 0$ for one set of factors

	$2x$
x	$2x^2$

(a)

	$2x$	3
x	$2x^2$	$3x$
-2	$-4x$	

(b)

	$2x$	3
x	$2x^2$	$3x$
-2	$-4x$	-6

(c)

We must build up a table for each set of factors and, initially, we do this for the factors 3 and -2, as shown in Table 4.1. Firstly, we write down the factors of $2x^2$, namely $2x$ and x, as shown in Table 4.1(a), and enter the *product* of the two factors in the top left-hand corner.

Next, in Table 4.1(b), we enter the first two factors of -6, namely 3 and -2 in the top row and the left-hand column, respectively. We then multiply each of these factors with the appropriate 'x' factor and show it inside the table. That is, we enter $(-2 \times 2x) = -4x$ by the side of the -2 factor, and enter $(3 \times x) = 3x$ below the 3 factor. We will refer to these two values as the 'diagonal' terms.

The complete version of the table is shown in Table 4.1(c), where we enter the product of the -2 and 3 factors in the bottom right-hand corner of the table. Let us consider the equation again, which is

$$2x^2 - 11x - 6 = 0$$

If we have selected the correct factors, the left-hand term of the equation ($2x^2$) should appear in the top left-hand corner of Table 4.1(c), and the right-hand term of the equation (-6) should appear in the bottom right-hand corner of the table.

The centre term of the equation ($-11x$) should be *equal to the sum of the 'diagonal' terms* of Table 4.1(c). In our case the sum of the diagonal terms is $(-4x + 3x) = -x$; clearly the factors $(2x - 3)$ and $(x - 2)$ *are incorrect*. To obtain the correct factors, we must repeat the tabular process until the conditions we have specified are satisfied. This is done in Table 4.2 for the factors (3, −2) (see also Table 4.1), (2, −3), (6, −1) and (1, −6) as shown in Table 4.2 (a), (b), (c) and (d), respectively.

Table 4.2 Complete table for the roots of $2x^2 - 11x - 6 = 0$

	$2x$	3
x	$2x^2$	$3x$
-2	$-4x$	-6

(a)

	$2x$	2
x	$2x^2$	$2x$
-3	$-6x$	-6

(b)

	$2x$	6
x	$2x^2$	$6x$
-1	$-2x$	-6

(c)

	$2x$	1
x	$2x^2$	x
-6	$-12x$	-6

(d)

We see that table 4.2(d) gives the correct solution for the sum of the 'diagonal' terms, namely $(-12x + x) = -11x$, hence the equation reduces to

$$2x^2 - 11x - 6 = (2x + 1)(x - 6) = 0$$

and the roots of the equations are obtained as follows.

$$2x + 1 = 0 \quad \text{or} \quad x = -\tfrac{1}{2}$$
$$x - 6 = 0 \quad \text{or} \quad x = 6$$

Obtaining the roots by factorisation is not always easy, or even possible!

(b) Solution of a quadratic equation by 'completing the square'

In this method, the quadratic equation is written in the form in which the variable, i.e., x, **appears only in a term which is 'squared'**. That is, an equation of the form

$$ax^2 + bx + c = 0$$

is written in the form

$$(x + M)^2 + N = 0$$

where a, b, c, M and N are constants. The reader is asked to note that the coefficient of x in the final form of the equation is unity; one of the first steps in this method of solution is, therefore, to divide throughout the equation by the coefficient a, so that it appears in the form

$$x^2 + \frac{b}{a}x + \frac{c}{a} = 0$$

Let us use this method to solve the equation

$$2x^2 - 8x - 24 = 0$$

Initially we reduce the coefficient of x^2 to unity by dividing throughout by 2, as follows

$$x^2 - 4x - 12 = 0$$

or

$$x^2 - 4x = 12$$

That is, we have kept all the terms containing the variable on the left-hand side of the equation. We *complete the square* of the left-hand side of the equation by *adding the square of half the coefficient of x to it*. We must balance the equation by adding the same value to the right-hand side of the equation as follows

$$x^2 - 4x + \left[\frac{4}{2}\right] = 12 + \left[\frac{4}{2}\right]^2 = 16$$

Writing the left-hand side of the equation as a 'square' we have

$$\left[x - \frac{4}{2}\right]^2 = 16$$

or

$$(x - 2)^2 = 16$$

Taking the square root of both sides of the equation gives

$$x - 2 = \sqrt{16} = \pm 4$$

that is

$$x = \pm 4 + 2 = +6 \text{ or } -2$$

therefore

$$x^2 - 4x - 12 = (x - 6)(x + 2) = 0$$

Worked Example 4.4

Solve the following quadratic equations by 'completing the square' (a) $x^2 - 5x + 4 = 0$, (b) $x^2 + x - 6 = 0$.

Solution

(a) Re-writing the equation in the form

$$x^2 - 5x = -4$$

hence

$$x^2 - 5x + \left[\frac{5}{2}\right]^2 = -4 + \left[\frac{5}{2}\right]^2 = 2.25$$

That is

$$\left[x - \frac{5}{2}\right]^2 = 2.25$$

or

$$x - \frac{5}{2} = \sqrt{2.25} = \pm 1.5$$

Therefore $x = \pm 1.5 + 2.5 = 4$ or 1

That is $x^2 - 5x + 4 = (x - 4)(x - 1) = 0$

(b) The equation is re-written

$$x^2 + x = 6$$

hence

$$x^2 + x + \left[\frac{1}{2}\right]^2 = 6 + \left[\frac{1}{2}\right]^2 = 6.25$$

therefore

$$\left[x + \frac{1}{2}\right]^2 = 6.25$$

or

$$x + \tfrac{1}{2} = \sqrt{6.25} = \pm 2.25$$

giving

$$x = \pm 2.5 - 0.5 = -3 \text{ or } 2$$

That is

$$x^2 + x - 6 = (x + 3)(x - 2) = 0$$

(c) Solving a quadratic equation using the quadratic formulae

The solution of a quadratic equation of the type

$$ax^2 + bx + c = 0$$

can be obtained using the equation

$$x = \frac{-b \pm \surd(b^2 - 4ac)}{2a}$$

We will use the equation to solve equations at this time, and will prove it a little later. The equation is, in fact, based on the solution of a quadratic equation by the method of 'completing the square'. Let us solve the equation

$$2x^2 - 10x + 8 = 0$$

In this case $a = 2$, $b = -10$ and $c = 8$. Substituting these values in the equation gives

$$x = \frac{-(-10) \pm \surd((-10)^2 - (4 \times 2 \times 8))}{2 \times 2}$$

$$= \frac{10 \pm \surd(100 - 64)}{4} = \frac{10 \pm \surd 36}{4} = \frac{10 \pm 6}{4}$$

$$= 4 \text{ or } 1$$

Substituting either of these values into the equation will satisfy it.

The term $(b^2 - 4ac)$ is known as the **discriminant** which, for the moment, *must either be zero or have a positive value*. Since we cannot, at the moment, take the square root of a negative quantity, we cannot deal with a negative discriminant.

If the discriminant is negative, the equation is said to have *imaginary roots*; we deal with 'imaginary' quantities in Chapter 11.

Next, we take a look at how the formulae is deduced. The original equation is re-written in the form

$$ax^2 + bx = -c$$

or

$$x^2 + \frac{b}{a}x = -\frac{c}{a}$$

Using the method of 'completing the square' gives

$$x^2 + \frac{b}{a}x + \left[\frac{b}{2a}\right] = -\frac{c}{a} + \left[\frac{b}{2a}\right]^2$$

$$= \frac{b^2}{4a^2} - \frac{c}{a} = \frac{b^2 - 4ac}{4a^2}$$

Writing the left-hand side as a 'square', we get

$$\left[x + \frac{b}{2a}\right]^2 = \frac{b^2 - 4ac}{4a^2}$$

Taking the square root of both sides of the equation yields

$$x + \frac{b}{2a} = \pm\sqrt{\left[\frac{b^2 - 4ac}{4a^2}\right]} = \frac{\pm\sqrt{(b^2 - 4ac)}}{2a}$$

or

$$x = -\frac{b}{2a} \pm \frac{\sqrt{(b^2 - 4ac)}}{2a} = \frac{-b \pm \sqrt{(b^2 - 4ac)}}{2a}$$

Worked Example 4.5

The e.m.f., E microvolts, produced by a thermocouple operating at temperature θ is given by the law

$$E = -0.019\theta^2 + 6.9\theta$$

The temperature is known to be in the range 250–400°C. If the thermocouple e.m.f. is $280\,\mu V$, determine the temperature measured.

Solution

Inserting the values given, the equation becomes

$$280 = -0.019\theta^2 + 6.9\theta$$

or

$$0.019\theta^2 - 6.9\theta + 280 = 0$$

Using the above values in the quadratic equation gives

$$\theta = \frac{-(-6.9) \pm \sqrt{(6.9^2 - (4 \times 0.019 \times 280))}}{2 \times 0.019}$$

$$\frac{6.9 \pm 5.131}{0.038} = 316.6°\text{C or } 46.5°\text{C}$$

Since the measured temperature is known to be in the range 250–400°C, the temperature is clearly 316.6°C.

Self-test questions

4.1 Simplify (a) $7x - 6y + 3x + 15y - 8y + 7x$,
(b) $5a + 10b - (-9a) - 6b + 4(a - b)$,
(c) $15x + 7b + 9(b - x) - 9x$.

4.2 Simplify (a) $x^2 + 2xy + y^2$,
(b) $a^3 + 2a^2b - 2ab^2 - b^3$.

4.3 Simplify (a) $(10x - 15y + 25xy)/5xy$,
(b) $xyz(x^2 + y^2(2 - w) + 4wx)/wxz$,
(c) $(a^2 + 2ab + b^2 + ab + b^2)/(a + b)$

4.4 Transpose the following equations so that the variable listed is the subject of the equation

(a) I in $H = NI/L$, (b) x in $B = I\mu_O/(2\pi x)$,

(c) B in $F = B^2a/(2\mu_O)$, (d) d in $L = (\mu/\pi)\ln(d/r)$,

(e) I_B in $I_{R2} = (I_R + a^2I_Y + aI_B)/3$,

(f) t in $i = (E/R)e^{-t/\tau}$,

(g) C_2 in $w_O = \sqrt{\left[\frac{1}{L}\left(\frac{1}{C_1} + \frac{1}{C_2}\right)\right]}$.

4.5 Factorise (a) $2x^2 + x - 15$, (b) $2x^2 + 4x - 6$.

4.6 Use the factors obtained in question 4.5 to simplify

$$\frac{1}{2x^2 + x - 15} + \frac{1}{2x^2 + 4x - 6}$$

4.7 Solve the following quadratic equations by factorisation

(a) $x^2 - 1 = 0$, (b) $2x^2 - 3x - 9 = 0$,

(c) $x^2 + 4x + 4 = 0$.

4.8 Solve the following quadratic equations by 'completing the square'

(a) $x^2 + 8x + 10 = 0$, (b) $x^2 + 10x + 15 = 0$,

(c) $4x^2 + 16x + 5 = 0$.

4.9 An unknown resistance is connected in series with a 10 Ω resistor, the voltage across the unknown resistor being 40 V. If the total power dissipated by the circuit is 120 W, deduce the quadratic equation relating the current, I, to the known factors. Solve the equation for I.

4.10 When two resistors are connected in parallel, the effective resistance is 4.8 Ω, and when they are connected in series the effective resistance is 20 Ω. Determine the resistance of each resistor.

Summary of important facts

An **algebraic expression** is any mathematical form which can be represented in symbols. An **equation** is true for certain values if the variable and an **identity** is true for all values of the variable.

When **transposing** or manipulating an equation, it is always necessary to make the same changes throughout the equation. **Factorisation** is the process of extracting common factors from an expression; after factorising an expression, it is advisable to check the answer by multiplying it out in full.

A **quadratic equation** is an equation of the *second degree*, i.e., one variable is raised to the power of 2. The four methods of solving a quadratic are (a) by *factorisation*, (b) by *completing the square*, (c) by using the *quadratic formulae* and (d) *graphically* (see Chapter 9).

5 Simultaneous equations

5.1 Introduction

The formulation and solution of simultaneous equations is a fairly problematical area for most young engineers, and it is the purpose of this chapter to establish the principles involved.

By the end of this chapter the reader will be able to

- write down the equations for a circuit,
- solve simultaneous linear equations by substitution and elimination,
- solve simultaneous equations by determinants,
- solve simultaneous equations using the BASIC programming language.

5.2 General principles

Many electrical circuit equations involve several variables, and gives rise to an equation such as

$$10 = 25I_1 + 20I_2 \tag{5.1}$$

Unfortunately, the equation does not give enough information to allow us to solve it, and it is necessary to have a second equation from the same circuit in order to determine the value of the variables I_1 and I_2. Such an equation may be

$$-10 = 5I_1 - 10I_2 \tag{5.2}$$

Equations (5.1) and (5.2) form a pair of **simultaneous equations**. In general, in order to solve a problem of this kind **we need as many simultaneous equations as there are unknown variables**. That is, if there are two unknowns, we need two simultaneous equations to determine their value.

A knowledge of the formulation and solution of simultaneous equations is most important to electrical and electronic engineers, and in this chapter we look at several methods of solution.

5.3 Deducing simultaneous equations for a circuit

Consider the circuit in Figure 5.1, which contains two sources of e.m.f., each supplying current to the circuit. The circuit has three **branches** or **paths** through which current can flow, and these meet at **node** 2 (and also at

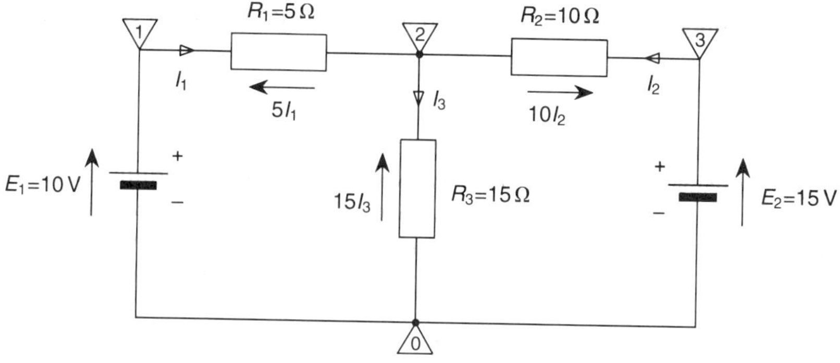

Figure 5.1 Analysis of an electrical circuit

node 0*): we allocate currents I_1, I_2 and I_3 to the branches. The direction of the current in any branch is selected at random, but the most sensible thing to do is to draw each current arrow in the direction in which the current is likely to flow.

At this stage, we need to know how many simultaneous equations are needed to solve the circuit. As mentioned above, the number of equations required is generally equal to the number of unknown variables in the problem.

If we apply **Kirchhoff's current law** (KCL) to node 2 (or to node 0), we see that

$$I_1 + I_2 - I_3 = 0$$

Clearly, if we know two of the three currents, we can calculate the third current. That is, there are only effectively two unknowns, and we only need two simultaneous equations. If we calculate the value of I_1 and I_2, then

$$I_3 = I_1 + I_2 \tag{5.3}$$

The two equations can be obtained by applying **Kirchhoff's voltage law** (KVL) to two **closed loops** in the circuit. The circuit contains three closed loops which are, respectively, loops 0120, 0230 and 01230.† It is important to note that each closed loop **starts and finishes at the same node**. Strictly

* The reader may ask why we have numbered the nodes or junctions rather than giving them alphabetical characters and, in particular, why we have used node zero (0) as one of them. The reason is that, in Chapter 16, we shall be looking at SPICE software (*Simulation Program with Integrated Circuit Emphasis*) for the solution of electrical and electronic circuits, and this uses numbered nodes, node zero being the reference node or zero voltage node. Where possible, we shall use this notation throughout the book.

† At this point we should differentiate between a *loop* and a *mesh* in a circuit. A mesh is a loop which does not contain any other loops within it. For the circuit drawn in Figure 5.1, the closed path 01230 is, strictly speaking, not a mesh since it contains loops 0120 and 0230 within it. For our purposes this difference is strictly academic, but for readers wishing to proceed to higher academic levels it is worth noting.

speaking, we can 'start' a closed loop at any node, and proceed around the circuit in either direction. That is, the loop 2102 is technically equivalent to the loop 0120. Since we only need two closed loops to solve for two unknowns, we select loops 0120 and 01230.

Before applying KVL to each closed loop, we must ensure that:

1. Current arrows are assigned to each branch in the loop.
2. Voltage arrows are assigned to each e.m.f. in the loop (the arrowhead pointing towards the more positive terminal).
3. Potential drop arrows are assigned to each resistor (the arrow pointing in the opposite direction to the current flow through the resistor).

We commence at the 'start' node for the loop, and proceed around it until we reach the 'finish' node, writing the loop equation as we pass round the loop as follows

(a) Assign a positive sign to any potential arrow which points in the direction in which we move around the loop.
(b) Assign a negative sign to any potential arrow pointing in the opposite direction to the way in which we move around the loop.
(c) Rearrange the equation with e.m.f.s on one side of the equation, and p.d.s on the other side.
(d) Rewrite the equation with all the variables, i.e., I_1, I_2 and I_3, written in terms of the unknowns, i.e., I_1 and I_2.

Loop 0120

Steps 1, 2 and 3 above have been completed in Figure 5.1, and we will proceed around the loop in the direction 0120, and will now apply steps (a)–(c) above. Starting at node 0, we note that the potential arrow associated with E_1 (10 V) points in the direction of travel around the loop, and the potential arrows associated with R_1 and R_3 oppose the direction of travel. Accordingly, the loop voltage equation from KVL for the loop is

$$10 - 5I_1 - 15I_3 = 0$$

or (step (c))

$$10 = 5I_1 + 15I_3$$

The use of (5.3) and step (d) above tell us that

$$\begin{aligned} 10 &= 5I_1 + 15(I_1 + I_2) \\ &= 20I_1 + 15I_2 \end{aligned}$$

We can also obtain this equation if we start at any node within the closed loop and proceed either in the same direction or in the reverse direction. For example, applying KVL to loop 2102 gives us the equation

$$5I_1 - 10 + 15I_3 = 0$$

or

$$-10 = -5I_1 - 15I_3$$

that is, using (5.3), we get

$$10 = 5I_1 + 15I_3 = 20I_1 + 15I_2$$

Loop 01230

Applying steps (a)–(d) above to this loop gives the equation

$$10 - 5I_1 + 10I_2 - 15 = 0$$

or

$$-5 = 5I_1 - 10I_2 \tag{5.5}$$

The complete solution of the circuit is obtained by solving (5.4) and (5.5).

5.4 Solving simultaneous linear equations by substitution

Using the **substitution** method of solution, the first equation is used to express one of the unknowns in terms of the other unknown. This relationship is then used in the second equation to allow one of the unknowns to be calculated, after which it is a simple matter to calculate the other unknown, as shown below. Let us solve for I_1 and I_2 in (5.4) and (5.5) as follows

$$10 = 20I_1 + 15I_2 \qquad ((5.4)\text{ rewritten})$$

$$-5 = 5I_1 - 10I_2 \qquad ((5.5)\text{ rewritten})$$

from (5.4) we get

$$20I_1 = 10 - 15I_2$$

or

$$I_1 = \frac{10}{20} - \frac{15}{20}I_2 = 0.5 - 0.75I_2 \tag{5.6}$$

This completes the first stage of the solution. The second stage is completed by substituting (5.6) into (5.5) as follows

$$-5 = 5I_1 - 10I_2 = 5(0.5 - 0.75I_2) - 10I_2$$
$$= 2.5 - 3.75I_2 - 10I_2 = 2.5 - 13.75I_2$$

or

$$-5 - 2.5 = -13.75I_2$$

that is

$$I_2 = \frac{-7.5}{-13.75} = 0.5455A$$

By substituting the value of I_2 into one of the other equations, we can calculate the value of I_1. Using (5.4) we get

$$10 = 20I_1 + 15I_2 = 20I_1 + (15 \times 0.5455)$$
$$= 20I_1 + 8.1825$$

that is

$$20I_1 = 10 - 8.1825 = 1.8175$$

therefore

$$I_1 = \frac{1.8175}{20} = 0.0909A$$

The solution of the circuit is

$$I_1 = 0.0909A$$
$$I_2 = 0.5455A$$
$$I_3 = I_1 + I_2 = 0.6364A$$

At this point we should apply some engineering common-sense to the solutions. We cannot, in practice, make measurements better than about 1 per cent accuracy. Furthermore, depending on the instrument, the accuracy may be much worse than this! The readings obtained with normal laboratory instruments may, typically be 0.09 A, 0.55 A and 0.64 A for the respective currents. In fact, if we connected three ammeters in the circuit as shown, the resistance of the meters would cause the current to be slightly different than the values calculated and, depending on the accuracy of the meters, it may be the case that $I_1 + I_2$ may not appear to be quite equal to I_3!

Do not despair. We are only commenting on the accuracy of instruments and of the readings, and not on the mathematics or the method of solution.

5.5 Solving simultaneous equations by elimination

In this method, one of the unknowns is eliminated by making the multiplying coefficient of that quantity the same in both equations. The two equations are, appropriately, either added or subtracted, so that the selected variable is eliminated from the equation, leaving one unknown. After calculating the value of that unknown, the remaining unknown is evaluated by substitution in one of the original simultaneous equations.

We will use this method to solve for I_1 and I_2 in the circuit in Figure 5.1. Once again, the circuit equations are

$$10 = 20I_1 + 15I_2 \qquad \text{((5.4) rewritten)}$$
$$-5 = 5I_1 - 10I_2 \qquad \text{((5.5) rewritten)}$$

We can make the coefficient of I_1 the same in both equations by multiplying (5.5) by 4; I_1 can then be eliminated between the two equations by subtracting them as follows

$$\begin{aligned} 10 &= 20I_1 + 15I_2 & &((5.4)\text{ rewritten}) \\ -20 &= 20I_1 - 40I_2 & &((5.5)\ \times 4) \\ \hline \text{SUBTRACT} \quad 30 &= \qquad\quad 55I_2 \end{aligned}$$

hence

$$I_2 = \frac{30}{55} = 0.5455 \text{ A}$$

Substituting this value into (5.4) gives

$$10 = 20I_1 + (15 \times 0.5455) = 20I_1 + 8.1825$$

that is

$$20I_1 = 10 - 8.1825 = 1.8175$$

and

$$I_1 = \frac{1.8175}{20} = 0.0909 \text{ A}$$

giving the results obtained in section 5.4. Hence

$$I_3 = I_1 + I_2 = 0.6364 \text{ A}$$

Once again, the values which are measured in practice may differ from the values calculated here for the reasons mentioned earlier.

5.6 Checking the calculated values

Once a calculation has been completed, it is important to check if the results agree with the original equations. This process takes a little time, but it is well worth doing. If the results and the equations do not agree, there are three general reasons, namely

1. An error in the original equations.
2. An error in the calculations.
3. The equations are not independent of one another.

Errors can be introduced when writing down the original equations, the simplest of all being drawing the potential arrows on the circuit incorrectly. Another source of errors is in manipulating the equations when getting them in the final form. The only solution is to be vigilant.

Many errors in calculations are due to elementary arithmetical operations, and a simple check on this cause is to solve the equations using another method, i.e., solve by substitution (section 5.3) rather than by elimination (section 5.4).

Two alternative methods of calculation will also be available to us later in this chapter, namely solution by determinants (section 5.7) or by computer solution (section 5.8), the latter also using the determinant method.

Let us check the solutions obtained for the circuit in Figure 5.1. The solutions were $I_1 = 0.0909\,\text{A}$ and $I_2 = 0.5455\,\text{A}$. The equations for the circuit are

$$10 = 20I_1 + 15I_2 \qquad \text{((5.4) rewritten)}$$
$$-5 = 5I_1 - 10I_2 \qquad \text{((5.5) rewritten)}$$

Substituting the solutions into (5.4) gives for the right-hand side of the equation

$$\begin{aligned}\text{RHS} &= (20 \times 0.0909) + (15 \times 0.5455)\\ &= 1.818 + 8.1825 = 10.0005\end{aligned}$$

and substituting them into (5.5) yields for the right-hand side

$$\begin{aligned}\text{RHS} &= (5 \times 0.0909) - (10 \times 0.5455)\\ &= 0.4545 - 0.5455 = -5.0005\end{aligned}$$

Since (5.4) was used to calculate I_1 then, strictly speaking, we should use (5.5) to check the results.

In both cases, the small difference between the left-hand and right-hand side of the equations are due to 'rounding' errors when writing the solution down in the first place. Since we have written down the solutions to four decimal places, the errors in the calculations are small enough to be ignored.

5.7 Further examples of simultaneous equations

In this section we look at the solution of three electrical circuits.

Worked Example 5.1

In the circuit in Figure 5.2, a battery of e.m.f. E_B and internal resistance $0.5\,\Omega$, is charged from two generators, having a respective internal resistance of $2\,\Omega$ and $3\,\Omega$ (see Figure 5.2), which are connected in parallel. Calculate

(a) the current supplied by each generator,
(b) the battery charging current when E_B is 10 V, and
(c) the terminal voltage E_B of the battery when E_B is 10 V.

Solution

(a) The arbitrarily chosen direction of current in each branch is shown in Figure 5.2; the directions chosen are thought to be reasonable. The circuit is redrawn in Figure 5.3, on which the direction of the 'potential' arrows are drawn (remember, the direction of a potential arrow associated with a resistor opposes the direction of current in the resistor).

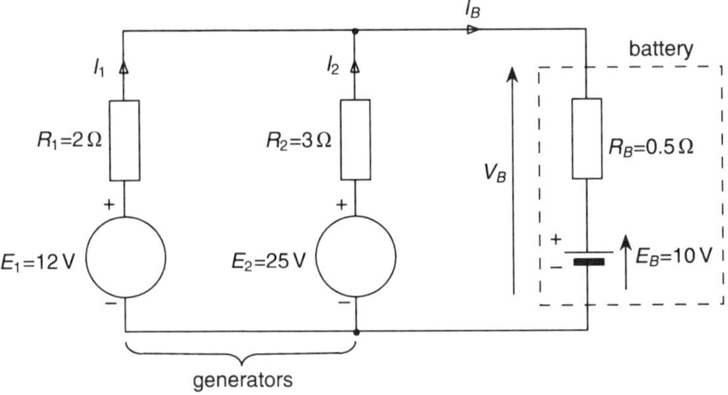

Figure 5.2 Worked Example 5.1

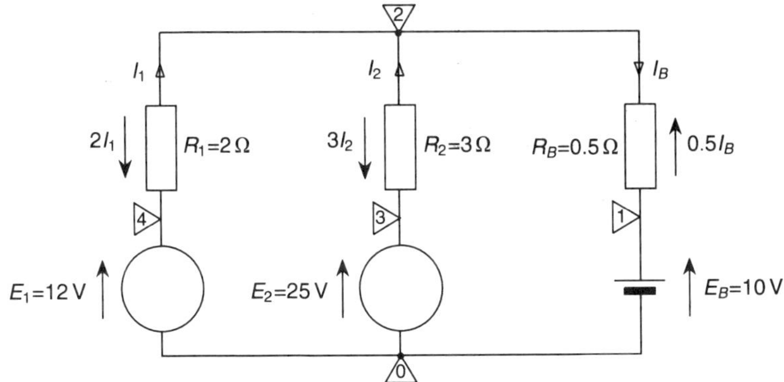

Figure 5.3 Solution of Worked Example 5.1

We can select any suitable pair of loops, and here we select loops 01230 and 01240, and applying KVL, we get the following equations.

Loop 01230

$$10 + 0.5I_B + 3I_2 - 25 = 0$$

or

$$-15 = -0.5I_B - 3I_2 \tag{5.7}$$

Loop 01240

$$10 + 0.5I_B + 2I_1 - 12 = 0$$

or

$$-2 = -0.5I_B - 2I_1 \tag{5.8}$$

Applying KCL to node 2 gives

$$I_B = I_1 + I_2 \tag{5.9}$$

Inserting the expression for I_B into (5.7) shows that

$$\begin{aligned}-15 &= -0.5I_B - 3I_2 = -0.5(I_1 + I_2) - 3I_2 \\ &= -0.5I_1 - 3.5I_2 \end{aligned} \qquad (5.10)$$

and into (5.8) yields

$$\begin{aligned}-2 &= -0.5I_B - 2I_1 = -0.5(I_1 + I_2) - 2I_1 \\ &= -2.5I_1 - 0.5I_2 \end{aligned} \qquad (5.11)$$

We can eliminate I_1 between (5.10) and (5.11) by multiplying (5.10) by 5 and subtracting (5.11) from it as follows

$$\begin{aligned} -75 &= -2.5I_1 - 17.5I_2 && ((5.10)\times 5) \\ -2 &= -2.5I_1 - 0.5I_2 && ((5.11)\text{ repeated}) \\ \hline \text{SUBTRACT} \quad -73 &= \qquad\quad - 17I_2 \end{aligned}$$

or

$$I_2 = -73/(-17) = 4.294 \text{ A}$$

I_1 is calculated by substituting the value of I_2 into (5.10) as follows

$$\begin{aligned}-15 &= -0.5I_1 - 3.5I_2 = -0.5I_1 - (3.5 \times 4.294) \\ &= -0.5I_1 - 15.029\end{aligned}$$

hence

$$I_1 = \frac{15 - 15.029}{0.5} = -0.058 \text{ A}$$

The reader should note here that I_1 has a negative value, implying that the 'generator' E_1 receives current, rather than exporting it, i.e., it is driven as a **motor** by generator E_1.
Check: Inserting the values of I_1 and I_2 into (5.11) gives

$$\begin{aligned}\text{RHS} &= -2.5I_1 - 0.5I_2 \\ &= -(2.5 \times (-0.058)) - (0.5 \times 4.29) \\ &= 0.145 - 2.145 = -2\end{aligned}$$

which agrees with the left-hand side of (5.11).

(b) From (5.9), the battery charging current is

$$I_B = I_1 + I_2 = -0.058 + 4.294 = 4.236 \text{ A}$$

(c) We can calculate the terminal voltage V_B of the battery by writing down the equation for the voltage across branch 012, and inserting appropriate values as follows

$$V_B = E_B + 0.5I_B = 10 + (0.5 \times 4.236) = 12.118 \text{ V}$$

In practice we cannot measure these values quite as accurately as they can be calculated.

Worked Example 5.2

Three d.c. generators are connected in parallel with one another. The e.m.f. and internal resistance of the generators are

Generator 1: $E_1 = 100\,\text{V}$, $R_1 = 4\,\Omega$
Generator 2: $E_2 = 90\,\text{V}$, $R_2 = 3\,\Omega$
Generator 3: $E_3 = 80\,\text{V}$, $R_3 = 5\,\Omega$

Calculate the terminal voltage of the generators.

Solution

The circuit is shown in Figure 5.4, together with the assumed direction of current flow and the associated p.d. arrows across the resistors. Applying KCL at node 4 (or node 0) gives

$$I_1 + I_2 + I_3 = 0$$

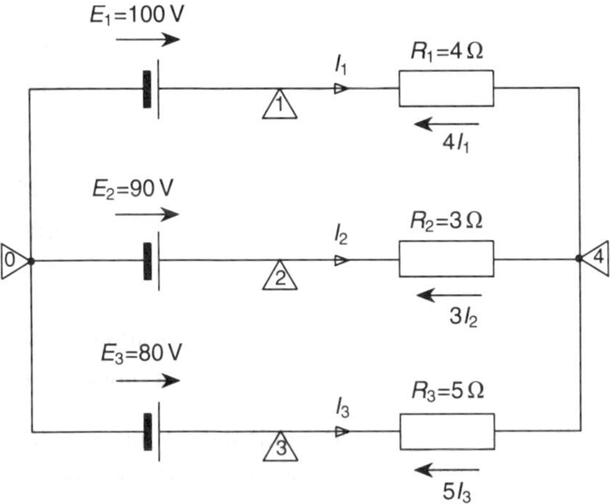

Figure 5.4 Worked Example 5.2

There are three variables, but we only need two simultaneous equations because, if we can calculate I_1 and I_2, we can determine I_3 from the following

$$I_3 = -(I_1 + I_2) \tag{5.12}$$

Using KVL, we will write down equations for two of the closed loops in the circuit as follows.

Loop 01420

$$100 - 4I_1 + 3I_2 - 90 = 0$$

or

$$10 = 4I_1 - 3I_2 \tag{5.13}$$

Loop 02430

$$90 - 3I_2 + 5I_3 - 80 = 0$$

or

$$10 = 3I_2 - 5I_3$$

that is

$$10 = 3I_2 - 5(-(I_1 + I_2)) = 5I_1 + 8I_2 \tag{5.14}$$

I_1 can be eliminated from (5.13) and (5.14) by multiplying (5.14) by 0.8 and subtracting it from (5.13) as follows.

$$\begin{aligned} 10 &= 4I_1 - 3\ I_2 && \text{((5.13) rewritten)} \\ 8 &= 4I_1 + 6.4I_2 && (0.8\times\ (5.14)) \end{aligned}$$

SUBTRACT $\quad 2 = \quad - 9.4I_2$

or

$$I_2 = 2/(-9.4) = -0.213 \text{ A}$$

Substituting this value in (5.13) gives

$$10 = 4I_1 - 3I_2 = 4I_1 - 3 \times (-0.213) = 4I_1 + 0.639$$

that is

$$I_1 = \frac{10 - 0.639}{4} = 2.34 \text{ A}$$

and from (5.12) we get

$$I_3 = -(I_1 + I_2) = -(2.34 + (-0.213)) = -2.127 \text{ A}$$

Check: Inserting the above values into (3.13) gives

$$\begin{aligned} \text{RHS} &= 4I_1 - 3I_2 = (4 \times 2.34) - (3 \times (-0.213)) \\ &= 9.999 \end{aligned}$$

which is in very close agreement with the value of 10 on the left-hand side of the equation.

It is interesting to note that, **with no external load connected** between nodes 0 and 4, current flows in all three generators; E_1 supplies a current of 2.34 A, whilst E_2 and E_3 absorb this amount of current between them! That is to say, with no load connected, 'generators' E_2 and E_3 operate as 'motors'. We look at the case when a load is connected to the generators in Worked Example 5.3.

The terminal voltage can be determined by following the voltages and p.d.s in any branch between nodes 0 and 4. Choosing the branch 024, we have

$$\begin{aligned} \text{Terminal voltage} &= V_{40} = 90 - 3I_2 \\ &= 90 - 3(-0.213) = 90.64 \text{ V} \end{aligned}$$

Worked Example 5.3

Calculate the current in each generator in Worked Example 5.2 if a 6 Ω load is connected between nodes 0 and 4. Determine also the current in the load and the voltage across it.

Solution

The circuit is drawn in Figure 5.5. Applying KCL to node E (or node A) tells us that

$$I_1 + I_2 + I_3 - I_L = 0$$

or

$$I_L = I_1 + I_2 + I_3 \tag{5.15}$$

where I_L is the load current. In other words, even though there are four variables in (5.15), there are only three unknowns because, once we have calculated three of them, we can determine the value of the fourth from (5.15). We therefore need three simultaneous equations from the circuit to solve for three unknowns; in this case we choose to solve for I_1, I_2 and I_3.

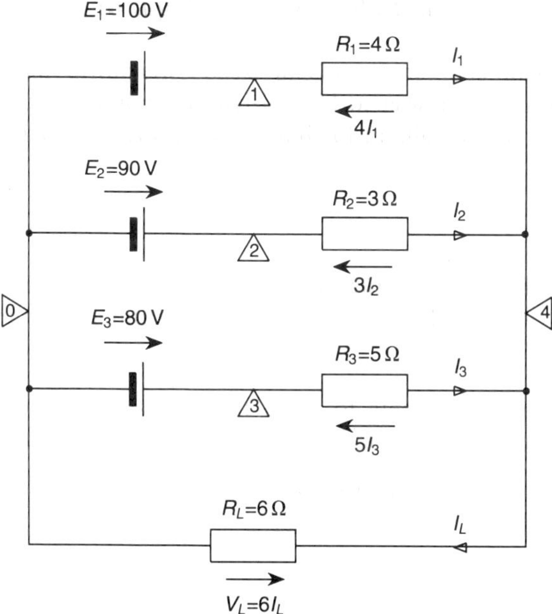

Figure 5.5 Worked Example 5.3

It is pointed out here that **the solution of three simultaneous equations is no more difficult than the solution of two simultaneous equations, it merely takes longer**.

There are four closed loops in the circuit, and we apply KVL to loops 01420, 02430 and 0340.

Loop 01420

$$100 - 4I_1 + 3I_2 - 90 = 0$$

or

$$10 = 4I_1 - 3I_2 \tag{5.16}$$

Loop 02430

$$90 - 3I_2 + 5I_3 - 80 = 0$$

that is

$$10 = 3I_2 - 5I_3 \tag{5.17}$$

Loop 0340

$$80 - 5I_3 - 6I_L = 0$$

or

$$\begin{aligned} 80 &= 5I_3 + 6I_L = 5I_3 + 6(I_1 + I_2 + I_3) \\ &= 6I_1 + 6I_2 + 11I_3 \end{aligned} \tag{5.18}$$

Next, we group the three equations together so that we can decide what steps to take.

$$\begin{aligned} 10 &= 4I_1 - 3I_2 && \text{((5.16) rewritten)} \\ 10 &= \quad\;\; 3I_2 - 5I_3 && \text{((5.17) rewritten)} \\ 80 &= 6I_1 + 6I_2 + 11I_3 && \text{((5.18) rewritten)} \end{aligned}$$

We can solve the three simultaneous equations **by elimination** if we take the following steps

1. Eliminate one variable (say I_2) from the first and second equations. This leaves a new equation.
2. Eliminate the same variable (I_2) from the first and third equations. This produces a second new equation.
3. Solve for the remaining unknowns (I_1 and I_3) from the two new equations.
4. Insert the value of I_1 and I_3 into one of the original equations, and determine I_2.

Step 1: To eliminate I_2 between (5.16) and (5.17), it is merely necessary to add the two equations together as follows

$$\begin{aligned} 10 &= 4I_1 - 3I_2 && \text{((5.16) rewritten)} \\ 10 &= \qquad\;\; 3I_2 - 5I_3 && \text{((5.17) rewritten)} \\ \hline \text{ADD} \quad 20 &= 4I_1 \qquad\quad - 5I_3 && (5.19) \end{aligned}$$

Step 2: To eliminate I_2 between (5.16) and (5.18), we multiply (5.18) by 0.5 and add it to (5.16)

$$10 = 4I_1 - 3I_2 \qquad \text{((5.16) rewritten)}$$
$$40 = 3I_1 + 3I_2 + 5.5I_3 \qquad (0.5\times\text{(5.18))}$$

$$\text{ADD} \quad 50 = 7I_1 + 5.5I_3 \qquad (5.20)$$

For clarity, we rewrite (5.19) and (5.20)

$$20 = 4I_1 - I_3 \qquad \text{((5.19) rewritten)}$$
$$50 = 7I_1 + 5.5I_3 \qquad \text{((5.20) rewritten)}$$

Step 3: To eliminate I_3 between these two equations, multiply (5.20) by $5/5.5 = 0.9091$, and add the resulting equation to (5.19), as follows

$$20 = 4I_1 - 5I_3 \qquad \text{((5.19) rewritten)}$$
$$45.45 = 6.36I_1 + 5I_3 \qquad (0.9091\times\text{(5.20))}$$

$$\text{ADD} \quad 65.45 = 10.36I_1$$

giving

$$I_1 = 65.45/10.36 = 6.32 \text{ A}$$

Substituting this value into (5.19) yields

$$20 = (4 \times 6.32) - 5I_3$$

hence

$$I_3 = (25.28 - 20)/5 = 1.06 \text{ A}$$

Step 4: Equation (5.16) enables us to calculate I_2 as follows

$$10 = 4I_1 - 3I_2 = (4 \times 6.32) - 3I_2$$

that is

$$I_2 = (25.28 - 10)/3 = 5.09 \text{ A}$$

The reader should observe that, when the load is connected, all the generators supply a 'positive' current (see Worked Example 5.2, where some supply a 'negative' current under no-load condition).
Check: Inserting these values into (5.18) gives

$$\begin{aligned}\text{RHS} &= 6I_1 + 6I_2 + 11I_3 \\ &= (6 \times 6.32) + (6 \times 5.09) + (11 \times 1.06) \\ &= 80.12\end{aligned}$$

which is within 0.2 per cent of the value of 80 on the left-hand side of the equation.

The load current I_L is calculated from (5.15) as shown below

$$I_L = I_1 + I_2 + I_3 = 6.32 + 5.09 + 1.06 = 12.47 \text{ A}$$

and the voltage across the load is

$$V_L = 6I_L = 6 \times 12.47 = 74.82 \text{ V}$$

5.8 Solution of simultaneous equations using determinants

The solution of simultaneous equations either by substitution or elimination (particularly when there are more than two unknowns) requires great care, and can be very time consuming.

An alternative method of solving simultaneous equations using what are known as **determinants** is less demanding, less error-prone and is quicker than the methods described hitherto. We will not give a general proof of the method used here, and the reader should refer to books on mathematics for the validity of the method.

Suppose we have the following simultaneous equations

$$V_1 = AI_1 + BI_2 \tag{5.21}$$

$$V_2 = CI_1 + DI_2 \tag{5.22}$$

where V_1, V_2, A, B, C and D are numerical values, and I_1 and I_2 are unknowns. If we arrange the **coefficients** A, B, C and D in determinant form we get

$$\begin{vmatrix} A & B \\ C & D \end{vmatrix}$$

The vertical lines on either side of the coefficients tell us that we are dealing with a determinant. The **numerical value** of the determinant (which we will call **det** in this case) is

$$\text{det} = \begin{vmatrix} A & B \\ C & D \end{vmatrix} = AD - BC \tag{5.23}$$

That is, we multiply the diagonal coefficients together, and subtract the diagonal product BC from the product AD.

The simultaneous equations (5.21) and (5.22) are solved using the following equation

$$\frac{1}{\text{det}} = \frac{I_1}{\text{det}\, I_1} = \frac{I_2}{\text{det}\, I_2} \tag{5.24}$$

where det is the determinant whose value was obtained from (5.23), and $\text{det}\, I_1$ and $\text{det}\, I_2$ are calculated as follows

$$\det I_1 = \begin{vmatrix} V_1 & B \\ V_2 & D \end{vmatrix} = V_1 D - V_2 B \tag{5.25}$$

$$\det I_2 = \begin{vmatrix} A & V_1 \\ C & V_2 \end{vmatrix} = AV_2 - CV_1 \tag{5.26}$$

That is, $\det I_1$ is obtained by replacing the coefficients A and C by V_1 and V_2, respectively in the determinant det, and $\det I_2$ is obtained by replacing the coefficients B and D by V_1 and V_2.

To summarise, from (5.24) we may say

$$\det I_1 = \frac{\det I_1}{\det} = \frac{\begin{vmatrix} V_1 & B \\ V_2 & D \end{vmatrix}}{\begin{vmatrix} A & B \\ C & D \end{vmatrix}} = \frac{V_1 D - V_2 B}{AD - BC}$$

$$I_2 = \frac{\det I_2}{\det} = \frac{\begin{vmatrix} A & V_1 \\ C & V_2 \end{vmatrix}}{\begin{vmatrix} A & B \\ C & D \end{vmatrix}} = \frac{AV_2 - CV_1}{AD - BC}$$

Let us use this method to solve the circuit in Figure 5.1, for which the circuit equations are

$$10 = 20I_1 + 15I_2 \qquad \text{((5.4) rewritten)}$$
$$-5 = 5I_1 - 10I_2 \qquad \text{((5.5) rewritten)}$$

From (5.23), the value of det is

$$\det = \begin{vmatrix} 20 & 15 \\ -5 & -10 \end{vmatrix} = (20 \times (-10)) - (5 \times 15)$$
$$= -200 - 75 = -275$$

From (5.25), the value of $\det I_1$ is

$$\det I_1 = \begin{vmatrix} 10 & 15 \\ -5 & -10 \end{vmatrix} = (10 \times (-10)) - (-5 \times 15)$$
$$= -100 + 75 = 25$$

and from (5.26), $\det I_2$ is

$$\det I_2 = \begin{vmatrix} 20 & 10 \\ 5 & -5 \end{vmatrix} = (20 \times (-5)) - (10 \times 5)$$
$$= -100 - 50 = -150$$

(5.24) tells us that

$$I_1 = \frac{\det I_1}{\det} = \frac{25}{-275} = -0.909 \text{ A}$$

and

$$I_2 = \frac{\det I_2}{\det} = \frac{-150}{-275} = 0.5455 \text{ A}$$

which values agree with the solutions obtained in sections 5.3 and 5.4.

The reader will see that this is a quicker and less error-prone method of solving a pair of simultaneous equations because it is more systematic than other methods; it will be an interesting exercise to use this method to solve other simultaneous equations containing two unknowns.

If there are three simultaneous equations of the form

$$V_1 = AI_1 + BI_2 + CI_3$$
$$V_2 = DI_1 + EI_2 + FI_3$$
$$V_3 = GI_1 + HI_2 + JI_3$$

The general solution is obtained from

$$\frac{1}{\det} = \frac{I_1}{\det I_1} = \frac{I_2}{\det I_2} = \frac{I_3}{\det I_3} \tag{5.27}$$

All we need to know now is how to evaluate the four determinants det, $\det I_1$, $\det I_2$ and $\det I_3$. Once again, the procedure is fairly straightforward using a mathematical procedure known as the **rule of Sarrus**. Let us apply this to the determinant det as follows

$$\det = \left|\begin{array}{ccc|cc} A & B & C & A & B \\ D & E & F & D & E \\ G & H & J & G & H \end{array}\right.$$

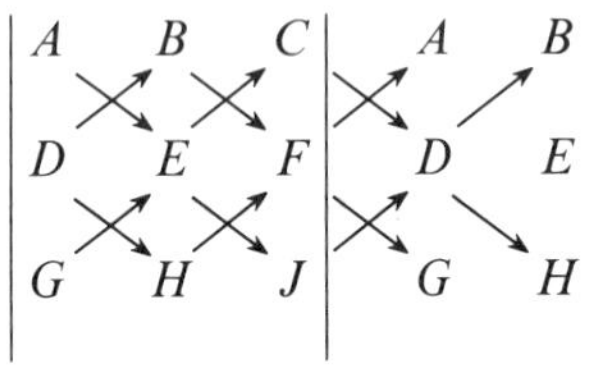

$$= (AEJ) + (BFG) + (CDH) - (GEC) - (HFA) - (JDB)$$

The steps involved are as follows

1. Repeat the first two columns in the determinant, but on the right-hand side of the determinant.
2. Mentally draw diagonal lines joining sets of three determinants.
3. Multiply the value of the three elements on each diagonal line. The product terms *AEJ*, *BFG* and *CDH* are given a positive sign, and the terms *GEC*, *HFA* and *JDB* are given a negative sign.
4. The value of the determinant is the sum of all the diagonal products.

The determinant $\det I_1$ is obtained by replacing the first column (column A, D, G) in the determinant det by the column V_1, V_2, V_3 as shown below. The value of $\det I_1$ is obtained by applying the rule of Sarrus as outlined above

$$\det I_1 = \begin{vmatrix} V_1 & B & C \\ V_2 & E & F \\ V_3 & H & J \end{vmatrix}$$

$$= V_1EJ + BFV_3 + CV_2H - V_3EC - HFV_1 - JV_2B$$

and I_1 is calculated as follows (see (5.27))

$$I_1 = \frac{\det I_1}{\det}$$

Similarly

$$\det I_2 = \begin{vmatrix} A & V_1 & C \\ D & V_2 & F \\ G & V_3 & J \end{vmatrix}$$

$$= AV_2J + V_1FG + CDV_3 - GV_2C - V_3FA - JDV_1$$

$$\det I_3 = \begin{vmatrix} A & B & V_1 \\ D & E & V_2 \\ G & H & V_3 \end{vmatrix}$$

$$= AEV_3 + BV_2G + V_1DH - GEV_1 - HV_2A - V_3DB$$

also

$$I_2 = \det I_2 / \det \text{ and } I_3 = \det I_3 / \det$$

It is important to note that **the rule of Sarrus applies only to third-order determinants**.

Whilst the general procedure for working out the value of determinants is fairly simple, errors can easily occur when changing the values in the columns associated with the different determinants. **Do take care** (the author speaks from experience!).

Let us apply this to the circuit in Worked Example 5.3, for which the equations are

$$10 = 4I_1 - 3I_2 \qquad \text{((5.16) rewritten)}$$

$$10 = 3I_2 - 5I_3 \qquad \text{((5.17) rewritten)}$$

$$80 = 6I_1 + 6I_2 + 11I_3 \qquad \text{((5.18) rewritten)}$$

For these equations

$$\det = \begin{vmatrix} 4 & -3 & 0 \\ 0 & 3 & -5 \\ 6 & 6 & 11 \end{vmatrix}$$

$$= 4.3.11 + (-3).(-5).6 + 0.0.6 - 6.3.0. - 6.(-5).4 - 11.0.(-3)$$
$$= 132 + 90 + 0 - 0 + 120 - 0 = 342$$

$$\det I_1 = \begin{vmatrix} 10 & -3 & 0 \\ 10 & 3 & -5 \\ 80 & 6 & 11 \end{vmatrix}$$

$$= 10.3.11 + (-3).(-5).80 + 0.10.6 - 80.3.0 - 6.(-5).10 - 11.10.(-3)$$
$$= 330 + 1200 + 0 - 0 + 300 + 330 = 2160$$

$$\det I_2 = \begin{vmatrix} 4 & 10 & 0 \\ 0 & 10 & -5 \\ 6 & 80 & 11 \end{vmatrix}$$

$$= 4.10.11 + 10.(-5).6 + 0.0.80 - 6.10.0 - 80.(-5).4 - 11.0.10$$
$$= 440 - 300 + 0 - 0 + 1600 - 0 = 1740$$

$$\det I_3 = \begin{vmatrix} 4 & -3 & 10 \\ 0 & 3 & 10 \\ 6 & 6 & 80 \end{vmatrix}$$

$$= 4.3.80 + (-3).10.6 + 10.0.6 - 6.3.10 - 6.10.4 - 80.0.(-3)$$
$$= 960 - 180 + 0 - 180 - 240 - 0 = 360$$

From (5.27) we may write

$$I_1 = \det I_1 / \det = 2160/342 = 6.32 \text{ A}$$
$$I_2 = \det I_2 / \det = 1740/342 = 5.09 \text{ A}$$
$$I_3 = \det I_3 / \det = 360/342 = 1.05 \text{ A}$$

which agree with the values obtained in Worked Example 5.3.

5.9 Programs for solving simultaneous equations using the BASIC language

In this section we will briefly describe BASIC language programs for solving simultaneous equations for two and three variables respectively.

As mentioned earlier, the programs given in this book are straightforward, and should run on most versions of BASIC. Some versions do not

```
10  CLS
20  PRINT TAB(3); "Solution of two simultaneous equations"
30  PRINT TAB(15); "of the form": PRINT
40  PRINT TAB(13); "V1 = A*X + B*Y"
50  PRINT TAB(13); "V2 = C*X + D*Y": PRINT
60  PRINT TAB(3); "Where V1 and V2 are numerical values,"
70  PRINT TAB(3); "A,B,C and D are numerical coefficients,"
80  PRINT TAB(3); "and X and Y are the variables."
90  PRINT
100 INPUT "V1 = ", V1
110 INPUT "A = ", A
120 INPUT "B = ", B
130 PRINT
140 INPUT "V2 = ", V2
150 INPUT "C = ", C
160 INPUT "D = ", D
170 PRINT
180 Det = (A * D) - (B * C)
190 REM ** There is no solution if Det = 0 **
200 IF Det = 0 THEN PRINT TAB(3); "The equations cannot be solved.": END
210 REM ** Calculate Det X and Det Y **
220 DetX = (V1 * D) - (V2 * B): DetY = (A * V2) - (C * V1)
230 REM ** Calculate the value of the variables **
240 PRINT TAB(3); "X = "; DetX / Det: PRINT TAB(3); "Y = "; DetY / Det
250 END
```

Figure 5.6 Solution of two simultaneous equations

use line numbers, but these will operate even if the line numbers are included. However it is pointed out that the programs are merely a 'tool', and do not help the learning process.

Both programs operate in much the same way, and use determinants to solve the problem. Firstly, they display the general form of the equation, and then they ask for the data associated with each equation (see Figure 5.6). The numerical values on the left-hand side of the equation are V_1 and V_2 (or V_1, V_2 and V_3 in the case of three unknowns), and the numerical coefficients on the right-hand side of the equation are A, B, C and D (or A–H and J (I is omitted for obvious electrical reasons)). The unknowns are X and Y (or X, Y and Z in the case of three unknowns (see Figure 5.7)).

Should the determinant 'det' have zero value, the equation cannot be solved.

In the case of two unknowns, the value of Det X and Det Y are evaluated directly. For three unknowns, $D1$ is the sum of the terms which are given a 'positive' sign by the rule of Sarrus (see section 5.7), and $D2$ is the sum of the terms given a 'negative' sign.

```
10  CLS
20  PRINT TAB(3); "Solution of three simultaneous equations"
30  PRINT TAB(15); "of the form": PRINT
40  PRINT TAB(11); "V1 = A*X + B*Y + C*Z"
45  PRINT TAB(11); "V2 = D*X + E*Y + F*Z"
50  PRINT TAB(11); "V3 = G*X + H*Y + J*Z": PRINT
60  PRINT TAB(3); "Where V1, V2 and V3 are numerical values,"
70  PRINT TAB(3); "A to H and J are numerical coefficients,"
80  PRINT TAB(3); "and X, Y and Z are the variables."
90  PRINT
100 INPUT "V1 = ", V1
110 INPUT "A = ", A
120 INPUT "B = ", B
130 INPUT "C = ", C
140 PRINT
150 INPUT "V2 = ", V2
160 INPUT "D = ", D
170 INPUT "E = ", E
180 INPUT "F = ", F
190 PRINT
200 INPUT "V3 = ", V3
210 INPUT "G = ", G
220 INPUT "H = ", H
230 INPUT "J = ", J: PRINT
240 D1 = (A * E * J) + (B * F * G) + (C * D * H)
250 D2 = (G * E * C) + (H * F * A) + (J * D * B)
260 Det = D1 - D2
270 REM ** There is no solution if Det = 0 **
280 IF Det = 0 THEN PRINT TAB(3); "The equations cannot be solved.": END
290 REM ** Calculate Det X, Det Y and Det Z **
300 D1 = (V1 * E * J) + (B * F * V3) + (C * V2 * H)
310 D2 = (V3 * E * C) + (H * F * V1) + (J * V2 * B)
320 DetX = D1 - D2
330 D1 = (A * V2 * J) + (V1 * F * G) + (C * D * V3)
340 D2 = (G * V2 * C) + (V3 * F * A) + (J * D * V1)
350 DetY = D1 - D2
360 D1 = (A * E * V3) + (B * V2 * G) + (V1 * D * H)
370 D2 = (G * E * V1) + (H * V2 * A) + (V3 * D * B)
380 DetZ = D1 - D2
390 REM ** Calculate the value of the variables **
400 PRINT TAB(3); "X = "; DetX / Det
410 PRINT TAB(3); "Y = "; DetY / Det
420 PRINT TAB(3); "Z = "; DetZ / Det
430 END
```

Figure 5.7 Solution of three simultaneous equations

Self-test questions

5.1 Solve the following equations for x and y

$$5 = 4x + 3y$$
$$10 = 2x + 5y$$

5.2 Solve the following for x and y

$$\frac{8}{14} = \frac{2x}{5} + \frac{2y}{3}$$
$$\frac{5}{9} = \frac{2x}{9} - \frac{y}{3}.$$

5.3 If, in Worked Example 5.2, the e.m.f.s are

$$E_1 = 100\,\text{V},\ E_2 = 110\,\text{V},\ E_3 = 120\,\text{V}$$

and the resistance values are

$$R_1 = 1\,\Omega,\ R_2 = 2\,\Omega,\ R_3 = 3\,\Omega$$

write down a set of simultaneous equations for the solution of the circuit. Calculate the current in each battery, and determine the voltage of node 4 with respect to node 0 (see also Figure 5.4).

5.4 If a 5 Ω resistance is connected between nodes E and A in question 5.3, evaluate the voltage across the resistor.

5.5 Solve the equations

$$14.5 = 5x + 6y + 7z$$
$$13.6 = x - y + 3.5z$$
$$-6.8 = 2x - 3y - 5z$$

5.6 Calculate the current in each battery in Figure 5.8.

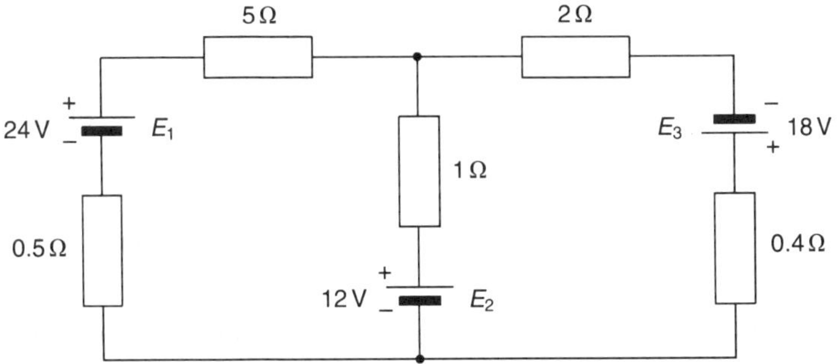

Figure 5.8 Self-test question 5.6

5.7 What current is drawn from each generator, and what is the battery charging current, if the voltage E_B in Worked Example 5.1 (see Figure 5.2) is 8 V?

Summary of important facts

Linear equations contain only variables raised to the power unity, i.e., x, y, I_1, V_1, etc., and do not contain variables raised to any other power, i.e., x^2, $y^{3.1}$, etc.

Simultaneous equations relate to a number of variables, and occur frequently in electrical and electronic circuits.

Simultaneous linear equations may be solved *by hand* either by **substitution** or by **elimination**. Solution by substitution is carried out by expressing one variable in terms of another; once its value is known, it can be inserted in another equation to allow the calculation of a second unknown. Solution by elimination involves multiplying through one equation by a constant, allowing one variable to be eliminated from the equations.

An alternative method of solution by hand is to use **determinants**. This method is generally more straightforward and less error-prone than solution by substitution or elimination. **Computer solution** of simultaneous equations often involves solution by determinants.

Another method of computer solution of electric circuits is by the use of special software such as **SPICE** (see Chapter 16). This software does not solve the equations of the circuit by conventional methods, but uses numerical methods which are beyond the scope of this book.

6 Trigonometry

6.1 Introduction

Trigonometry is concerned with the solution of triangles using **trigonometric functions**, and is of immense practical value in all branches of engineering. The earliest rudiments of trigonometry date back to 1900 BC, and there is an Egyptian papyrus (c. 1650 BC) containing trigonometric calculations relating to the pyramids.

In this chapter we look at methods of **angular measurement**, the **solution of triangles** and many other aspects of trigonometry which concern electrical and electronic engineers.

By the end of this chapter the reader will be able to

- recognise acute, obtuse and reflex angles,
- calculate angles in degrees and radians,
- perform calculations using sine, cosine, tangent, cosecant, secant and cotangent functions,
- manipulate angles in any of the four quadrants, and angles which are greater than 360°,
- draw sine, cosine and tangent curves,
- determine the amplitude, phase angle, period and frequency of a sinusiodal wave.

6.2 Angles and angular measure

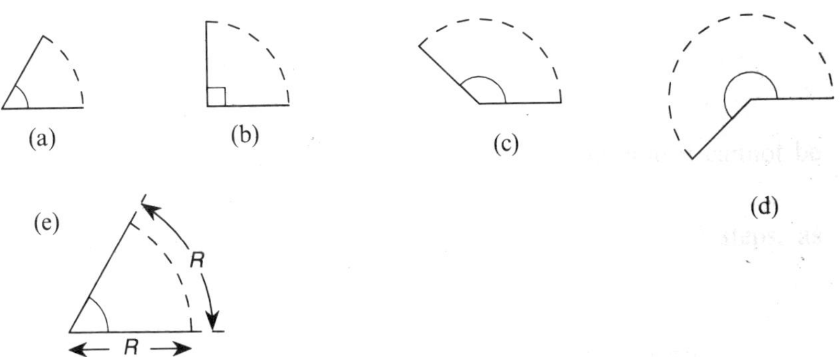

Figure 6.1 (a) an acute angle, (b) a right angle, (c) and obtuse angle, (d) a reflex angle, (e) the radian

An **angle** is a measure of the 'rotation' between two lines which meet at a point or **vertex** (see Figure 6.1). There are four general types of angle, namely **acute**, **obtuse** and **reflex** (the latter expression is not used very frequently in engineering), together with the **right-angle** or quadrant of a circle.

The most popular unit of angular measurement is the **degree**, in which a circle is divided into 360 degrees or 360°; this subdivision dates back to Babylonian times. Formerly the degree was itself subdivided into *sixty minutes*, and each minute was divides into *sixty seconds*. Today, however, the degree has been decimalised. For example, and angle of 26.32° corresponds to 26°, 19 minutes and 12 seconds, and is written in the form

$$26.32^\circ = 26^\circ 19' 12''$$

Yet another angular measure used in engineering is the **radian** (often abbreviated to rad), and 1 radian is the angle subtended at the centre of a circle by an arc of length equal to the radius (see Figure 6.1 (e)). The name 'radian' is said to have been invented by James Thomson for an examination paper in Belfast in 1870. There are 2π radians in a complete circle, so that

$$2\pi \text{ radians} \equiv 360^\circ$$

or

$$1 \text{ radian} \equiv 57.3^\circ$$

Both the degree and radian are widely employed in engineering, and we shall use both of them in this chapter. Referring to Figure 6.1, the angles are classified as follows

(a) **Acute angle** – less than 90° or $\pi/2$ rad.
(b) **Right angle** – 90° or $\pi/2$ rad (quarter of a complete circle).
(c) **Obtuse angle** – between 90° and 180° (between $\pi/2$ and π rad).
(d) **Reflex angle** – between 180° and 360° (between π and 2π rad).

The small rectangular shape drawn in the corner of the angle in Figure 6.1(b) indicates that the angle is a right-angle.

If two angles have a sum of 90° they are said to be **complementary angles**. That is if

$$A + B = 90^\circ$$

then

$$A = 90^\circ - B \text{ and } B = 90^\circ - A$$

Each of the above angles is said to the *complement* of the other.

Two angles that have a sum of 180° are said to be **supplementary angles**. For example, if

$$C + D = 180^\circ$$

then

$$C = 180^\circ - D \text{ and } D = 180^\circ - C$$

C and D are said to be the *supplement* of one another.

6.3 Trigonometric ratios of acute angles

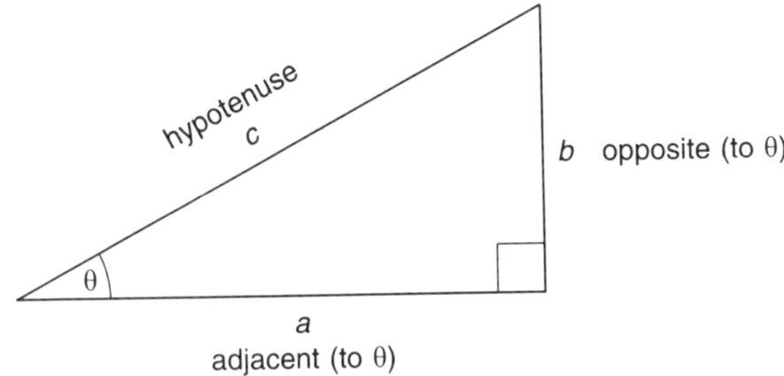

Figure 6.2 The names of the sides of a right-angled triangle

With reference to Figure 6.2, the three sides of the **right-angled triangle** are:

adjacent – the side which commences at the vertex of the angle and terminates at the right angle. It is said to be *adjacent* to the angle.
opposite – the side which is *opposite* to the angle.
hypotenuse – the side which commences at the vertex of the angle and terminates at the top of the opposite side.

The three principal *trigonometric ratios* or *functions* are:

$$\text{sine}\,\theta = \frac{\text{opposite}}{\text{hypotenuse}} \quad \text{or} \quad \sin\theta = \frac{b}{c}$$

$$\text{cosine}\,\theta = \frac{\text{adjacent}}{\text{hypotenuse}} \quad \text{or} \quad \cos\theta = \frac{a}{c}$$

$$\text{tangent}\,\theta = \frac{\text{opposite}}{\text{adjacent}} \quad \text{or} \quad \tan\theta = \frac{b}{a}$$

Also we see that

$$\frac{\sin\theta}{\cos\theta} = \frac{b/c}{a/c} = \frac{b}{a} = \tan\theta$$

Other ratios are

$$\text{cosecant}\ \theta = \frac{\text{hypotenuse}}{\text{opposite}} \quad \text{or} \quad \text{cosec}\,\theta = \frac{c}{b}$$

$$\text{secant}\,\theta = \frac{\text{hypotenuse}}{\text{adjacent}} \quad \text{or} \quad \sec\theta = \frac{c}{a}$$

$$\text{cotangent}\,\theta = \frac{\text{adjacent}}{\text{opposite}} \quad \text{or} \quad \cot\theta = \frac{a}{b}$$

6.4 Inverse trigonometric functions

These are the inverse of the trigonometric functions (also known as **anti-trigonometric functions**). If

$$q = \sin \theta$$

The inverse is written

$$\theta = \arcsin q$$

and is described as 'θ is the angle whose sine is q'. Similarly we have $\arccos q$ and $\arctan q$.

The inverse sine function is also described as $\sin^{-1} q$; similarly we have $\cos^{-1} q$ and $\tan^{-1} q$. The reader is cautioned against the use of these because $\sin^{-1} q$ **is not** $1/\sin q$; $1/\sin q$ is, in fact, $(1/\sin q)^{-1}$. To avoid any confusion, $\arcsin q$, $\arccos q$ and $\arctan q$ will be used in this book.

6.5 The four quadrants

An angle may lie at any point within a circle, and we define the four quadrants of a circle as (see Figure 6.3)

first quadrant: 0°–90°

second quadrant: 90°–180°

third quadrant: 180°–270°

fourth quadrant: 270°–360°

second quadrant	first quadrant
third quadrant	fourth quadrant

Figure 6.3 The four quadrants of a circle

As is shown below, the *mathematical sign* of the function of an angle (sin, cos, tan, etc.) may change from one quadrant to another. In fact, a simple rule is given below which allows us to predict the mathematical sign of the function of the angle (see also Figure 6.6).

In the *first quadrant*, all the sides of the triangle, i.e., ON_1, N_1M_1 and OM_1 are all positive, and **all the trigonometric ratios of the triangle are positive in this quadrant**.

In the *second quadrant* the adjacent side is negative, the other sides of the triangle having a positive value. That is, the **sine of the angle is positive**; its cosine and tangent are negative.

In the *third quadrant* the adjacent and opposite sides are both negative, so that the **tangent of the angle** is positive, whilst the sine and cosine of the angle are negative.

In the *fourth quadrant* the opposite side is negative, so that the **cosine of the angle** is positive and its sine and tangent are negative.

Figure 6.4 shows which trigonometric ratio is positive in each of the four quadrants of the circle. Moving in an anticlockwise direction we have

ALL, SIN, TAN, COS

which can be remembered by either of the following mnemonics.

All ***S***tations ***T***o ***C***rewe
All ***S***tudents of a ***T***echnical ***C***ourse

SIN	ALL
TAN	COS

Figure 6.4 Trigonometric ratios are always positive

6.6 Angles greater than 360° and negative angles

By convention, *the measurement of angles is positive in an anticlockwise direction*, and the horizontal direction is normally taken as the **reference direction**. Thus an angle of 150° implies a rotation of 150° in an anticlockwise direction, and −40° implies a rotation of 40° in a clockwise direction.

So far as trigonometrical ratios are concerned, we must reduce any angle (even one greater than +360° or −360°) to within 360°. For example, we regard 370° as an angle of $(360° + 10°) \equiv 10°$; that is 370° is equivalent to +10°, so that any trigonometric ratio of 370° has the same value as the identical trigonometric ratio of 10°. Similarly, we can regard 560° as being equivalent to an angle of $(360° + 200°) \equiv 200°$, i.e., we think of it as being equivalent to 200°. An angle of 800° is regarded as being $((2 \times 360°) + 80°)$, and its trigonometric ratios are the same as those of 80°.

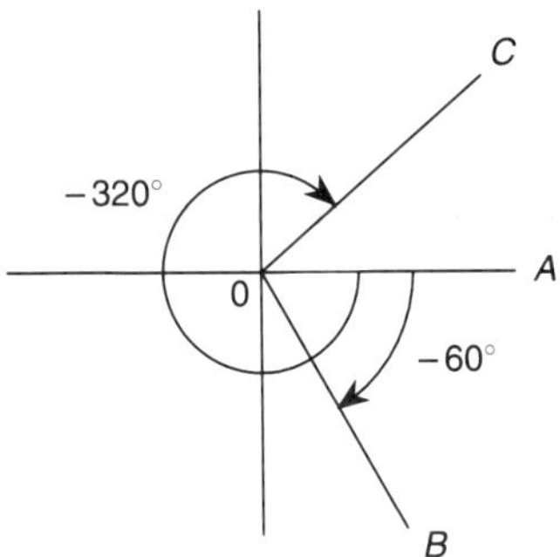

Figure 6.5 Negative angles

If the line *OA* in Figure 6.5 rotates in a clockwise direction to position *OB*, then we can say that its angle is −60°. If it continues to rotate in a clockwise direction to position *OC*, its angle is −320°.

Alternatively, we may reach *OB* and *OC* by assuming that the line has rotated in an anticlockwise direction. Clearly, the angle of −60° can be regarded as a positive angle of $(360 - 60)° = +300°$, and the angle of −320° is equivalent to $(360 - 320)° = 40°$.

6.7 The sine ratio

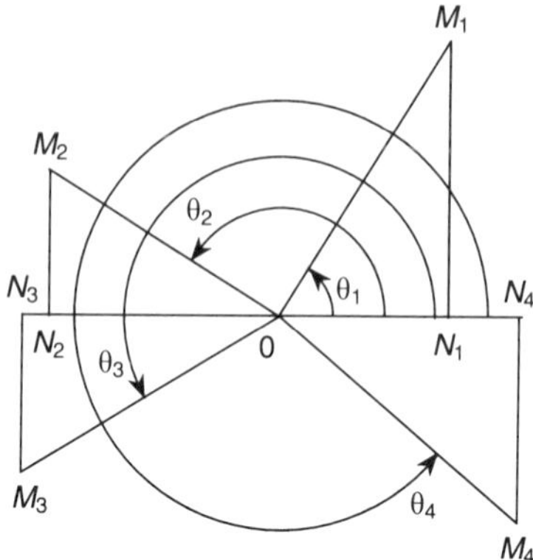

Figure 6.6 Angles in the four quadrants

In the following we will refer to Figure 6.6, and see that the sine of any angle is the ratio of the length NM (i.e., N_1M_1, N_2M_2, etc.) to OM (i.e. OM_1, OM_2, etc.). Since the maximum value of the ratio NM to OM can never exceed either +1 or −1 (when NM is negative), the maximum value of the sine of any angle is either +1 or −1.

First quadrant

In this case.

$$\sin\theta_1 = \frac{N_1M_1}{OM_1}$$

Since both N_1M_1 and OM_1 are positive, the sine of *any angle* in this quadrant has a positive sign. When N_1M_1 and ON_1 have the same value, the angle is 45°, and

$$OM_1 = \sqrt{(1^2 + 1^2)} = \sqrt{2}$$

hence

$$\sin 45^\circ = \frac{N_1M_1}{\sqrt{2}N_1M_1} = \frac{1}{\sqrt{2}} = 0.7071$$

We can also say that $\arcsin 0.7071 = 45^\circ$ (or $\pi/4$ rad).

We can also see that when

$$\theta_1 = 0^\circ, \text{ then } N_1M_1 = 0 \text{ and } \sin 0^\circ = 0$$

also when

$$\theta_1 = 90^\circ, \text{ then } N_1M_1 = OM_1 \text{ and } \sin 90^\circ = 1.$$

Second quadrant

Referring again to Figure 6.6, we see that

$$\sin\theta_2 = \frac{N_2M_2}{OM_2}$$

Once again, both the numerator and the denominator of this equation are positive, so that *the sine of the angle in this quadrant is always positive.*

When $\theta_2 = 180°$, then $N_2M_2 = 0$, and $\sin 180° = 0$.

Third quadrant

In this case

$$\sin\theta_3 = \frac{N_3M_3}{OM_3}$$

Here N_3M_3 is negative and OM_3 is positive, so that the sine of any angle in this quadrant is negative.

When $\theta_3 = 270°$, $N_3M_3 = OM_3$ so that $\sin 270° = -1$.

Fourth quadrant

We see from Figure 6.6 that

$$\sin\theta_4 = \frac{N_4M_4}{OM_4}$$

In this case N_4M_4 is negative and OM_4 is positive, so that the sine of any angle in this quadrant is negative.

When $\theta_4 = 360°$ ($\equiv 0°$), then $N_4M_4 = 0$ and $\sin 360° = 0$.

Worked Example 6.1

Determine the sine of (a) 10.1°, (b) 90°, (c) 0.722π rad, (d) 180°, (e) 220°, (f) 5.59 rad, (g) 400°, (h) −100°, (i) 15°10′5″.

Solution

We can use either a set of sine tables or a calculator to determine the answers, which are as follows.

(a) $\sin 10.1° = 0.1754$
Note: 10.1° is equivalent to $360° + 10.1 = 370.1°$, or $(2 \times 360°) + 10.1° = 730.1°$, etc.

(b) $\sin 90° = 1$.

(c) In this case $0.722\pi \times 57.3 \equiv 130°$, and $\sin 130° = 0.766$.

(d) $\sin 180° = 0$.
(e) $\sin 220° = -0.6428$.
(f) Converting the angle into degrees gives
$5.59\text{ rad} \equiv 5.59 \times 57.3° = 320°$, and $\sin 320° = -0.6428$.
Note that the answers in (e) and (f) are the same.
(g) $\sin 400° = 0.6428$.
Note: $400° = 360° + 40° \equiv 40°$
That is $\sin 400° \equiv \sin 40°$.
(h) $\sin(-100°) = -0.9848$.
Note: $-100° \equiv 360 - 100° = 260°$, so that
$\sin(-100°) \equiv \sin 260° = 0.9848$.
(i) In this case $10' = (10/60)° = 0.1667°$, and
$5'' = (5/(60 \times 60))° = 0.0014°$, so that
$15°10'5'' = (15 + 0.1667 + 0.0014)° = 15.1681°$
Using a calculator we find that

$$\sin 15°10'5'' = \sin 15.1681° = 0.2617$$

Worked Example 6.2

In the following $a =$ length of adjacent side, $b =$ length of opposite side, and $c =$ length of the hypotenuse (see also Figure 6.2). Using the sine relationship, evaluate the angle corresponding to the following: (a) $a = 2$, $c = 3$, (b) $a = -5$, $b = 4$, (c) $a = -3.3$, $b = -2$, and (d) $a = 3.1$, $b = -2.5$.

Solution

(a) In this case a is positive, so that the angle lies *either in the first quadrant or in the fourth quadrant*. Since we are to use the sine relationship we must, initially, evaluate the length of the opposite side of the triangle using Pythagorus's theorem as follows. Since

$$c^2 = a^2 + b^2$$

then

$$b = \surd(c^2 - a^2) = \surd(3^2 - 2^2) = 2.2361$$

If the angle lies in the first quadrant, then

$$\theta_a = \arcsin(b/c) = \arcsin(2.2361/3)$$
$$= \arcsin 0.7454 = 48.19°$$

If the angle lies in the fourth quadrant then

$$\text{angle} = -\theta_a = -48.19°$$
$$\text{or } 180° - 48.19° = 131.81°.$$

(b) In this case $a = -5$ and $b = 4$, i.e. *the angle must lie in the second quadrant*. Clearly, it is advisable to sketch the angle (see Figure 6.7) and treat the calculation on its merits.

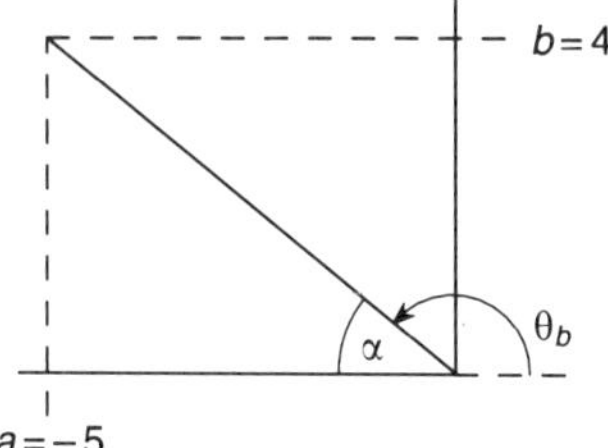

Figure 6.7 Solution to Worked Example 6.2(b)

We see that

$$\sin\alpha = \frac{\text{magnitude of opposite side}}{\text{magnitude of the hypotenuse}}$$

The length of the hypotenuse is

$$c = \sqrt{(a^2 + b^2)} = \sqrt{((-5)^2 + 4^2)} = 6.4031$$

hence

$$\sin\alpha = 4/6.4031 = 0.6247$$

or

$$\alpha = \arcsin 0.6247 = 38.66^\circ$$

If the reader were to insert the above values into a calculator, it would simply indicate that the answer is 38.66°! It is very clear that we must apply our experience to the data given in order to obtain the correct solution. That is the reason why we should draw a diagram which displays the data before we rush into the solution. Clearly, from Figure 6.7 we see that

$$\theta_b = 180^\circ - \alpha = 141.34^\circ$$

(c) In this case $a = -3.3$ and $b = -2$, so that the angle lies in the third quadrant; once again, we should draw a diagram which shows the angle (see Figure 6.8).

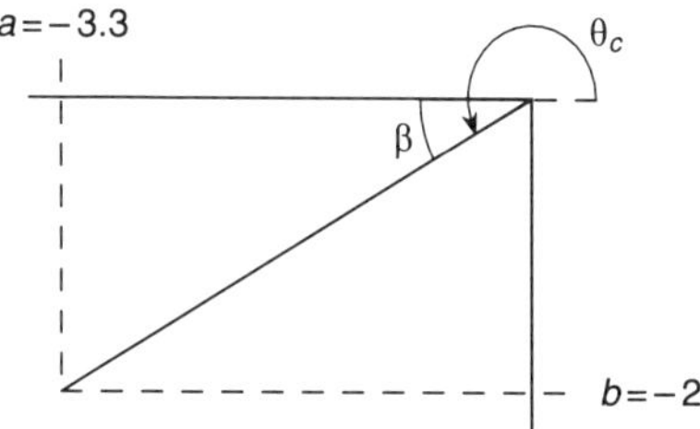

Figure 6.8 Solution to Worked Example 6.2(c)

In this case

$$\sin\beta = \frac{\text{length of opposite side}}{\text{length of hypotenuse}}$$

and the length of the hypotenuse is

$$c = \sqrt{(a^2 + b^2)} = \sqrt{((-3.3)^2 + (-2)^2)} = 3.86$$

hence the *magnitude* of $\sin\beta$ is

$$\sin\beta = 2/3.86 = 0.5181$$

and

$$\beta = \arcsin 0.5181 = 31.21^\circ$$

Referring to Figure 6.8 we see that

$$\theta_c = 180^\circ + \beta = 180^\circ + 31.21^\circ = 211.21^\circ$$
$$\text{or } (211.21 - 360)^\circ = -148.79^\circ$$

(d) Here $a = 3.1$ and $b = -2.5$, so that the angle lies in the fourth quadrant (see Figure 6.9).

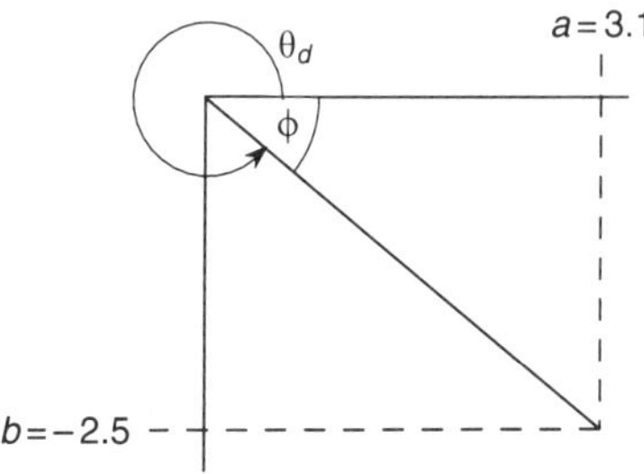

Figure 6.9 Solution to Worked Example 6.2(d)

In this case, the length of the hypotenuse is

$$c = \sqrt{(a^2 + b^2)} = \sqrt{(3.1^2 + (-2.5)^2)} = 3.98$$

hence

$$\sin\theta_d = \frac{\text{length of opposite side}}{\text{length of hypotenuse}} = \frac{-2.5}{3.98} = -0.6281$$

or

$$\theta_d = \arcsin(-0.6281) = -38.91^\circ$$
$$\text{or } (-38.91 + 360)^\circ = 321.09^\circ$$

Worked Example 6.3

The number of *kilo volt-amperes reactive*, kVAr, consumed by a three-phase load is given by the equation

$$kVAr = \frac{\sqrt{3}V_L I_L \sin\phi}{1000}$$

where V_L is the *line voltage*, I_L is the *line current*, and ϕ is the *phase angle* between V_L and I_L (see also section 6.9). Determine the value of ϕ if V_L is 3300 V, I_L is 150 A, and the kVAr consumed is 742.5.

Solution

Initially we will transpose the equation in terms of $\sin\phi$ as follows

$$kVAr \times \frac{1000}{\sqrt{3}V_L I_L} = \frac{\sqrt{3}V_L I_L \sin\phi}{1000} \times \frac{1000}{\sqrt{3}V_L I_L}$$

that is

$$kVAr \times \frac{1000}{\sqrt{3}V_L I_L} = \sin\phi$$

hence

$$\sin\phi = 742.5 \times \frac{1000}{\sqrt{3} \times 3300 \times 150} = 0.866$$

therefore

$$\phi = \arcsin 0.866 = 60^\circ$$

Note: the theory of three-phase work is outside the scope of this book, and the reader should refer to Noel Morris, *Mastering Electrical Engineering* (Macmillan, 2nd edn 1991).

Worked Example 6.4

In alternating current circuits the *power consumed* in watts is represented by P (see Figure 6.10), and the volt-amperes reactive consumed or *reactive power* in VAr is represented by Q, and these are related by the *power triangle* in Figure 6.10. The number of *volt-amperes* consumed in VA is represented by S, and ϕ is the *phase angle* of the circuit. If $Q = 200$ VAr and $\phi = 40^\circ$, determine the value of S and P.

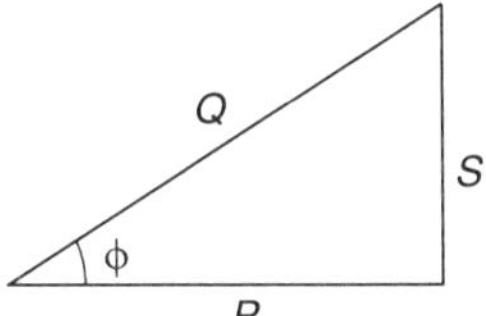

Figure 6.10 Worked Example 6.4

Solution

From Figure 6.10 we see that

$$\sin\phi = \frac{Q}{S}$$

or

$$S = Q/\sin\phi = 200/\sin 40^\circ = 311.1 \text{ VA}$$

From Pythagorus's theorem $S^2 = P^2 + Q^2$. Transposing for P gives

$$P = \sqrt{(S^2 - Q^2)} = \sqrt{(311.1^2 - 200^2)} = 238.3 \text{ W}$$

6.8 The graph of a sine wave

Graphs show the relationship between two variables and, strictly speaking, are the subject of Chapter 9. However, at this stage, we need to understand the way in which a function such as $\sin\theta$ varies with θ, and we therefore need to introduce the graph concept; readers needing more detail should study Chapter 9.

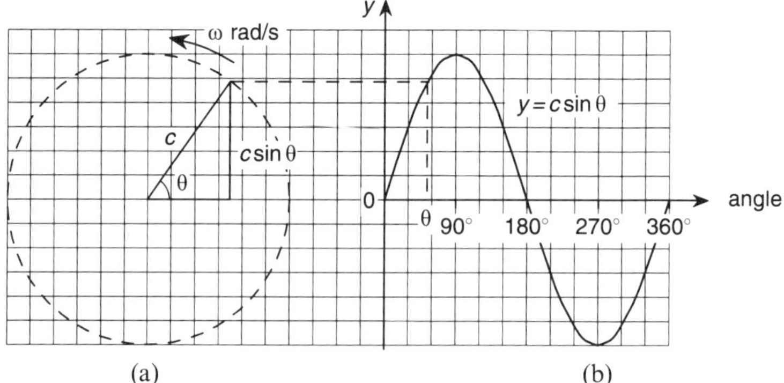

Figure 6.11 Graph of $y = c\sin\theta$

If a line of length c (see Figure 6.11(a)) is rotated at a constant speed *in an anticlockwise direction* then, at some point in time, it reaches angle θ. The vertical projection of this line (the 'opposite' side of the triangle) has a value $c\sin\theta$. If we plot the length of this line in the 'y direction' or vertical direction, to a base of the angle of rotation (which is in the 'x direction' or horizontal direction), we get the curve in Figure 6.11(b) as the line completes one complete revolution.

This curve is known as a **sine curve**, and has a **sinusoidal** shape. Its value is zero at angles of 0°, 180°, 360° and ($n \times 180°$), where n is an integer. The curve reaches its first maximum positive value of c at 90°, and its first maximum negative value at 270°. If the line which produces the curve continues to rotate, the sine curve is repeated over and over again, and is said to be a **repetitive wave** or a **periodic function**. That is a positive maximum occurs at $(90 + (n \times 360))^\circ$, and a negative maximum occurs at $(270 + (n \times 360))^\circ$, where n is an integer.

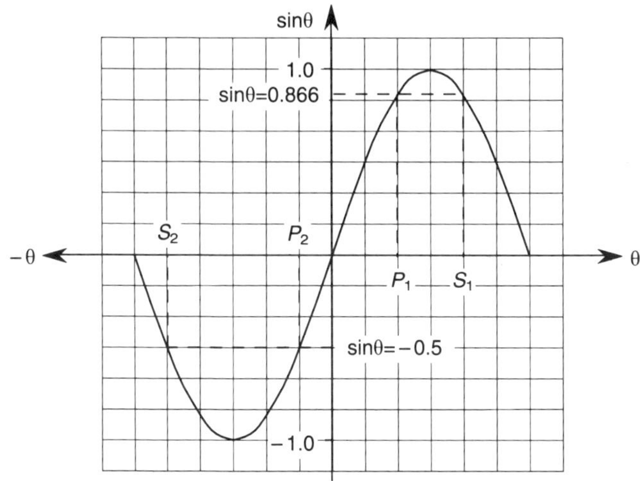

Figure 6.12 Primary and secondary solutions of a sine equation

If you use a calculator or a set of sine tables to determine θ from the expression $\sin\theta = 0.866$, you will get the solution $\theta = 60^\circ$; this is known as the **primary solution** of the equation, and is labelled P_1 in Figure 6.12. However the graph shows that, in the first positive half cycle of the wave, there is another solution known as the **secondary solution**, S_1. We can also see from the graph that

$$S_1 = 180^\circ - P_1$$

In our case, $S_1 = 180^\circ - 60^\circ = 120^\circ$; a calculator shows that $\sin 120^\circ = 0.866$. As shown in section 6.5, the sine of angles in the first and second quadrants are both positive, which agrees with the above. It is very clear that we should take great care when using a calculator to determine the value of an angle from the value of its sine because *it could lie in either of two quadrants.*

Similarly, if $\sin\theta = -0.5$, the calculator shows that $\theta = -30^\circ$. This is the *primary solution*, P_2, of the equation in the negative half cycle of the sine wave (see Figure 6.12). Similarly, there is a *secondary solution*, S_2, which is determined from the equation

$$S_2 = -180^\circ - P_2 = -180^\circ - (-30^\circ) = -150^\circ$$

The reader should verify that $\sin(-150^\circ) = -0.5$.

Since the sinewave is symmetrical about the origin we can see, without mathematical proof, that

$$\sin\theta = -\sin(-\theta) \text{ or } \sin(-\theta) = -\sin\theta$$

For example, if $\theta = 45°$ then $\sin 45° = 0.7071$, and

$$-\sin(-45°) = -(-0.7071) = 0.7071$$

Any function with this type of characteristic, i.e. one which is symmetrical about the origin, is known mathematically as an **odd function**.

6.9 Period, frequency, angular frequency, amplitude and phase angle

We saw in Figure 6.11 that a sine wave repeats itself every 360°; one complete cycle is known as the **period** of the wave.

The time taken for the line which draws out the wave to make one complete revolution or 360° is known as the **periodic time**, T, of the wave. In fact, *any periodic function* (not just a sine wave) has its own periodic time, and is the time between *any point on the wave to the next identical point on the wave*. For example, it could be the time between the start of the wave and the next start, or the time between a positive maximum and the next positive maximum, etc.

Since T is the periodic time of the wave, and ω the angular frequency which produces it, one complete cycle (2π rad) is complete in a time of ωT seconds. That is

$$\omega T = 2\pi$$

or

$$T = \frac{2\pi}{\omega}$$

The **frequency**, f, of a periodic function is the number of cycles occurring per second, and is given the dimensions of hertz (Hz), named after H.R. Hertz. The shorter the periodic time, the greater the frequency; the frequency and periodic time are related by the equation

$$f = 1/T \text{ Hz}$$

A wave with a periodic time of 20 ms has a frequency of

$$f = 1/(20 \times 10^{-3}) = 50 \text{ Hz}$$

and if the periodic time is 0.1 ms, the frequency is

$$f = 1/(0.1 \times 10^{-3}) = 10\,000 \text{ Hz or } 10 \text{ kHz}$$

If the frequency is 1.0 cycle per second or 1.0 Hz, then the wave completes 2π radians in one second, and a wave of frequency f Hz completes $2\pi f$ radians in one second. This frequency is known as the **angular frequency** of the wave, and is given the Greek symbol ω, that is

$$\omega = 2\pi f \text{ rad/s}$$

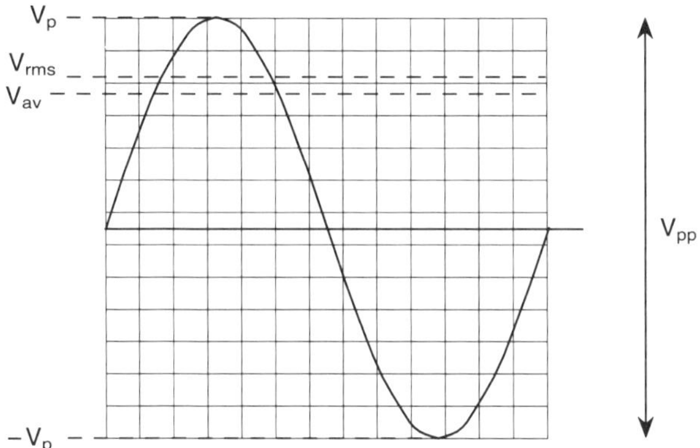

Figure 6.13 Amplitude values of a sine wave

When describing a sinusoidal wave, there are various amplitude values that may be used to define it (see Figure 6.13).

The simplest is the **peak value**, V_p, which occurs at each positive peak of the wave; alternatively, a negative peak, $-V_p$, occurs once in each cycle. Sometimes we need to know the **peak-to-peak value**, V_{pp}, which, in the case of the sine wave, is $2V_p$.

The usual value used when stating the value of a sinusoidal voltage is the **root-mean-square value** (r.m.s.), V_{rms}, or the **effective value**, which, in the case of a sine wave is given by

$$V_{rms} = V_p/\sqrt{2}$$

Details of the method of calculation of the r.m.s. value of a sine wave is given in Chapter 13. Another value associated with sinusoidal waves is the **average value** or **mean value**, V_{av}, which for a sinewave is

$$V_{av} = \frac{2V_p}{\pi} = 0.637V_p$$

Details of the method of calculation of the electrical average value of a sine wave is also given in Chapter 13.

Consider the two rotating lines in Figure 6.14, of length V_m* and I_m, respectively, which are displaced from one another by angle ϕ. Both lines rotate at ω rad/s in an anticlockwise direction, and the vertical displacement of the tip of each line traces out one of the sinewave on the right of the figure. The equation of the curve traced out by V_{m1} is

$$v = V_{m1} \sin \theta = V_{m1} \sin \omega t = V_{m1} \sin 2\pi ft$$

where v is the instantaneous voltage of the wave at angle θ (or, alternatively, at time t), and V_{m1} is the maximum value of the waveform. When $\theta = 0$ (or

---

* The subscripts m and p are interchangeable in electrical and electronic engineering, m meaning *maximum* and p meaning *peak*. That is, V_m and V_p are taken to mean the same thing.

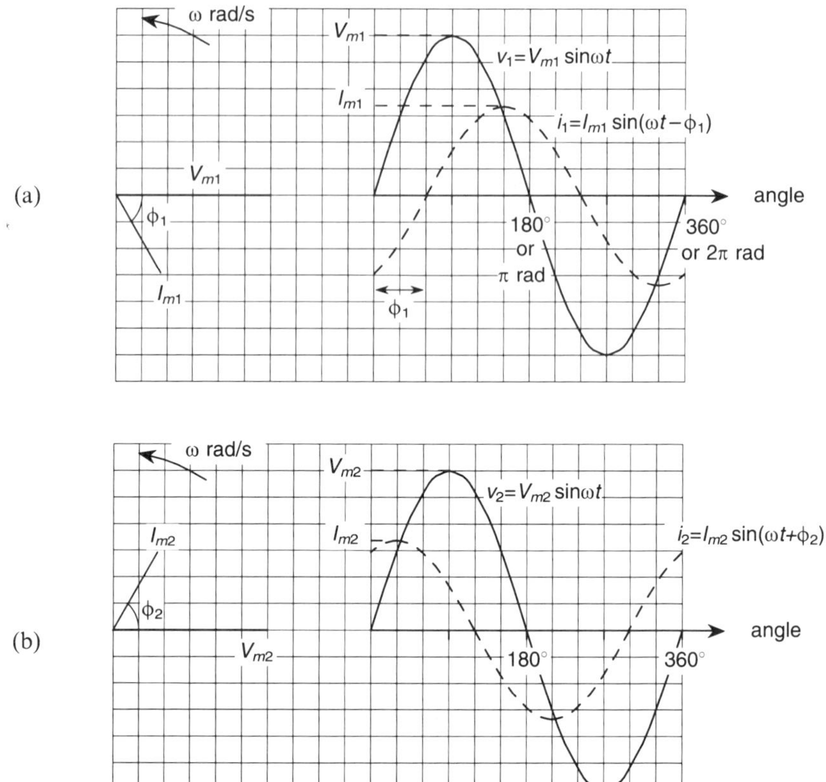

Figure 6.14 Phase angle

$t = 0$), the instantaneous value of the wave is $V_{m1} \sin 0 = 0\,\text{V}$ but, at this angle (or time), the rotating line represented by I_{m1} has not reached the horizontal, so that its vertical component has a negative value.

Since V_{m1} and I_{m1} rotate at the same speed, we see that I_{m1} reaches the horizontal some time after $t = 0$, that is I_{m1} **lags behind** V_{m1} by angle ϕ_1. Alternatively, we may say that V_{m1} **leads** I_{m1} by angle ϕ_1. The concept of lagging and leading phase angles is widely used in electrical and electronic engineering. We can describe the sinewave drawn out by the rotating line I_{m1} by means of the equation

$$i_1 = I_{m1} \sin(\omega t - \phi_1)$$

which tells us that the line I_{m1} is at angle $-\phi_1$ when $t = 0$, i.e. the current lags behind the reference direction when $t = 0$.

In the case of Figure 6.14(b), we see that I_{m2} *leads* V_{m2} by ϕ_2 (or V_{m2} *lags behind* I_{m2} by ϕ_2), and the equation for the sinewave of i_2 is

$$i_2 = I_{m2} \sin(\omega t + \phi_2)$$

Worked Example 6.5

For the following voltage waves, determine (a) the maximum voltage, (b) the periodic time, (c) the frequency, (d) the instantaneous value of each wave when $t = 2$ ms and (e) the phase relationship between the two voltages

(i) $v_1 = 100 \sin(100\pi t + 20^\circ)$

(ii) $v_2 = 50 \sin(314.2t - 30^\circ)$

Solution

The general equation for the instantaneous value of both waves is of the form

$$v = V_m \sin(\omega t + \phi)$$

where V_m is the maximum value, ω is the angular frequency of the wave, and ϕ is the phase angle of the wave.

(a) (i) Comparing the above equation with the equation for v_1, we see that

$$V_{m1} = 100 \text{ V}$$
$$\omega_1 = 100\pi = 314.2 \text{ rad/s}$$
$$\phi_1 = +20^\circ$$

That is, v_1 has a maximum value of 100 V, its angular frequency is 100π rad/s, and its phase angle at $t = 0$ is $+20^\circ$.

(ii) When we look at the equation for v_2, we see that

$$V_{m2} = 50 \text{ V}$$
$$\omega_1 = 314.2 = 100\pi \text{ rad/s}$$
$$\phi_1 = -30^\circ$$

The waveform for v_2 therefore has a maximum value of 50 V, its angular frequency is 100π rad/s, and its phase angle at $t = 0$ is -30°.

(b) Since the angular frequency of both waves is 100π rad/s, the periodic time of both waves is

$$T = 2\pi/\omega = 2\pi/100\pi = 1/50 = 0.02 \text{ s or } 20 \text{ ms}$$

(c) The frequency of both waves is

$$f = 1/T = 1/0.02 = 50 \text{ Hz}$$

(d) (i) The value of v_1 when $t = 2$ ms or 0.002 s is

$$\begin{aligned} v_1 &= 100 \sin(100\pi t + 20^\circ) \\ &= 100 \sin((100\pi \times 0.002) + 20^\circ) \\ &= 100 \sin(0.2\pi + 20^\circ) \end{aligned}$$

At this point the reader should note that the angle within the brackets contains one part in radians, and a second part in degrees. We will convert the part in radians into degrees as follows.

$$0.2\pi \equiv 0.2\pi \times 57.3^\circ = 36^\circ$$

Hence the value of v_1 when $t = 2\,\text{ms}$ is

$$v_1 = 100\sin(36^\circ + 20^\circ) = 100\sin 56^\circ = 82.9\ \text{V}$$

(ii) The value of v_2 when $t = 2\,\text{ms}$ is

$$\begin{aligned} v_2 &= 50\sin(314.2t - 30^\circ) \\ &= 50\sin(0.6284\ \text{rad} - 30^\circ) \\ &= 50\sin(36^\circ - 30^\circ) = 50\sin 6^\circ = 5.23\ \text{V} \end{aligned}$$

(e) The voltage waveform equations tell us that when $t = 0$, the angle of the rotating line which traces out v_1 is at $+20^\circ$ to the reference direction, and the line tracing out v_2 is at -30°. That is, v_1 leads v_2 by $(20 - (-30))^\circ = 50^\circ$ or, alternatively, v_2 lags behind v_1 by 50°.

6.10 The cosine ratio

In the following we refer to Figure 6.6 (see also section 6.7).

First quadrant

Since $\cos\theta$ = adjacent/hypotenuse, we see that in the first quadrant

$$\cos\theta_1 = ON_1/OM_1$$

and we observe that

1. the cosine is always positive since both ON_1 and OM_1 are positive, and
2. when $\theta_1 = 0^\circ$, $\cos\theta_1 = 1$ (since $ON_1 = OM_1$); when $\theta_1 = 90^\circ$, $\cos\theta_1 = 0$ (since $ON_1 = 0$).

That is the value of $\cos\theta$ falls from 1 to 0 as θ changes from 0° to 90°.

Second quadrant

In this case

$$\cos\theta_2 = ON_2/OM_2$$

and we note that

1. since ON_2 is negative, the cosine is always negative in this quadrant, and
2. when $\theta_2 = 90^\circ$ then $\cos\theta_2 = 0$, and when $\theta_2 = 180^\circ$ then $\cos\theta_2 = -1$ (since $ON_2 = -OM_2$).

That is $\cos\theta$ changes from 0 to -1 as θ changes from 90° to 180°.

Third quadrant

In this case

$$\cos\theta_3 = ON_3/OM_3$$

and we see that

1. since ON_3 is negative, the cosine is always negative in this quadrant, and
2. when $\theta_3 = 180^\circ$ then $\cos\theta_3 = -1$, and when $\theta_3 = 270^\circ$ then $\cos\theta_3 = 0$ (since $ON_3 = 0$).

That is $\cos\theta$ rises from -1 to 0 as θ changes from 180° to 270°.

Fourth quadrant

We see that

$$\cos\theta_4 = ON_4/OM_4$$

and

1. since both ON_4 and OM_4 are positive, the cosine is always positive in this quadrant, and
2. when $\theta_4 = 270^\circ$ then $\cos\theta_4 = 0$, and when $\theta_4 = 360^\circ$ then $\cos\theta_4 = 1$ (since $ON_4 = OM_4$).

That is $\cos\theta$ rises from 0 to 1 as θ changes from 270° to 360°.

6.11 Graph of cosine θ

Using a calculator we can obtain the cosine of any angle, and the graph of $\cos\theta$ over the range -90° to 360° is shown in Figure 6.15.

We see that the graph has a generally similar shape to that for $\sin\theta$, with the exception that the $\sin\theta$ graph has a positive peak at 90°, and a negative peak at 270°. We can therefore conclude that

$$\cos\theta = \sin(\theta + 90^\circ)$$

and

$$\sin\theta = \cos(\theta - 90^\circ)$$

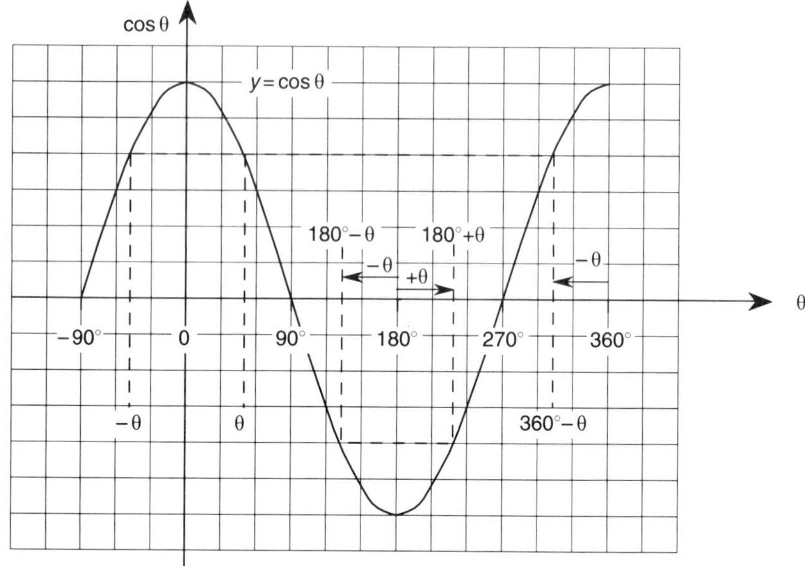

Figure 6.15 Graph of cos θ for the range of θ = −90° to θ = 360°

for example

$$\cos 30^\circ = \sin(30^\circ + 90^\circ) = \sin 120^\circ = 0.866$$
$$\sin 30^\circ = \cos(30^\circ - 90^\circ) = \cos(-60^\circ) = 0.5$$

Also from Figure 6.15 we see that

$$\cos(-\theta) = \cos\theta$$

and

$$\cos\theta = \cos(360^\circ - \theta)$$

also

$$\cos\theta = -\cos(180^\circ - \theta) = -\cos(180^\circ + \theta)$$

For example,

$$\text{if } \theta = 60^\circ \text{ then } \cos\theta = 0.5 \text{ and}$$
$$\cos(-60^\circ) = \cos 60^\circ = 0.5$$
$$\cos(360^\circ - 60^\circ) = \cos 300^\circ = 0.5 = \cos 60^\circ$$
$$-\cos(180^\circ - 60^\circ) = -\cos 120^\circ = 0.5 = \cos 60^\circ$$
$$-\cos(180 + 60^\circ) = -\cos 240^\circ = 0.5 = \cos 60^\circ$$

Worked Example 6.6

In alternating current theory, electrical engineers are concerned about the *power factor* of a.c. circuits, the power factor being defined as

$$\text{power factor} = \frac{\text{power consumed in watts}}{\text{volts} \times \text{amperes}}$$

The power factor is also given by $\cos\phi$, where ϕ is the *phase angle* between the sinusoidal applied voltage and the sinusoidal current in the circuit. That is

$$\cos\phi = \frac{\text{power in watts}}{\text{volts} \times \text{amperes}}$$

If an a.c. circuit energised by a 440 V sinusoidal supply draws a current of 60 A, and consumes a power of 18.48 kW, calculate the power factor and the phase angle of the circuit.

Solution

From the equations given

$$\text{power factor} = \frac{\text{watts}}{\text{volts} \times \text{amperes}} = \frac{18.48 \times 10^3}{440 \times 60}$$
$$= 0.7$$

That is to say, the power factor of the circuit is 0.7. Using our calculator

$$\phi = \arccos 0.7 = 45.57^\circ$$

In fact, from the work in this section, we know that

$$\cos\phi = \cos(-\phi)$$

which means that the phase angle could be either 45.57° or -45.57°. Unless we know more about the circuit (which, at this stage, we do not), either of these solutions could be correct!

Worked Example 6.7

In alternating current theory, the total opposition of a circuit to current flow is known as the *impedance*, Z, of the circuit (see Figure 6.16). The impedance is calculated from Figure 6.16 using the *resistance* R of the circuit, and the *reactance* X. The phase angle, ϕ, of the circuit is the angle between R and Z. The triangle in Figure 6.16 is known as the *impedance triangle* of the a.c. circuit.

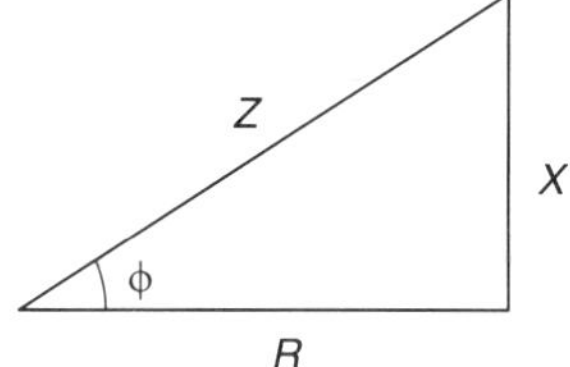

Figure 6.16 Worked Example 6.7

If $R = 10\,\Omega$ and $Z = 11.55\,\Omega$, determine the power factor ($\cos\phi$), the phase angle ϕ, and the reactance X of the circuit.

Solution

The power factor of the circuit is

$$\cos\phi = R/Z = 10/11.55 = 0.866$$

hence

$$\phi = \arccos 0.866 = 30^\circ$$

From Pythagorus's theorem

$$Z = \sqrt{(R^2 + X^2)}$$

therefore

$$X = \sqrt{(Z^2 - R^2)} = \sqrt{(11.55^2 - 10^2)} = 5.78\,\Omega$$

6.12 The tangent ratio

Once again we refer to Figure 6.6.

First quadrant

Since $\tan\theta$ = opposite/adjacent, we see that in the first quadrant

$$\tan\theta_1 = N_1M_1/ON_1$$

and we observe that

1. the tangent is always positive since both N_1M_1 and ON_1 are positive, and
2. when $\theta_1 = 0^\circ$, $\tan\theta_1 = 0$ (since $N_1M_1 = 0$); when $\theta_1 = 90^\circ$, $\tan\theta_1 = +\infty$ (since $ON_1 = 0$).

That is the value of $\tan\theta$ rises from 0 to $+\infty$ as θ changes from 0° to 90°.

Second quadrant

In this case

$$\tan\theta_2 = N_2M_2/ON_2$$

and we observe that

1. the tangent is always negative since ON_2 is negative, and
2. when θ_2 is slightly greater than 90°, $\tan\theta_2 \approx -\infty$ (since ON_2 is both negative and practically zero); when $\theta_2 = 180°$, $\tan\theta_2 = 0$ (since $N_2M_2 = 0$).

That is the value of $\tan\theta$ changes from $-\infty$ to 0 as θ changes from 90° to 180°.

Third quadrant

Here we have

$$\tan\theta_3 = N_3M_3/ON_3$$

and

1. the tangent is always positive since both N_3M_3 and ON_3 are both negative, and
2. when $\theta_3 = 180°$, $\tan\theta_3 = 0$; when $\theta_3 = 270°$, $\tan\theta_3 = +\infty$ (since $ON_3 = 0$).

That is the value of $\tan\theta$ rises from 0 to $+\infty$ as θ changes from 180° to 270°.

Fourth quadrant

In this case

$$\tan\theta_4 = N_4M_4/ON_4$$

and we see that

1. the tangent is always negative in this quadrant because N_4M_4 is negative, and
2. when $\theta_4 = 270°$, $\tan\theta_4 = -\infty$ (since ON_4 is negative and practically zero in the region of 270°); when $\theta_4 = 360°$, $\tan\theta_4 = 0$ (since $N_4M_4 = 0$).

That is the value of $\tan\theta$ changes from $-\infty$ to 0 as θ changes from 270° to 360°.

6.13 The graph of $\tan\theta$

The value of $\tan\theta$ over the range -90° to 360° can be obtained from a calculator or set of tangent tables, and the resulting graph is plotted in Figure 6.17.

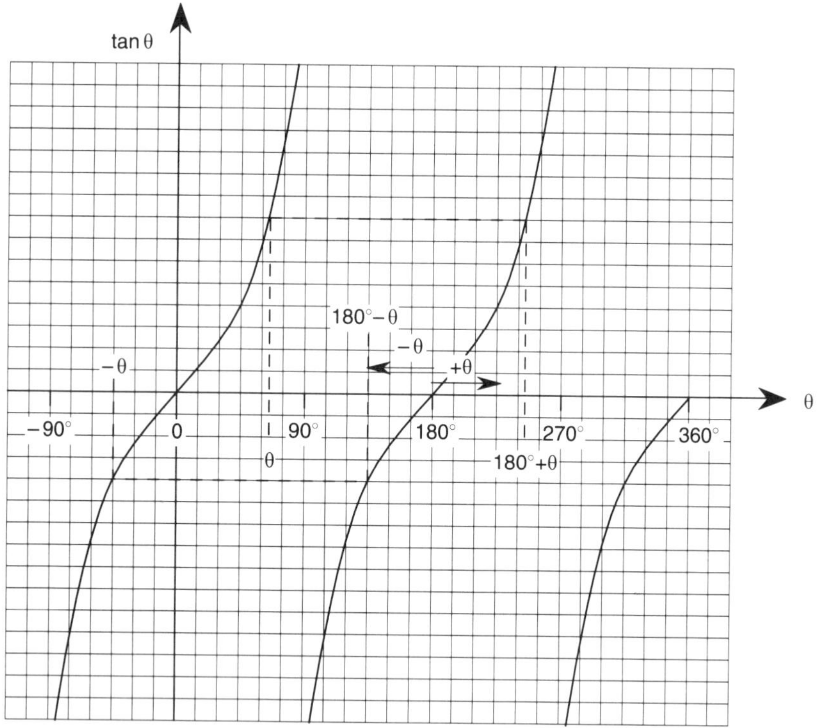

Figure 6.17 Graph of $\tan\theta$ for the range of $\theta = -90^\circ$ to $\theta = 360^\circ$

We see from the graph that

$$\tan\theta = -\tan(-\theta)$$
$$\tan(180^\circ + \theta) = \tan\theta$$
$$\tan(180^\circ - \theta) = \tan(-\theta)$$

For example,

$$\text{if } \theta = 60^\circ \text{ then } \tan\theta = 1.732 \text{ and}$$
$$-\tan(-60^\circ) = -(-1.732) = 1.732 = \tan 60^\circ$$
$$\tan(180^\circ + 60^\circ) = \tan 240^\circ = 1.732 = \tan 60^\circ$$
$$\tan(180^\circ - 60^\circ) = \tan 120^\circ = -1.732 = \tan(-60^\circ)$$

Worked Example 6.8

An engineer needs to determine the length of a lightning conductor to be fixed to the side of a substation. Using a theodolite positioned 20 m from the side of the building, the angle of elevation of the top of the building is 30°; the height of the theodolite above the ground is 1.6 m. What length of lightning conductor is needed to reach from the top of the building to the ground?

Solution

A diagram showing the problem is given in Figure 6.18. The distance A is calculated from

$$\tan 30^\circ = \frac{A}{20\ \text{m}}$$

or

$$A = 20 \times \tan 30^\circ = 11.55\ \text{m}$$

hence

$$\text{height of building} = A + 1.6 = 13.15\ \text{m}$$

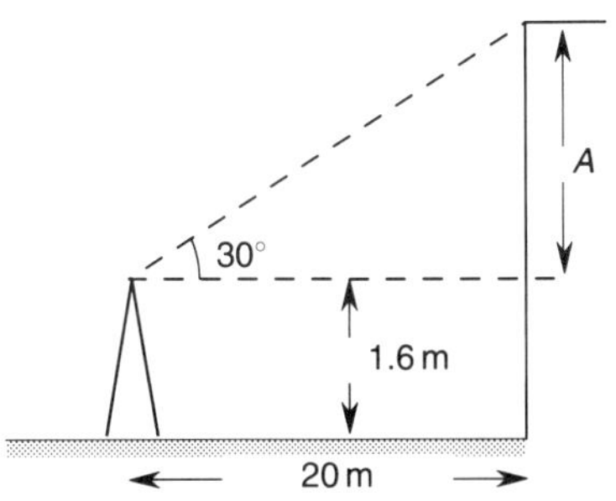

Figure 6.18 Solution to Worked Example 6.8

Note: the engineer must also allow for the length of conductor required to terminate it at either end.

Worked Example 6.9

The phase angle of a *balanced 3-phase load* can be determined by the *two-wattmeter method* of measuring power, in which two wattmeters P_1 and P_2 are used to measure the total power consumed. The tangent of the phase angle, ϕ, of the load is calculated from

$$\tan \phi = \sqrt{3}\left[\frac{P_1 - P_2}{P_1 + P_2}\right]$$

Determine the phase angle of the load if $P_1 = 7\,\text{kW}$, and $P_2 = 3.5\,\text{kW}$.

Solution

From the equation given

$$\tan \phi = \sqrt{3}[(7 - 3.5)/(7 + 3.5)] = 0.5774$$

We can calculate the phase angle from the inverse trigonometric function as follows

$$\phi = \arctan 0.5774 = 30^\circ \text{ or } -30^\circ.$$

Self-test questions

6.1 Determine the following: (a) $\sin 45.6°$, (b) $\cos 50°26'$, (c) $\tan 148.2°$, (d) $\sin 230.7°$, (e) $\cos 300.6°$, (f) $\tan 386.2°$, (g) $\sin(-102.5°)$, (h) $\cos(-200.5°)$, (i) $\tan(-796.3°)$. Note: In part (b) there are 60 minutes in one degree.

6.2 Given the following inverse trigonometric ratios, determine the angle: (a) $\arcsin \phi = 0.866$, (b) $\arccos \phi = 0.1736$, (c) $\arctan \phi = 0.1763$, (d) $\arcsin \phi = -0.2079$.

6.3 For the following periodic functions, calculate the periodic time, the frequency, and the maximum amplitude given that the instantaneous amplitude is 2 when $t = 4$ ms.
(a) $v = V_m \sin 100\pi t$
(b) $i = I_m \cos 600t$

6.4 State the phase relationship between the following
(a) $v_1 = 100 \sin \theta$ and $v_1 = 20 \sin(\theta + 2\pi/3)$
(b) $i_1 = 20 \cos \omega t$ and $i_2 = 30 \sin(\omega t - 40°)$
(c) $v_1 = 90 \sin(\omega t + \pi/2)$ and $V_2 = 40 \sin(\omega t - \pi/4)$
(d) $i_1 = 80 \cos \theta$ and $v_2 = 90 \sin(\theta - \pi/3)$

6.5 Given that an angle lies in the third quadrant, and that its sine is -0.4, calculate the angle, its cosine and its tangent.

6.6 If $\cos \theta = -0.08$, determine all possible values of θ up to 360°.

6.7 Evaluate
(a) $\cos(\pi/2).\sin(3\pi/2) + \cos(3\pi/2).\sin(\pi/2)$
(b) $\cos(\pi/6).\cos(\pi/4) - \cos(\pi/6).\sin(\pi/4)$

Summary of important facts

Angles are measured in **degrees** and in **radians**, where

$$1 \text{ rad} = 57.3°$$

Positive angles are measured in an *anti-clockwise direction*, and **negative angles** in a *clockwise direction.*

An **acute angle** is one less than 90°, a **right-angle** is one whose angle is 90°, an **obtuse angle** is one between 90° and 180°, and a **reflex angle** is one between 180° and 360°.

Two angles whose sum is 90° are **complementary angles**, and if the sum of two angles is 180° they are **supplementary angles**.

The three sides of a right-angled triangle are the hypotenuse, the opposite side and the adjacent side. The **hypotenuse** is the side opposite to the right-angle, the **opposite side** is the side which is opposite to the angle (and is one of the sides forming the angle), and the **adjacent side** is the side which is adjacent to the angle which is not the hypotenuse (see Figure 6.2).

The usual trigonometric ratios are the sine, the cosine and the tangent, which are defined as

$\sin\theta$ = opposite/hypotenuse
$\cos\theta$ = adjacent/hypotenuse
$\tan\theta$ = opposite/adjacent = $\sin\theta/\cos\theta$

Other ratios are the cosecant, the secant and the cotangent, which are defined as

$\text{cosec}\,\theta = 1/\sin\theta$ = hypotenuse/opposite
$\sec\theta = 1/\cos\theta$ = hypotenuse/adjacent
$\cot\theta = 1/\tan\theta$ = adjacent/opposite

Inverse trigonometric functions are the inverse of the above trigonometric functions. If $y = \cos\theta$, the inverse trigonometric function is $\theta = \arccos y$ (or $\cos^{-1} y$). Other inverse trigonometric functions are $\arcsin y$ (or $\sin^{-1} y$), and $\arctan y$ (or $\tan^{-1} y$).

The circle is divided into **four quadrants** as follows

first quadrant – 0° to 90°
second quadrant – 90° to 180°
third quadrant – 180° to 270°
fourth quadrant – 270° to 360°

All trigonometric ratios are positive in the first quadrant, the **sine ratio is positive** in the second quadrant, the **tangent ratio is positive** in the third quadrant, and the **cosine ratio is positive** in the fourth quadrant. This sequence can be remembered by either of the following mnemonics.

All ***S***tations ***T***o ***C***rewe
All ***S***tudents of a ***T***echnical ***C***ourse

Both the sine and the cosine waves are known as **sinusoidal waves**, and are related by

$$\cos\theta = \sin(\theta + 90^\circ)$$
$$\sin\theta = \cos(\theta - 90^\circ)$$

A waveform which repeats itself periodically is known as a **periodic wave**, and the time taken for one complete cycle of the wave is its **periodic time**, T. The **frequency** of a periodic wave is

$$f = 1/T \text{ hertz (Hz)}$$

The **angular frequency** of a wave is given by

$$\omega = 2\pi f = 2\pi/T$$

The **instantaneous value** of a sine wave is given by

$$y = Y_m \sin\theta = Y_m \sin\omega t = Y_m \sin 2\pi ft$$

where Y_m is the **maximum value** or **peak value** of the wave. If the wave has a **phase angle** ϕ, the equation of the sine wave becomes

$$\begin{aligned} y &= Y_m \sin(\theta \pm \phi) = Y_m \sin(\omega t \pm \phi) \\ &= Y_m \sin(2\pi ft \pm \phi) \end{aligned}$$

where ϕ may be in degrees or radians.

7 Further trigonometric skills

7.1 Introduction

In this chapter we look at further skills which are particularly useful in trigonometric applications related to some of the problems involved in electrical and electronic circuits. By the end of this chapter, the reader will be able to

- solve problems involving the sine rule and the cosine rule,
- appreciate and apply trigonometric identities,
- use compound and double angle formulae,
- solve equations involving the product of sines and cosines.

7.2 The sine rule

Electrical and electronic engineers frequently need to solve alternating current circuit problems which involve phasors (see Chapter 10 for details), in which the sine rule is invaluable.

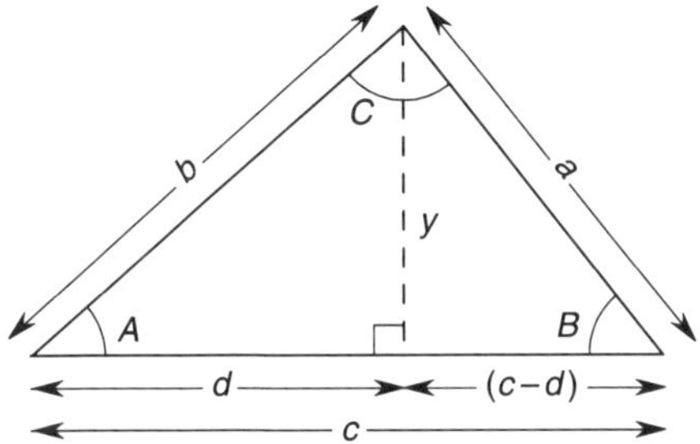

Figure 7.1 The sine rule

Consider the triangle in Figure 7.1 in which side a is opposite to angle A, side b is opposite to angle B, and side c is opposite to angle C. Length y is a perpendicular drawn from side c to angle C. From basic trigonometry, we get

$$\sin A = \frac{y}{b} \quad \text{and} \quad \sin B = \frac{y}{a}$$

That is

$$y = b \sin A = a \sin B$$

hence

$$a \sin B = b \sin A$$

or

$$\frac{a}{\sin A} = \frac{b}{\sin B}$$

This argument can be extended to show that

$$\boldsymbol{\frac{a}{\sin A} = \frac{b}{\sin B} = \frac{c}{\sin C}}$$

This relationship is known as the **sine rule**, and applies to any triangle whether the angle is acute or obtuse.

The sine rule allows us to solve a triangle if we know either

1. two sides and one of the opposite angles, or
2. two angles and the length of the side between them.

Worked Example 7.1

A triangle has the following dimensions: $a = 30\,\text{m}$, $c = 25\,\text{m}$, $\angle A = 17°$. Determine the remaining side and angles.

Solution

From the sine rule we see that

$$\frac{a}{\sin A} = \frac{c}{\sin C}$$

or

$$\sin C = \frac{c}{a} \sin A = \frac{25}{30} \sin 17° = 0.2436$$

hence

$$\angle C = \arcsin 0.2436 = 14.1°$$

Since the sum of the angles in a triangle is 180°, then

$$\angle A + \angle B + \angle C = 180°$$

or

$$\angle B = 180° - \angle B - \angle C = 180° - 17° - 14.1° = 148.9°$$

and

$$\frac{b}{\sin B} = \frac{a}{\sin A}$$

or

$$b = a\frac{\sin B}{\sin A} = 30 \times \frac{\sin 148.9°}{\sin 17°} = 53 \text{ m}$$

7.3 The cosine rule

As with the sine rule, the cosine rule is very useful for the solution of triangles.

The vertical broken line y in Figure 7.1 splits the main triangle into two smaller right-angles triangles for which

$$b^2 = d^2 + y^2 \quad \text{and} \quad a^2 = (c - d)^2 + y^2$$

or

$$y^2 = b^2 - d^2 \quad \text{and} \quad y^2 = a^2 - (c - d)^2$$

That is

$$b^2 - d^2 = a^2 - (c - d)^2$$

or

$$a^2 = b^2 - d^2 + (c - d)^2 = b^2 - d^2 + c^2 - 2cd + d^2$$
$$= b^2 + c^2 - 2cd \qquad (7.1)$$

From the left-hand triangle in Figure 7.1 we see that

$$\cos A = d/b$$

that is

$$d = b \cos A$$

Substituting the above expression into equation (7.1) gives

$$\boldsymbol{a^2 = b^2 + c^2 - 2bc \cos A}$$

which is one expression of the **cosine rule**. Similarly, it may be shown that

$$\boldsymbol{b^2 = a^2 + c^2 - 2ac \cos B}$$

and

$$\boldsymbol{c^2 = a^2 + b^2 - 2ab \cos C}$$

The cosine rule allows us to determine:

1. the third side of a triangle if we know two sides and the included angle, or
2. any angle if we know all three sides.

Worked Example 7.2

The following data refers to a triangle: $a = 4\,\text{m}$, $b = 7\,\text{m}$ and $\angle C = 28^\circ$. Using the cosine rule, determine the other side and angles of the triangle.

Solution

From the cosine rule

$$c^2 = a^2 + b^2 - 2ab\cos C$$
$$= 4^2 + 7^2 - (2 \times 4 \times 7)\cos 28^\circ = 15.55$$

hence

$$c = \sqrt{15.55} = 3.94\ \text{m}$$

Since we know all three sides and one angle of the triangle, the other angles can be calculated using either the cosine rule or the sine rule. We will use the former. Transposing for $\cos A$ from the equation

$$a^2 = b^2 + c^2 - 2bc\cos A$$

gives

$$\cos A = \frac{b^2 + c^2 - a^2}{2bc}$$
$$= (7^2 + 3.94^2 - 4^2)/(2 \times 7 \times 3.94) = 0.8797$$

hence

$$\angle A = \arccos 0.8797 = 28.4^\circ$$

We know that

$$\angle A + \angle B + \angle C = 180^\circ$$

hence

$$\angle B = 180^\circ - (\angle A + \angle C) = 180^\circ - (28.4^\circ + 28^\circ)$$
$$= 123.6^\circ$$

At this stage it pays to get a mental image of the triangle so that you can 'see' if the answer appears to be correct. Clearly, our solution indicates that the longest side is opposite the largest angle (side b and angle B), and the shortest side is opposite to the smallest angle (side c and angle C), which agrees with common sense.

7.4 Trigonometric identities

An **identity** is a statement which is true *for all values of the variable.* For example

$$\tan\theta \equiv \frac{\sin\theta}{\cos\theta}$$

is true for all values of θ. The identity sign '≡' should be used, but is often replaced by the '=' sign.

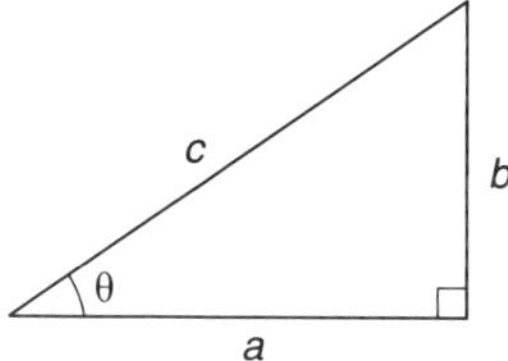

Figure 7.2 Trigonometrical identities

Consider the right-angled triangle in Figure 7.2, for which

$$a^2 + b^2 = c^2$$

Dividing throughout the equation by c^2 gives

$$\left[\frac{a}{c}\right]^2 + \left[\frac{b}{c}\right]^2 = \left[\frac{c}{c}\right]^2 = 1$$

or

$$\mathbf{\cos^2\theta + \sin^2\theta = 1}$$

Although this is written in the form of an equation it is, in fact, an identity because it is true for all values of θ. For example, if $\theta = 35.6°$, then $\cos\theta = 0.8131$ and $\sin\theta = 0.5821$, and

$$\cos^2\theta + \sin^2\theta = 0.6611 + 0.3389 = 1.0$$

Other identities can be obtained from the original equation. For example, dividing through by a^2 gives

$$\left[\frac{a}{a}\right]^2 + \left[\frac{b}{a}\right]^2 = \left[\frac{c}{a}\right]^2$$

or

$$\mathbf{1 + \tan^2\theta = \sec^2\theta}$$

and dividing through by b^2 results in

$$\mathbf{\cot^2\theta + 1 = cosec^2\theta}$$

7.5 Compound angle formulae

When two angles are added or subtracted, such as $(A+B)$ or $(A-B)$, they are known as **compound angles**. Sines and cosines formulae for the sum and difference of two angles are

$$\sin(A+B) = \sin A\cos B + \cos A\sin B$$
$$\sin(A-B) = \sin A\cos B - \cos A\sin B$$
$$\cos(A+B) = \cos A\cos B - \sin A\sin B$$
$$\cos(A-B) = \cos A\cos B + \sin A\sin B$$

The reader is asked to particularly note that $\sin(A+B)$ *is not equal to* $(\sin A + \sin B)$, and $\cos(A+B)$ *is not equal to* $(\cos A + \cos B)$, etc. For example, if $\angle A = 30^\circ$ and $\angle B = 60^\circ$, then

$$\begin{aligned}\sin(30^\circ + 60^\circ) &= \sin 30^\circ\cos 60^\circ + \cos 30^\circ\sin 60^\circ\\ &= (0.5\times 0.5) + (0.866\times 0.866)\\ &= 1.0 = \sin 90^\circ\end{aligned}$$

Note: $\cos 30^\circ + \sin 60^\circ = 0.5 + 0.866 = 1.366$!

Since compound angle formulae are true for all angles, they may be used in trigonometrical identities. For example

$$\begin{aligned}\tan(A+B) &= \frac{\sin(A+B)}{\cos(A+B)}\\ &= \frac{\sin A\cos B + \cos A\sin B}{\cos A\cos B - \sin A\sin B}\end{aligned}$$

which, by further manipulation, can be reduced to the following (the reader will find it an interesting exercise to verify them)

$$\mathbf{tan}(A+B) = \frac{\mathbf{tan}\,A + \mathbf{tan}\,B}{1 - \mathbf{tan}\,A\times\mathbf{tan}\,B}$$

and

$$\mathbf{tan}(A-B) = \frac{\mathbf{tan}\,A - \mathbf{tan}\,B}{1 + \mathbf{tan}\,A\times\mathbf{tan}\,B}$$

A sine wave which has been subjected to a phase shift of ϕ (see Chapter 10) can be represented in the form $Y\sin(\omega t + \phi)$, where Y is the maximum value of the wave and ω its angular frequency. Since we are dealing with an angle of $(\omega t + \phi)$, which is a compound angle, the expression can be expanded using the compound angle formulae as follows:

$$\begin{aligned}Y\sin(\omega t + \phi) &= Y(\sin\omega t\cos\phi + \cos\omega t\sin\phi)\\ &= Y\sin\omega t\cos\phi + Y\cos\omega t\sin\phi\end{aligned}$$

Since Y and ϕ are 'fixed' factors, i.e., they do not vary with time, we can group the fixed factors together to give

$$Y\sin(\omega t + \phi) = (Y\cos\phi)\sin\omega t + (Y\sin\phi)\cos\omega t$$

That is to say, the sine wave $Y\sin(\omega t + \phi)$ can be thought of as the addition of a sine wave ($\sin\omega t$) and a cosine wave ($\cos\omega t$), each wave being multiplied by a constant coefficient. That is we may write

$$Y\sin(\omega t + \phi) = A\sin\omega t + B\cos\omega t$$

where $A = Y\cos\phi$ and $B = Y\sin\phi$. If we now 'square' each of these terms we get $A^2 = Y^2\cos^2\phi$ and $B^2 = Y^2\sin^2\phi$. Next we add the 'squared' terms as follows

$$\begin{aligned} A^2 + B^2 &= Y^2\cos^2\phi + Y^2\sin^2\phi \\ &= Y^2(\cos^2\phi + \sin^2\phi) = Y^2 \end{aligned}$$

that is

$$Y = \sqrt{(A^2 + B^2)}$$

Also we see that

$$\frac{B}{A} = \frac{Y\sin\phi}{Y\cos\phi} = \tan\phi$$

or

$$\phi = \arctan\frac{B}{A}$$

Worked Example 7.3

Alternating voltages of $100\sin 500t$ V and $150\cos 500t$ V are connected in series. Express the resultant voltage in the form $Y\sin(500t + \phi)$; determine also the frequency of the wave.

Solution

The instantaneous voltage applied to the circuit is

$$v = 100\sin 500t + 150\cos 500t$$

Relating the values in the problem to the equation developed in section 7.5, we see that

$$100\sin 500t = A\sin\omega t$$

and

$$150\cos 500t = B\cos\omega t$$

That is $A = 100$, $B = 150$ and $\omega = 500$. It follows that

$$Y = \sqrt{(A^2 + B^2)} = \sqrt{(100^2 + 150^2)} = 180.3$$

That is to say, the peak value of the resultant wave is 180.3 V, and its r.m.s. voltage is $180.3/\sqrt{2} \approx 127.5$ V. Also

$$\phi = \arctan\frac{B}{A} = \arctan\frac{150}{100} = 56.3^\circ$$

We may therefore say that the resultant voltage is

$$v = 180.3 \sin(500t + 56.3^\circ)$$

The angular frequency of the wave is $\omega = 500$ rad/s, or

$$f = 500/2\pi = 79.6 \text{ Hz}$$

That is, the applied voltage is

$$180.3 \sin(500t + 56.3^\circ)$$

7.6 Product of sines and cosines

If we add together the equations for $\sin(A + B)$ and $\sin(A - B)$ listed in section 7.5, we get

$$\begin{aligned}&\sin(A + B) + \sin(A - B)\\ &\quad = (\sin A \cos B + \cos A \sin B) + (\sin A \cos B - \cos A \sin B)\\ &\quad = 2 \sin A \cos B\end{aligned}$$

or

$$\mathbf{\sin A \cos B = \tfrac{1}{2}(\sin(A + B) + \sin(A - B))}$$

Similarly, if we subtract $\sin(A - B)$ from $\sin(A + B)$ we get

$$\mathbf{\cos A \sin B = \tfrac{1}{2}(\sin(A + B) - \sin(A - B))}$$

Next, adding $\cos(A + B)$ to $\cos(A - B)$ gives

$$\mathbf{\cos A \cos B = \tfrac{1}{2}(\cos(A + B) + \cos(A - B))}$$

and subtracting $\cos(A + B)$ from $\cos(A - B)$ gives

$$\mathbf{\sin A \sin B = \tfrac{1}{2}(\cos(A - B) - \cos(A + B))}$$

These equations allow us to manipulate the product of angles, as seen from the following.

$$\begin{aligned}\cos 5\theta \cos 2\theta &= \tfrac{1}{2}(\cos(5\theta + 2\theta) + \cos(5\theta - 2\theta))\\ &= \tfrac{1}{2}(\cos 7\theta + \cos 3\theta)\end{aligned}$$

7.7 Double-angle formulae

If, in the compound-angle formulae (see section 7.5) we let $\angle B = \angle A$, then

$$\begin{aligned}\sin 2A = \sin(A + A) &= \sin A \cos A + \cos A \sin A \\ &= 2 \sin A \cos A \\ \cos 2A = \cos(A + A) &= \cos A \cos A - \sin A \sin A \\ &= \cos^2 A - \sin^2 A\end{aligned}$$

Cos $2A$ may, alternatively, be written as

$$(2\cos^2 A - 1) \text{ or as } (1 - 2\sin^2 A)$$

As an exercise, the reader should prove these. Also

$$\begin{aligned}\tan 2A = \tan(A + A) &= \frac{\tan A + \tan A}{1 - \tan A \tan A} \\ &= \frac{2 \tan A}{1 - \tan^2 A}\end{aligned}$$

Self-test questions

Use only the trigonometric formulae provided in this chapter to answer the following questions.

7.1 Solve the following triangles: (a) $\angle A = 60°$, $b = 4.75$, $c = 5$, (b) $b = 19$, $c = 22$, $\angle C = 60°$, (c) $\angle A = 88°$, $\angle B = 36°$, $a = 9.5$, (d) $a = 38$, $b = 25$, $\angle C = 78°$, (e) $a = 27$, $c = 21$, $\angle B = 60°$.

7.2 Given that $\sin A = 0.342$ and $\cos B = 0.766$, and that A and B are acute, determine the value of (a) $\sin(A + B)$, (b) $\sin(A - B)$, (c) $\cos(A + B)$, (d) $\cos(A - B)$, (e) $\tan(A + B)$, (f) $\tan(A - B)$.

7.3 Show that (a) $\cos(\theta - \pi) = -\cos\theta$, (b) $\sin(\theta + \pi) = -\sin\theta$, (c) $\tan(\theta + \pi) = \tan\theta$.

7.4 Convert each of the following in the form $Y\sin(\omega t + \phi)$ (a) $6\sin\omega t + 8\cos\omega t$, (b) $4\cos\omega t - 6\sin\omega t$, (c) $30\sin\omega t + 42\cos\omega t$.

7.5 If θ is acute, and given that $\sin 2\theta = 0.719$, determine the value of $\sin\theta$ and $\sin(\theta/2)$.

7.6 Prove that $\cos(\theta + 45°) + \sin(\theta - 45°) = 0$.

7.7 Solve for θ in $\cos 2\theta = 1 - 6\cos^2\theta$ for all positive values of θ up to 360°.

Summary of important facts

A triangle having sides a, b and c with opposite angles A, B and C, respectively, can be solved by the **sine rule** as follows

$$\frac{a}{\sin A} = \frac{b}{\sin B} = \frac{c}{\sin C}$$

Similarly, a triangle can be solved by the cosine rule which states

$$a^2 = b^2 + c^2 - 2bc\cos A$$
$$b^2 = a^2 + c^2 - 2ac\cos B$$
$$c^2 = a^2 + b^2 - 2ab\cos C$$

A **trigonometric identity** is true for all angles, and typical identities include

$$\tan\theta \equiv \sin\theta/\cos\theta$$
$$\cos^2\theta + \sin^2\theta \equiv 1$$
$$1 + \tan^2\theta \equiv \sec^2\theta$$
$$\cot^2\theta + 1 \equiv \operatorname{cosec}^2\theta$$

A **compound angle** is formed either by the addition or subtraction of two angles. Compound angle equations include the following

$$\sin(A+B) = \sin A\cos B + \cos A\sin B$$
$$\sin(A-B) = \sin A\cos B - \cos A\sin B$$
$$\cos(A+B) = \cos A\cos B - \sin A\sin B$$
$$\cos(A-B) = \cos A\cos B + \sin A\sin B$$
$$\tan(A+B) = (\tan A + \tan B)/(1 - \tan A\tan B)$$
$$\tan(A-B) = (\tan A - \tan B)/(1 + \tan A\tan B)$$

The equation $Y\sin(\omega t + \phi)$ can be written in the form

$$Y\sin(\omega t + \phi) = A\sin\omega t + B\cos\omega t$$

where

$$Y = \sqrt{(A^2 + B^2)},\ \phi = \arctan(B/A)$$
$$A = Y\cos\phi,\ B = Y\sin\phi$$

Equations for the **product of sines and cosines** are

$$\sin A\cos B = \tfrac{1}{2}[\sin(A+B) + \sin(A-B)]$$
$$\cos A\sin B = \tfrac{1}{2}[\sin(A+B) - \sin(A-B)]$$
$$\cos A\cos B = \tfrac{1}{2}[\cos(A+B) + \cos(A-B)]$$
$$\sin A\sin B = \tfrac{1}{2}[\cos(A-B) - \cos(A+B)]$$

If angle A = angle B, the compound angle formulae give the following **double-angle formulae**

$$\sin 2A = 2 \sin A \cos A$$

$$\cos 2A = \cos^2 A - \sin^2 A$$

$$= 2\cos^2 A - 1 = 1 - 2\sin^2 A$$

$$\tan 2A = 2 \tan A/(1 - \tan^2 A)$$

8 Mensuration

8.1 Introduction

Mensuration is a branch of mathematics involved in the determination of the length, area or volume of geometrical shapes and figures. In engineering we are concerned not only with the more usual shapes such as rectangles, triangles, circles, etc., but also irregular shapes. These include the area under a graph which may represent the variation of voltage, current or power plotted to a base of time or angle.

By the end of this chapter, the reader will be able to

- recognise the shapes of polygons,
- calculate the areas of plane figures,
- determine the volume and surface area of solids,
- evaluate the area of irregular figures using the mid-ordinate rule and Simpson's rule,
- calculate the average value or mean value of a waveform.

8.2 Introduction to polygons

A **polygon** is a closed shape bounded by straight lines, and the more usual polygons are

a **triangle** which has three sides
a **quadrilateral** which has four sides
a **pentagon** which has five sides
a **hexagon** which has six sides
a **heptagon** which has seven sides
a **octagon** which has eight sides

In particular, there are several types of *triangle*, including the **equilateral triangle** in which all three sides are of equal length, the **isosceles triangle** in which two sides have equal length, the **right-angled triangle** in which one angle is a right-angle, and the **scalene triangle** in which all three sides are of unequal length. A feature of a triangle is that the sum of the three internal angles is 180°.

There are several types of *quadrilateral* (see Figure 8.1) including the following:

(a) a **rectangle**, which has four internal angles which are all right-angles, and opposite sides are parallel and equal in length,
(b) a **square**, which has four internal right-angles, and all sides have equal length,

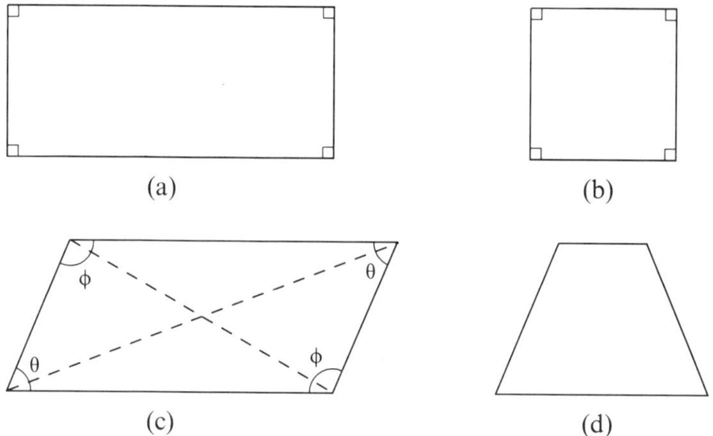

Figure 8.1 (a) A rectangle, (b) a square, (c) a parallelogram, (d) a trapezium

(c) a **parallelogram**, in which opposite sides are equal in length and are parallel to one another, and the diagonals bisect one another, and
(d) a **trapezium**, in which only one pair of sides are parallel.

8.3 Areas of plane figures

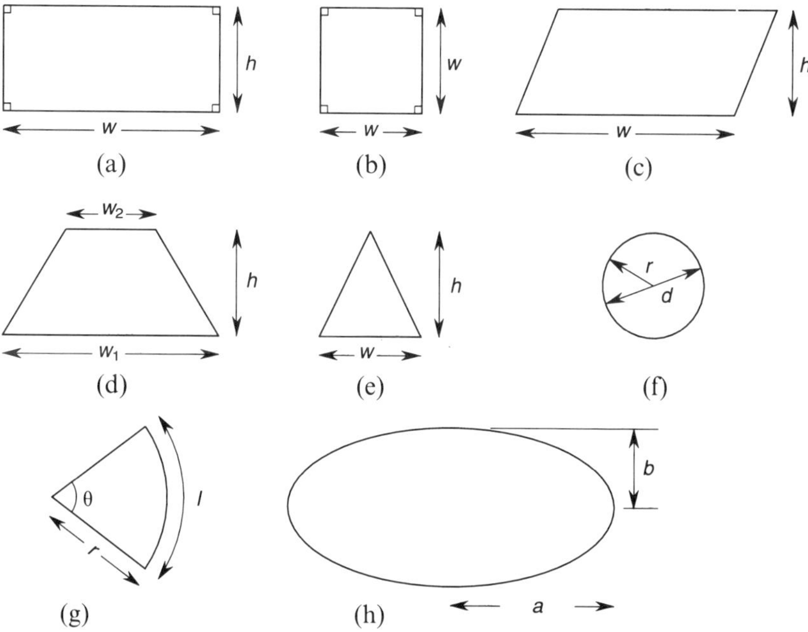

Figure 8.2 A number of shapes occurring in engineering practice

In the following, the area and (where of interest) the perimeter of the shapes in Figure 8.2 are quoted.

(a) Rectangle: Area $= wh$
(b) Square: Area $= w^2$
(c) Parallelogram: Area $= wh$
(d) Trapezium: Area $= \frac{1}{2}(w_1 + w_2)h$
(e) Triangle: Area $= \frac{1}{2}wh = \sqrt{(s(s-a)(s-b)(s-c))}$ where s is one-half of the total perimeter of the triangle, in which a, b and c are the length of the sides.
(f) Circle: Area $= \pi r^2 = \pi d^2/4$
    Circumference $= \pi d$
(g) Arc: Area $= \pi r^2\theta^\circ/360 = \frac{1}{2}r^2\theta$ (θ in rad)
    Arc length $= \pi r\theta^\circ/180 = r\theta$ (θ in rad)
(h) Ellipse: Area $= \pi ab$
    Perimeter $= \pi(a+b)$

Worked Example 8.1

Determine the area of the hexagon in Figure 8.3, each side of the hexagon being 2 cm.

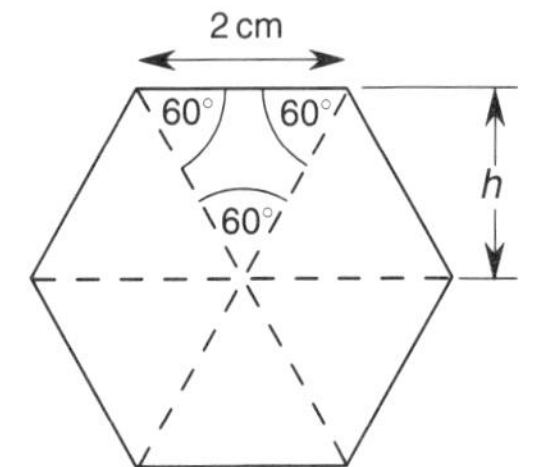

Figure 8.3 Worked Example 8.1

Solution

The hexagon can be divided into six equilateral triangles, as shown by the dotted lines in Figure 8.3. It is of interest to note that an equilateral triangle is equi-angular, and all internal angles are 60°. The height h of each triangle is calculated from

$$\tan 60^\circ = \frac{h}{(2\text{cm})/2}$$

or

$$h = 1\text{ cm} \times \tan 60^\circ = 1.732\text{ cm}$$

and

$$\begin{aligned}\text{area of one triangle} &= \tfrac{1}{2} \times \text{base} \times \text{height} \\ &= \tfrac{1}{2} \times 2\,\text{cm} \times h = h\,\text{cm}^2 \\ &= 1.732\,\text{cm}^2\end{aligned}$$

Alternatively, the length of half the perimeter of one triangle is

$$s = \tfrac{1}{2}(2 + 2 + 2) = 3\,\text{cm}$$

and

$$\begin{aligned}\text{area} &= \sqrt{(s(s-a)(s-b)(s-c))}\\ &= \sqrt{(3(3-2)(3-2)(3-2))} = 1.732\,\text{cm}^2\end{aligned}$$

The total area of the hexagon is, therefore

$$\text{total area} = 6 \times 1.732 = 10.392\,\text{cm}^2$$

8.4 Volume and surface area of solids

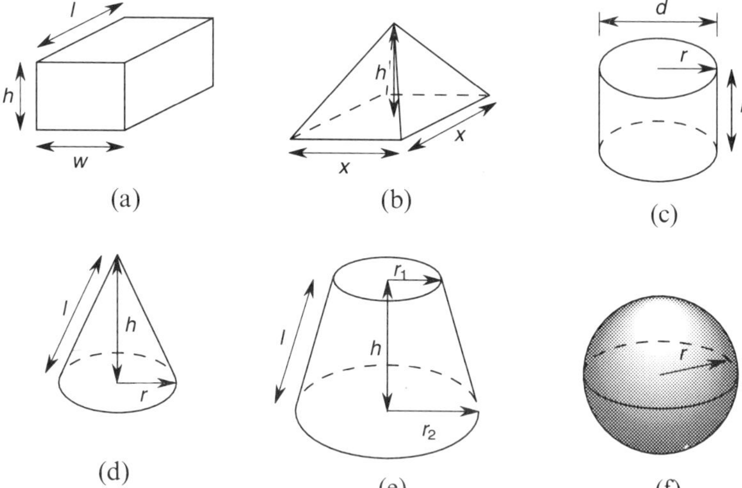

Figure 8.4 Surface area and volume of some solids

In the following, the volume and surface area of the solid shapes in Figure 8.4 is given.

(a) Rectangular prism: Volume $= whl$
Surface area $= 2(hw + wl + hl)$

(b) Pyramid: Volume $= x^2h/3$
Surface area $= x^2 + 4$(area of each triangle forming the side)

(c) Cylinder: Volume $= \pi r^2 h = \pi d^2 h/4$
Surface area $= 2(\pi r^2 + \pi rh) = 2\pi r(r + h)$

(d) Cone: Volume $= \pi r^2 h/3$
Surface area $= \pi r^2 + \pi rl = \pi r(r + l)$

(e) Frustum of a cone: Volume $= \pi h({r_1}^2 + r_1 r_2 + {r_2}^2)/3$

Surface area $= \pi l(r_1 + r_2) + \pi {r_1}^2 + \pi {r_2}^2$

$= \pi(l(r_1 + r_2) + {r_1}^2 + {r_2}^2)$

(f) Sphere: Volume $= 4\pi r^3/3$

Surface area $= 4\pi r^2$

Worked Example 8.2

A hollow shaft of internal diameter 10 cm has the same volume and length as a solid shaft whose diameter is 5 cm. Determine the thickness, t, of the material in the hollow shaft (see Figure 8.5).

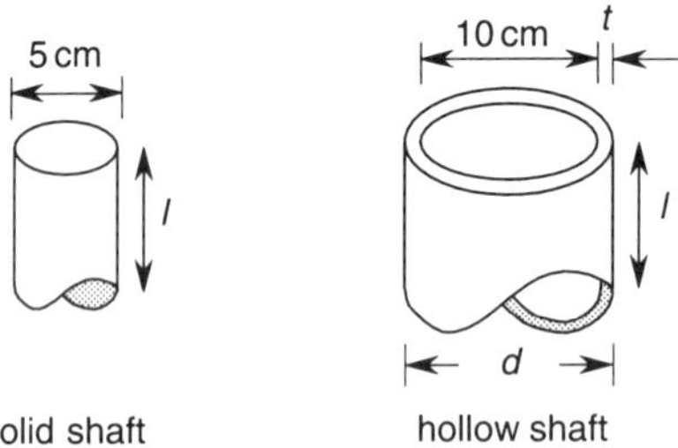

Figure 8.5 Worked Example 8.2

Solution

The volume of the solid shaft is

$$\frac{\pi}{4} \times 5^2 \times l$$

and the volume of the hollow shaft is

$$\frac{\pi}{4}(d^2 - 10^2)l$$

Since the two volumes are the same, then

$$\frac{\pi}{4}(d^2 - 10^2)l = \frac{\pi}{4} \times 5^2 \times l$$

hence

$$d^2 - 10^2 = 5^2$$

or

$$d^2 = 10^2 + 5^2 = 125$$

therefore

$$d = \sqrt{125} = 11.18\,\text{cm}$$

That is, the thickness of the hollow shaft is

$$t = (11.18 - 10)/2 = 0.59\,\text{cm}.$$

8.5 Area of irregular shapes

The area of an irregular shape can be determined *approximately* by several methods, each of which is a form of *numerical integration*. The two most popular methods are the *mid-ordinate rule* and *Simpson's rule*, the latter being named after Thomas Simpson, a British mathematician. Alternatively, an instrument known as a *planimeter* can be used, in which the outline of the figure is traced out manually using the instrument.

The mid-ordinate rule and Simpson's rule are described in sections 8.6 and 8.7.

8.6 The mid-ordinate rule

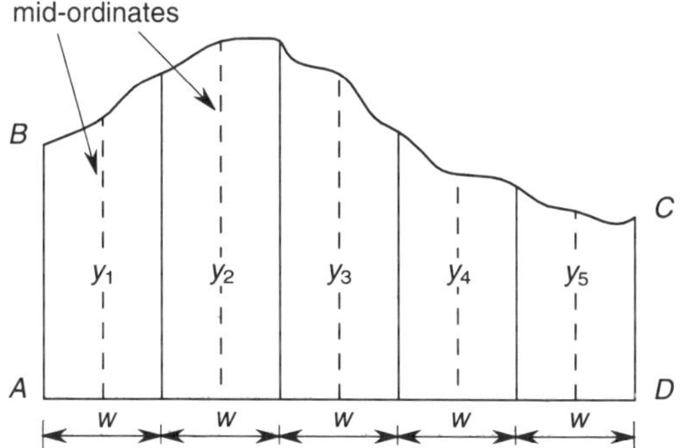

Figure 8.6 The mid-ordinate rule

To determine the area *ABCD* in Figure 8.6, the base (*AD*) is divided into a number of equal parts, each of width w (the number of parts could either be odd or even). The greater the number of parts, the more accurate the result will be. Next, the height of the *mid-ordinates* ($y_1, y_2, y_3 \ldots$) are measured at the centre of each part, and their values are added together.

The mid-ordinate rule states that the approximate value of the area of *ABCD* is

$$\begin{aligned} \text{area} &= w \times \text{sum of the mid-ordinates} \\ &= w(y_1 + y_2 + y_3 \ldots y_5) \\ &= \frac{\textbf{sum of mid-ordinates}}{\textbf{number of mid-ordinates}} \times \textbf{length } \boldsymbol{AD} \end{aligned}$$

This method is, perhaps, the simplest of all the available methods of estimating the area of an irregular shape.

8.7 Simpson's rule

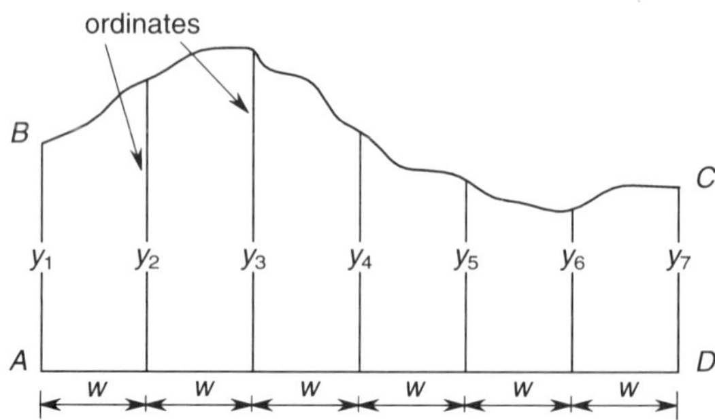

Figure 8.7 Simpson's rule

This rule provides perhaps what is one of the most accurate of the 'strip' methods and, although the method is difficult to prove, is easy to apply. In this case, the base line under the curve is divided into an *even number of strips* of equal width, and ordinates are erected at each point of division (there is, therefore, an *odd number of ordinates*) – see Figure 8.7. Simpson's rule states that the area $ABCD$ of the curve in Figure 8.7 is:

$$\frac{w}{3} \times \left[\begin{bmatrix} \textbf{first + last} \\ \textbf{ordinate} \end{bmatrix} + 4 \begin{bmatrix} \textbf{sum of even} \\ \textbf{ordinates} \end{bmatrix} + 2 \begin{bmatrix} \textbf{sum of odd} \\ \textbf{ordinates} \end{bmatrix} \right]$$

Note: the sum of the odd ordinates *does not include the first and the last ordinates*, since they have already been used.

Worked Example 8.3

The graph of a current waveform plotted to a base of time is divided into ten strips, each having a width of 1 second. The ordinates and mid-ordinates are listed in Table 8.1. Determine the area of the graph using (a) Simpson's rule and (b) the mid-ordinate rule.

Solution

(a) When determining the area by Simpson's rule we use the value of the *ordinates* as follows.

$$\text{area} = \frac{w}{3} \times [(y_1 + y_{11}) + 4(y_2 + y_4 + y_6 + y_8 + y_{10}) + 2(y_3 + y_5 + y_7 + y_9)]$$

$$= \frac{1}{3} \times [(29 + 12) + 4(33 + 44 + 36 + 22 + 17) + 2(40 + 43 + 28 + 18)]$$

$$= \frac{1}{3} \times [41 + 608 + 258] = 302.3 \text{ ampere-seconds}$$

Table 8.1 Data for Worked Example 8.3; the ordinates (for Simpson's rule) are listed as *y* values, and mid-ordinates (for the mid-ordinate rule) are listed as *m* values

	Ordinates (amperes)	*Mid-ordinates (amperes)*
y_1	29	
m_1		31
y_2	33	
m_2		36.5
y_3	40	
m_3		42
y_4	44	
m_4		43.5
y_5	43	
m_5		39.5
y_6	36	
m_6		32
y_7	28	
m_7		25
y_8	22	
m_8		20
y_9	18	
m_9		17.5
y_{10}	17	
m_{10}		14.5
y_{11}	12	

(b) We use the *mid-ordinate values* when calculating the area by the mid-ordinate rule, as shown below.

$$\begin{aligned}\text{area} &= w(m_1 + m_2 + m_3 + \ldots + m_{10}) \\ &= 1(31 + 36.5 + 42 + 43.5 + 39.5 + 32 + 25 + 20 \\ &\qquad + 17.5 + 14.5) \\ &= 301.5 \text{ ampere-seconds}\end{aligned}$$

In this case, the difference between the two methods is only about 0.3 per cent, which is small enough to be ignored, and either solution is acceptable.

8.8 The average value or mean value of a waveform

The *mathematical average value* of a waveform is its *average value taken over a complete cycle*. That is, the mathematical average value is

$$\frac{\textbf{area under the waveform}}{\textbf{length of the base}}$$

(a)

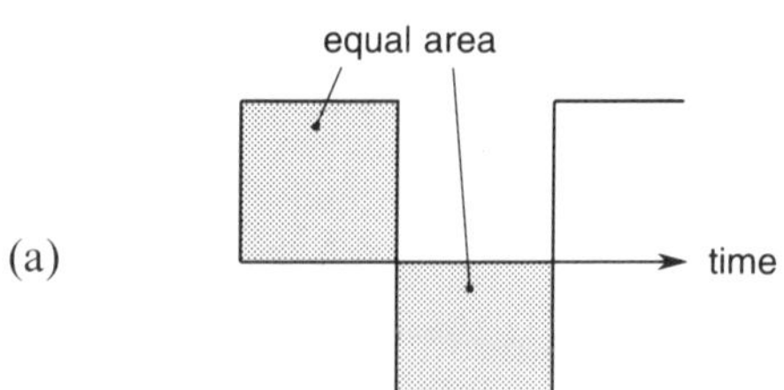

(b)

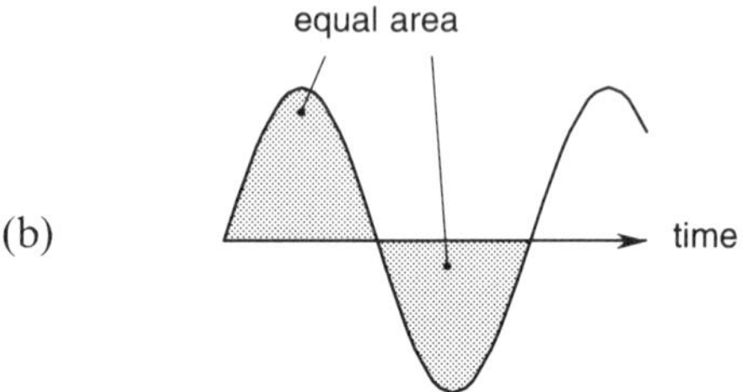

Figure 8.8 (a) A rectangular or square wave, (b) a sine wave

Figure 8.8 shows two types of **alternating waveform**; that in Figure 8.8(a) is a **rectangular wave** or **square wave**, and that in Figure 8.8(b) is a **sine wave**. It is an interesting fact that a *true alternating wave* has an equal area under both the positive and negative half-cycles, so that the total area taken over the whole cycle is zero. That is, *the mathematical average value of any alternating wave is zero*!

However, electrical engineers put a different interpretation on the meaning of 'average' when dealing with waveforms. They say that the average value or mean value of a waveform is **the average value of the positive half-cycle**. This is sometimes known as the *rectified value* of the wave.

Worked Example 8.4

Using the mid-ordinate rule, determine the average value or mean value of a sinusoidal alternating voltage of peak value 100 V.

Solution

Since we are dealing with an alternating voltage wave, we will determine the average value of the positive half-cycle of the wave. Initially, we divide the first 180° of the wave into ten strips of width 18°, and then take the mid-ordinates of the strips. These can be determined from a calculator (you can also obtain them by drawing out the sinewave, and measuring the mid-ordinates, but this is not quite so accurate).

The first mid-ordinate is at 9°, and others occur at 18° intervals up to and including 171° as follows

Mid-ordinate number	*Value*
1	$100 \sin 9^\circ = 15.64$
2	$100 \sin 27^\circ = 45.4$
3	$100 \sin 45^\circ = 70.71$
4	$100 \sin 63^\circ = 89.1$
5	$100 \sin 81^\circ = 98.77$
6	$100 \sin 99^\circ = 98.77$
7	$100 \sin 117^\circ = 89.1$
8	$100 \sin 135^\circ = 70.71$
9	$100 \sin 153^\circ = 45.4$
10	$100 \sin 171^\circ = 15.64$
sum	639.24

Hence the average value of the wave is

$$\frac{\text{sum of mid-ordinates}}{\text{number of mid-ordinates}} = \frac{639.24}{10} = 63.924 \text{ V}$$

As mentioned earlier, the mid-ordinate method provides an approximate result (but reasonably accurate), but Simpson's rule gives a more accurate result of 63.66 V (the reader should verify this fact). A true value is only obtained by using *integral calculus* (see Chapter 13 for details), which uses an infinite number or 'strips' of 'zero' width to determine the area.

Self-test questions

8.1 If the width of one face of a hexagon is w, what is the area of the hexagon?

8.2 If the radius of the tyre of a car is 0.25 m, calculate the rotational speed of the wheel in rev/s when the car is travelling at 50 km/h.

8.3 If the maximum allowable speed of the rim of a flywheel is 30 m/s, determine the maximum rotational speed in rev/s of the flywheel if its radius is 1.4 m.

8.4 A pyramid is constructed from four isosceles triangles having two sides 6 m in length, and a square base whose side is 5 m in length. Determine the total surface area of the pyramid.

8.5 Determine the area of the largest hexagonal shank that can be cut from a circular bar 2 cm in diameter.

8.6 Determine the relative volumes of a cylinder, a sphere and a cone which have the same diameter (of the base in the case of the cone), and height (diameter in the case of a cone).

8.7 A cathode-ray tube of a laboratory oscilloscope can be regarded as consisting of a cylinder of diameter 4 cm and length 15 cm, and a frustum of a cone of length from the end of the cylinder to the flared end of 15 cm, the diameter of the flared end of the frustum being 20 cm. Calculate (a) the total surface area of the tube and (b) its total volume.

8.8 Estimate the area under a curve and its mathematical average value given that the *ordinates* are 2.3, 3.8, 4.4, 6.0, 7.1, 8.3, 8.2, 7.9, 6.2, 5.0 and 3.9.

8.9 The waveshape of a current applied to a circuit is shown in Figure 8.9. Determine the average current in the circuit.

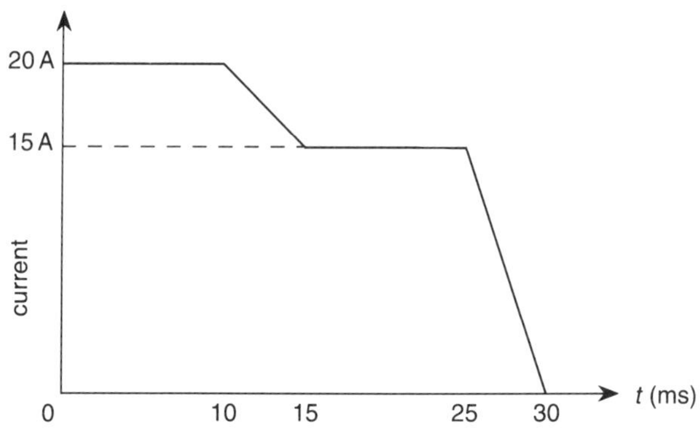

Figure 8.9 Self-test question 8.9

8.10 The instantaneous values of an alternating current waveform taken over one half-cycle are as follows

Time (ms)	0	1	2	3	4	5	6	7	8
Current (A)	0	92	160	200	86	132	100	64	0

The second half-cycle is a mirror-image of the first half-cycle. Determine the frequency of the wave and its mean value.

Summary of important facts

Mensuration is concerned with the determination of *lengths*, *areas* and *volumes* of shapes and figures, including **polygons**, the most important of which are the *triangle*, the *quadrilateral*, the *pentagon*, the *hexagon*, the *heptagon* and the *octagon*.

The area of an irregular shape can be determined *approximately* by a number of methods, which include forms of *numerical integration*. The principal methods are the **mid-ordinate rule** and **Simpson's rule**, which require the shape to be divided into strips. Simpson's rule requires an *even number of strips*, whilst the mid-ordinate rule can employ either an *odd number* or an *even number of strips*. The mid-ordinate rule is the simpler of the two to understand, but Simpson's rule is generally more accurate.

An instrument known as a **planimeter** can be used manually to estimate the area of a figure drawn on a piece of paper.

The **mathematical mean** value or average value of an alternating waveform is the average taken over a complete cycle, and has zero value. The **electrical (rectified) average value** or mean value of an alternating wave is the average value taken over the positive half-cycle of the wave.

9 Graphs

9.1 Introduction

In this chapter we look at graphs which are frequently encountered in electrical and electronic engineering including the straight line graph, inverse proportion graphs, parabolas, graphs of cubic equations, graphs having a law of the form $y = Ax^n$, and exponential curves such as may be encountered in transients in electrical circuits. We will also see how to obtain the graphical solution of simultaneous equations.

By the end of this chapter the reader will be able to

- understand basic facts about graphs,
- draw a straight line graph, and determine the equation of the graph,
- predict the 'best' straight-line graph from a set of 'points' or experimental results,
- solve linear simultaneous equations by means of a graph,
- understand the meaning of direct and inverse proportionality,
- plot graphs of quadratic equations, and graphically solve quadratic equations,
- plot graphs of cubic equations,
- plot graphs of the form $y = Ax^n$, and graphically solve an equation of the form $y = Ax^n + B$,
- use logarithmic graph paper,
- plot exponential graphs of the form $y = Ae^{-t/\tau}$ and $y = A(1 - e^{-t/\tau})$, such as occur in transients in electrical circuits,
- determine the settling time, rise time and fall time of transients in R-C and R-L circuits.

9.2 Basic facts about graphs

A **graph** is simply a way of representing pictorially how a quantity or **variable** changes with another. If, for example, we change the voltage applied to a circuit, the current in the circuit changes. The quantity which we control is known as the **independent variable** since the circuit itself has no control over the value of the voltage. However, since a change in the value of the voltage causes the current in the circuit to alter, the current is known as the **dependent variable**.

Graphs are usually drawn on a paper using axes which are at right-angles to one another (see Figure 9.1), the points on the graph are defined using **rectangular co-ordinates** or **cartesian co-ordinates** (after René Decartes in the

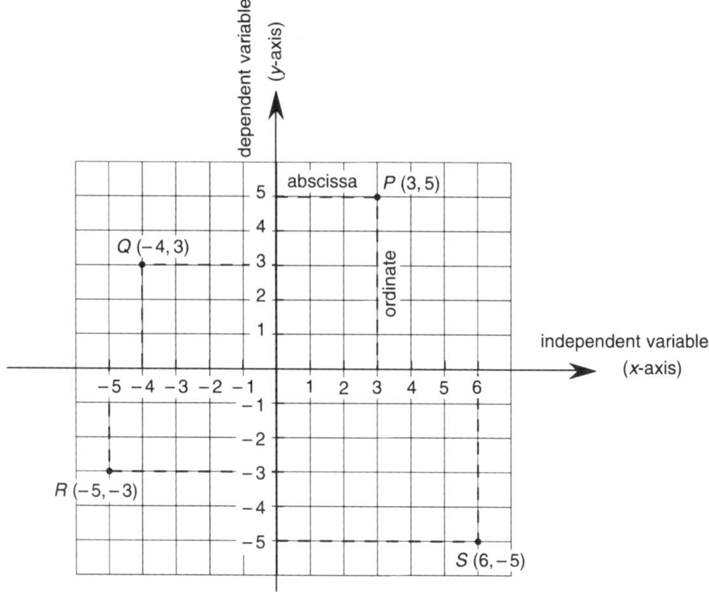

Figure 9.1 Defining points on a graph using cartesian or rectangular co-ordinates

17th century). The point of intersection of the two axes of the graph in Figure 9.1 is known as the **origin** of the graph.

The vertical axis or ***y*-axis** is reserved for the dependent variable, and the horizontal axis or ***x*-axis** is reserved for the independent variable. Distances above and to the right of the origin of the graph are positive, and distances below and to the left of the origin are negative. The x co-ordinate of a point on the graph is the **abscissa**, and the y co-ordinate is called the **ordinate**. The four quadrants of the graph are defined in the same way as those for angles (see chapter 6) namely the first, second, third and fourth quadrants, respectively, starting at the top right and moving anticlockwise to the bottom right quadrant.

The rectangular co-ordinates of any point on the graph in Figure 9.1 are written in the order (x, y), so that point P is defined as the point $(3, 5)$, Q is defined as $(-4, 3)$, R as $(-5, -3)$ and S as $(6, -5)$.

As stated above, a graph is a line or curve showing the relationship between two variables which, in many cases, are linked by an equation. For example, we can plot the following equations using cartesian co-ordinates.

$$y = 2x + 3$$

$$y = 10 \sin \theta$$

$$y = x^2 + 5x + 6, \text{ etc.}$$

The dependent variable, y, in the above equations is written on the left-hand side of the expression, and the independent variable is on the right-hand side.

9.3 The straight-line graph

In a **straight-line graph**, the independent variable, x, is raised to the power unity. For example

$$y = 2x + 3$$
$$y = 2x + 1$$
$$y = 2x - 1$$

are all examples of equations which have a straight-line graph. A table of values for y for each of these equations is given in Table 9.1, and values are plotted in Figure 9.2

TABLE 9.1 Data for some straight-line graphs

x	−2	−1	0	1	2	3
$y = 2x + 3$	−1	1	3	5	7	9
$y = 2x + 1$	−3	−1	1	3	5	7
$y = 2x - 1$	−5	−3	−1	1	3	5

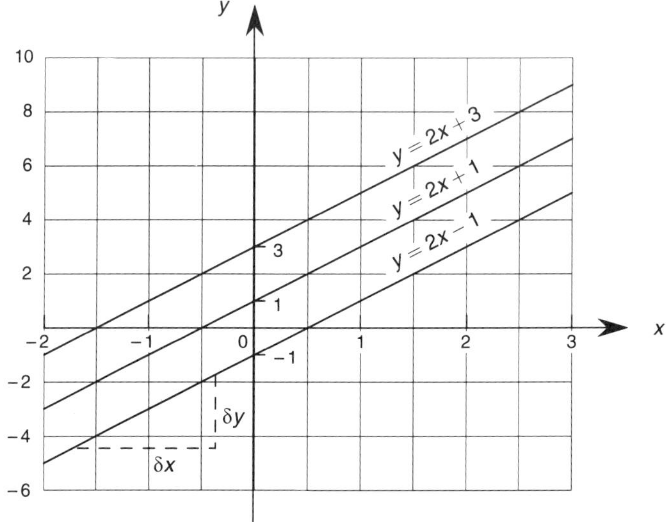

Figure 9.2 Straight-line graphs

Two parameters of great importance when defining a straight-line graph are the gradient and the y-axis intercept (also known as the vertical intercept).

The **gradient** is defined as

$$\text{gradient} = \frac{\text{change in } y}{\text{change in } x} = \frac{\delta y}{\delta x}$$

where δy and δx are shown in the graph for $y = 2x - 1$ in Figure 9.2. The gradient is, in fact, *the tangent of the angle that the graph makes with the x-axis*. Using the values for the graph of $y = 2x - 1$, we see that its tangent is

$$\text{gradient} = \frac{\delta y}{\delta x} = \frac{3 - 1}{2 - 1} = 2$$

Since all the graphs are parallel to one another, the slope of each graph in Figure 9.2 is 2 (the reader should verify this from the values in Table 9.1).

If the graph slopes upwards as x increases in value (as it does in all cases in Figure 9.2), *the gradient is positive*, and if it slopes downwards *the gradient is negative*. If the graph is horizontal, *the gradient is zero*, and if it is vertical, *the gradient is infinite*.

The **vertical intercept** or ***y*-intercept** is the distance from the origin to the point where the graph cuts the y-axis. In the case of the graph for $y = 2x + 3$ the y-intercept is 3 (see Figure 9.2), in the case of $y = 2x + 1$ it is 1, and in the case of $y = 2x - 1$ it is -1. That is, the y-intercept is equal to the constant in the equation.

The **law of a straight-line graph** can be stated as

$$y = mx + c$$

where m is the gradient and c is the y-intercept. In the case of the graph $y = 2x + 3$, we can observe that the graph has a gradient of $m = 2$, and a y-intercept of $c = +3$.

Worked Example 9.1

State the gradient and y-intercept of the following graphs

(a) $y = 4x + 6$, (b) $2y = 3x - 7$, (c) $-2y = 4x - 6$, (d) $\frac{y}{3} = \frac{x}{6} - \frac{2}{3}$, (e) $4x + 5y - 8 = 0$.

Solution

(a) In this case

$$y = 4x + 6 = mx + c$$

hence $m = 4$ and $c = 6$. That is, the gradient of the graph is $+4$, and the y-intercept is $+6$.

(b) Here the equation of the graph is

$$2y = 3x - 7$$

To reduce this to the 'standard' straight-line graph format, we must reduce the coefficient of y to unity by dividing throughout the equation by 2 as follows

$$y = 1.5x - 3.5 = mx + c$$

which has a gradient of $m = +1.5$ and a y-intercept of $c = -3.5$.

(c) The equation $-2y = 4x - 6$ is rewritten in the form

$$y = \frac{4x}{-2} - \frac{6}{-2} = -2x + 3 = mx + c$$

The gradient of the graph is $m = -2$ and the y-intercept is $c = +3$.

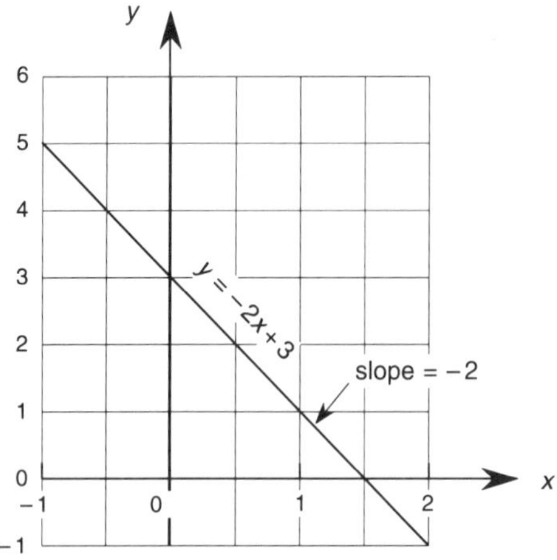

Figure 9.3 Solution of Worked Example 9.1(c)

The graph is shown in Figure 9.3, and we see that the negative gradient means that the graph slopes downwards as the value of x increases, and intersects the y-axis when $y = +3$. The reader should plot the graph over the range $x = -2$ to $x = +2$ to verify the shape of the graph.

(d) In this case the equation is $\frac{y}{3} = \frac{x}{6} - \frac{2}{3}$, which can be rewritten in the form

$$y = 3\left[\frac{x}{6} - \frac{2}{3}\right] = \frac{x}{2} - 2 = mx + c$$

From the above we see that the gradient is $m = +\frac{1}{2}$ and the y-intercept is $c = -2$.

(e) It is necessary to rewrite the equation in the form

$$5y = -4x + 8$$

or

$$y = -\frac{4}{5}x + \frac{8}{5} = mx + c$$

Clearly, the gradient of the graph is $m = -4/5 = -0.8$, and the y-intercept is $c = 8/5 = 1.6$

Worked Example 9.2

The way in which the terminal voltage, V_T volts, of an electronic power supply varies with the current, I amperes, in supplies is shown in the following table.

I	0	0.2	0.4	0.6	0.8	1.0
V_T	12	11.98	11.96	11.94	11.92	11.90

Determine the law relating I and V_T.

Solution

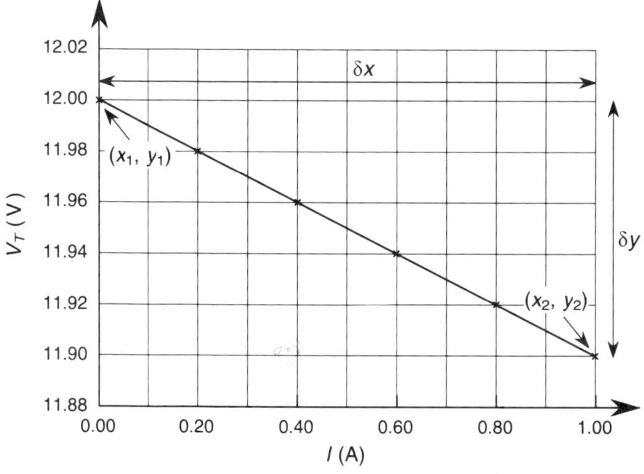

Figure 9.4 Solution of Worked Example 9.2

Since the value of I causes V_T to vary, I is the independent variable, and is plotted on the x-axis in Figure 9.4. The graph is plotted from a **false zero**; that is to say, the minimum value of V_T is not equal to zero (which enables us to show variations in V_T to a much greater scale). However, the current scale does start at zero, and we can see that

$$y\text{-intercept, } c = 12$$

The gradient of the graph can be determined from the points on the graph, and

$$\text{gradient, } m = \frac{\delta y}{\delta x} = \frac{y_2 - y_1}{x_2 - x_1} = \frac{11.9 - 12}{1 - 0} = \frac{-0.1}{1}$$
$$= -0.1$$

The law of the graph is therefore

$$V_T = -0.1I + 12 \text{ V}$$

Worked Example 9.3

The following results were obtained from an experiment in which the resistance of a wire-wound resistor was measured at different temperature values

Resistance, Ω	20.85	21.6	22.35	23.3	23.9	24.85
Temperature, °C	10.0	20.0	30.0	40.0	50.0	60.0

Determine the law relating the resistance of resistor to its temperature.

Solution

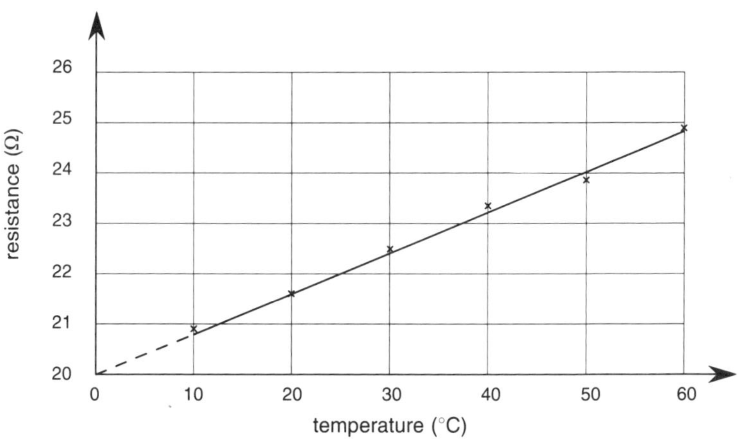

Figure 9.5 Solution of Worked Example 9.3

The points marked on the graph are plotted from the values in the table. Even though the results theoretically lie on a straight line, most of the points lie either side of the supposed position of the graph (typical of experimental results!).

The author has drawn what he considers to be the 'best' straight line. This line may not be what every reader considers to be the 'best' position for the graph, so that there will be a variation between individuals on the position of the graph. In fact, there is a mathematical method known as the *least squares method* of estimating the 'best fit' straight line (see section 9.4 for details). After reading section 9.4, the reader will find it interesting to predict the 'best fit' equation to the above set of values.

Once again, the graph is plotted with a 'false zero' and, since the independent variable (the temperature) results do not extend to zero, the graph must be extended or **extrapolated** (see the broken line in Figure 9.5) until it reaches the y-axis. Here we see that

resistance axis intercept, $c = 20\Omega$

When estimating the gradient of the graph, we must take the results from the 'best' straight line. In fact, it has been assumed that the points $(10\Omega, 20.8^\circ C)$ and $(60\Omega, 24.8^\circ C)$ lie on this line. That is

$$\text{gradient, } m = \frac{\delta y}{\delta x} = \frac{y_2 - y_1}{x_2 - x_1} = \frac{24.8 - 20.8}{60 - 10}$$

$$= \frac{4}{50} = 0.08\,\Omega/^\circ C$$

The estimated law of the graph is, therefore

$$\text{resistance} = m \times \text{temperature} + c$$

$$= 0.08\theta + 20\,\Omega$$

where θ is the temperature in °C.

9.4 Predicting the 'best fit' straight-line graph

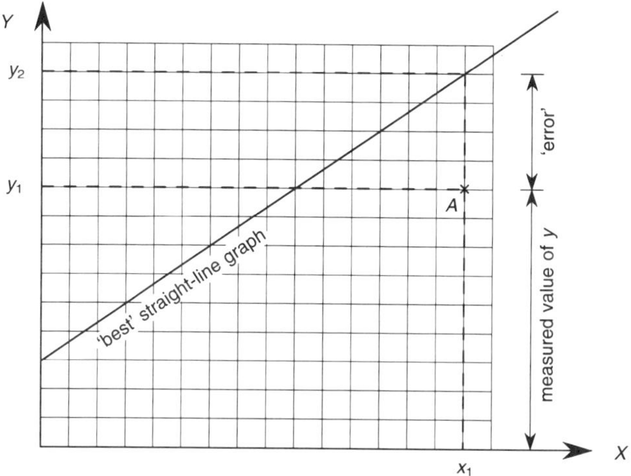

Figure 9.6 The effect of an 'error' in a measured value

If point A in Figure 9.6 corresponds to one point on a graph, and the estimated 'best fit' straight-line graph is shown in full line, there is an 'error' between the position of the point and the graph itself.

Mathematicians have devised a **method of least squares** technique for estimating the equation of the straight-line graph from a set of results. This method endeavours to reduce the value of $(\text{error})^2$ to the smallest value; the reason for this being that, since the error may either be positive or negative, then $(\text{error})^2$ is always positive. The resulting straight-line graph is known as the **line of regression of *X* on *Y*** or as the **line of prediction of *Y***.

Below we write down an expression for the method of calculation of the gradient, and one for the calculation of the y-intercept, and will apply them to a set of results.

The gradient is given by the expression

$$\text{gradient, } m = \frac{(N \times \sum XY) - (\sum X \times \sum Y)}{(N \times \sum(X^2)) - (\sum X)^2}$$

and the y-intercept is

$$\text{intercept, } c = \frac{\sum Y - (m \times \sum X)}{N}$$

where

$N =$ number of points on the graph

$\sum XY =$ sum of the products of X and Y

$\sum X =$ sum of the X-values

$\sum Y =$ sum of the Y-values

$\sum(X^2) =$ sum of the square values of X

Worked Example 9.4

The following table gives the resistance of a resistor as its temperature alters

Resistance, Ω	10.04	10.079	10.1	10.139
Temperature, °C	10.0	20.0	25.0	35.0

Using the least squares method, determine the equation relating resistance to temperature.

Solution

Before reading any further, the reader should plot the graph and estimate the equation of the graph. Since the temperature is the factor which controls the resistance of the resistor, we use the temperature as the independent variable, i.e., $X =$ temperature. This graph will be useful in assessing the accuracy of this method. Table 9.2 shows how the values in the least squares method are calculated.

TABLE 9.2 Method of least squares: solution to Worked Example 9.4

X	10.0	20.0	25.0	35.0	$\sum X = 90$
Y	10.04	10.079	10.1	10.139	$\sum Y = 40.358$
XY	100.4	201.58	252.58	354.87	$\sum XY = 909.35$
X^2	100.0	400.0	625.0	1225.0	$\sum(X^2) = 2350$

Substituting the values in the right-hand column of Table 9.2 into the equations in section 9.4 gives

$$\text{gradient, } m = \frac{(N \times \sum XY) - (\sum X \times \sum Y)}{(N \times \sum(X^2)) - (\sum X)^2}$$

$$= \frac{(4 \times 909.35) - (90 \times 40.358)}{(4 \times 2350) - 90^2}$$

$$= \frac{5.18}{1300} = 3.98 \times 10^{-3}$$

and

$$\text{intercept, } c = \frac{\sum Y - (m \times \sum X)}{N}$$

$$= \frac{40.358 - (3.98 \times 10^{-3} \times 90)}{4} = 10$$

That is

$$R = 3.98 \times 10^{-3}\theta + 10\,\Omega$$

where θ = temperature in °C.

9.5 Graphical solution of linear simultaneous equations

The mathematical solution of linear simultaneous equations was fully discussed in Chapter 5, but here we have the option of solving them graphically. Consider the circuit in Figure 9.7 (a), in which currents I_1 and I_2 are unknown. Using electrical circuit theory, we deduce the following simultaneous equations for the circuit which are (see also Chapter 5)

$$10 = 20I_1 + 10I_2$$

$$15 = 10I_1 + 30I_2$$

Since both currents are unknown, we cannot (strictly speaking) say which one of them is to be the independent variable. However, we must nominate one of them, and we choose I_2; that is, I_2 will be plotted on the x-axis. The above equations are therefore written in the form

$$20I_1 = -10I_2 + 10 \quad \text{or} \quad I_1 = -0.5I_2 + 0.5 \qquad (9.1)$$

$$10I_1 = -30I_2 + 15 \quad \text{or} \quad I_1 = -3I_2 + 1.5 \qquad (9.2)$$

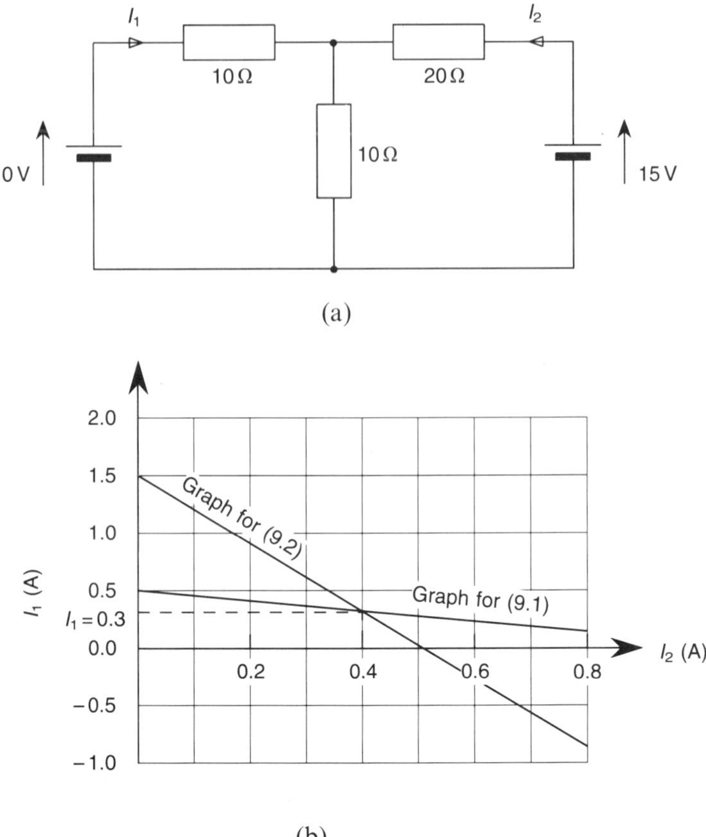

Figure 9.7 (a) An electrical circuit, (b) its graphical solution

TABLE 9.3 Graphical solution of linear equations

I_2	0.0	0.2	0.4	0.6	0.8
I_1 (from (9.1))	0.5	0.4	0.3	0.2	0.1
I_1 (from (9.2))	1.5	0.9	0.3	−0.3	−0.9

If we calculate I_1 for the range of I_2 values of 0 to 0.8 A we get the results in Table 9.3. The two graphs of I_1 plotted to a base of I_2 are shown in Figure 9.7(b). Clearly I_1 has the same value *for both equations* where the two graphs intersect; this occurs when

$$I_1 = 0.3 \text{ A and } I_2 = 0.4 \text{ A}$$

These values give the solution to the two simultaneous equations. The reader will find it an interesting exercise to verify the solution of the circuit using any of the methods outlined in Chapter 5.

9.6 Direct proportionality

The graph of a straight line is given by the law $y = mx + c$, where m and c have been defined earlier. In a relationship of this type, the variables y and x are said to be **linearly related to one another**. That is, a change in x produces a linear change in y.

In the special case when $c = 0$, i.e., *the graph passes through the origin*, then $k = mx$ (or, as is often quoted, $y = kx$), y and x are **directly proportional to one another**, that is $y \propto x$, where $\propto$ means 'is proportional to'. The shorter forms 'y is proportional to x' and 'y varies as x' are also used.

For example, the e.m.f. induced in the armature of a d.c. machine is given by the expression

$$E = \frac{2p}{c}\Phi Zn \text{ volts}$$

in which the factors p, c and Z are constants for a particular machine, whilst Φ (the magnetic flux in the machine) and n (the armature speed) can be controlled by the user, i.e. they are independent variables. If we write $K = 2pZ/c$, then the equation can be written in the form

$$E = K\Phi n \text{ volts}$$

or

$$E \propto \Phi n$$

On the other hand, if Φ is maintained at a constant value, it too is a constant and we may write $K_1 = K\Phi$, and

$$E = K_1 n$$

or

$$E \propto n$$

We frequently manipulate equations in this way in order to prove a particular point in electrical and electronic theory.

9.7 Inverse proportionality

If

$$y = \frac{k}{x} = kx^{-1}$$

where k is a constant, then y is **proportional to the reciprocal** of x, that is

$$y \propto 1/x$$

Here we say that ***y* varies inversely as *x***, or ***y* is inversely proportional to *x***. In this type of relationship, if x becomes very small (we say that it 'tends to' zero), then y becomes very large (it 'tends to' infinity); if x tends to infinity, then y tends to zero.

From the original expression we can say that

$$xy = k$$

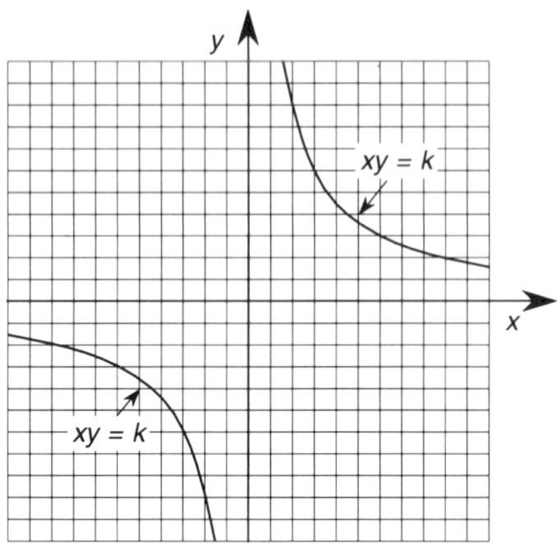

Figure 9.8 Graph of $xy = k$ or $y = k/x$

That is, the product of x and y always gives a constant value. The graph of such a curve is known as a **rectangular hyperbola**, and is shown in Figure 9.8. Clearly, in practice neither x or y can have an infinite value, and we say that the curve is asymptotic with the y and x axes (but does not touch them!) as x approaches zero and infinity, respectively. Let us consider practical situations in electrical engineering where this occurs.

Firstly, in Ohm's law $I = E/R$; if E is a constant voltage, then

$$I = \frac{\text{constant}}{R} = \frac{k}{R} = kR^{-1}$$

The graph of this relationship corresponds to the curve in the first quadrant of Figure 9.8, with R being plotted as the independent variable in the x-direction, the current I being the dependent variable. Clearly, as the resistance of the circuit reduces in value, the current increases, and as R tends to zero value, the circuit current tends to rise to an infinite value (which is prevented in a practical circuit by a fuse or overcurrent trip). Also, if the resistance of the circuit approaches an infinite value, the current in the circuit tends towards zero.

Next, let us look at the power rating of a semiconductor device. In practice, we design the circuit to work within the power rating of the semiconductor. The power, P, dissipated by the semiconductor is given by

$$P = VI$$

where V is the voltage drop across the device, and I is the current flowing in it. If P_{max} is the maximum power that the device can dissipate, we can re-write the above equation in the form

$$VI = P_{max}$$

That is if $P_{max} = 100\,\text{mW}$, and $V = 10\,\text{V}$, then the maximum current the device can carry is

$$I = P_{max}/V = 100/10 = 10 \text{ mA}$$

and if $V = 20\,\text{V}$, then the maximum current is

$$I = P_{max}/V = 100/20 = 5 \text{ mA}$$

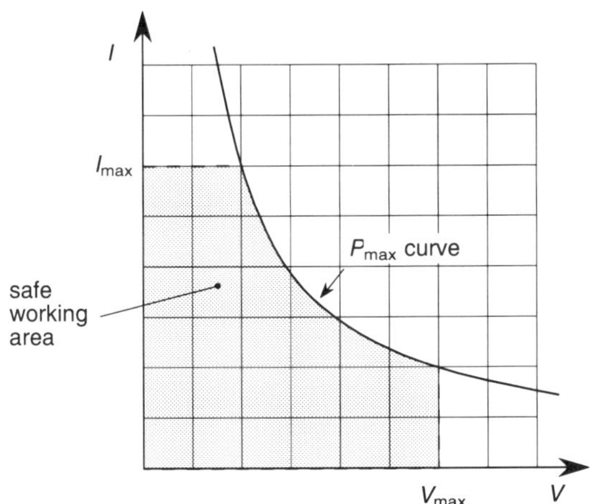

Figure 9.9 Safe working area for a semiconductor device

A typical graph for P_{max} is shown in Figure 9.9. Further, the **safe working area** under the P_{max} curve is bounded by the maximum current (I_{max}) the device will carry, and the maximum voltage (V_{max}) that the device will support.

9.8 Graphs of quadratic equations

The general form of **quadratic equation** (or, more strictly, a *second order polynomial*) is

$$y = ax^2 + bx + c$$

where a, b and c are constants, and the shape of the x-y graph is called a **parabola**.

An interesting point about a parabola is that if it is rotated about its axis, it produces a shape known as the **paraboloid of revolution**, and is the shape of optical reflectors and radar antennae. A property of this shape is that if a source of light or electronic radiation is placed at its *focal point*, the beam it produces is parallel to the axis. Also, in radar applications, the waves impinging on it are focused onto the focal point.

To get an idea of the general shape of the parabola, we will consider one or two special cases as follows *(a)* **The case where $b = 0$ and $c = 0$**; that is $y = ax^2$.

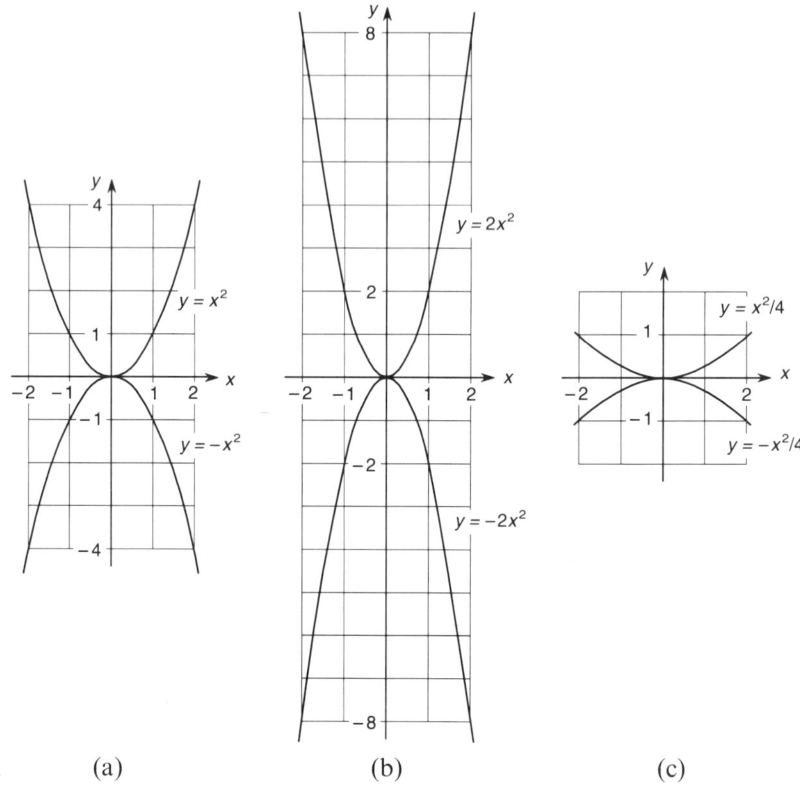

Figure 9.10 Parabolas for which parameters *b* and *c* are both zero

The graphs for $y = x^2$ and $y = -x^2$, i.e., parameter $a = \pm 1$, are shown in Figure 9.10(a). In this case we can see that the graph has a **turning point** at $(0, 0)$, i.e., $x = 0$, $y = 0$, and the slope of the tangent to the curve at this point is zero. If the value of parameter a is increased to ± 2, i.e., $y = 2x^2$ and $y = -2x^2$ (see Figure 9.10(b)), the graph has a turning point as $(0, 0)$ again, but the shape of the graph is much sharper than for $a = \pm 1$. If $a = \pm\frac{1}{4}$, the curve is much more shallow (see Figure 9.10(c)).

We also see that if the sign of parameter a is positive the graph is concave looking from the top, and if the sign is negative it is concave from below.

The case where $b = 0$; that is $y = ax^2 + c$.

We see in figures 9.11(a) and (b) that when parameter c is positive, the turning point occurs when $x = 0$ and y has a positive value. When c is negative, the turning point occurs when $x = 0$ and y has a negative value. Moreover, the y-intercept of the curve is equal to the value of parameter c.

The reader should also note, in Figure 9.11(a), *the curves do not touch or intersect the x-axis*. We will return to this fact later.

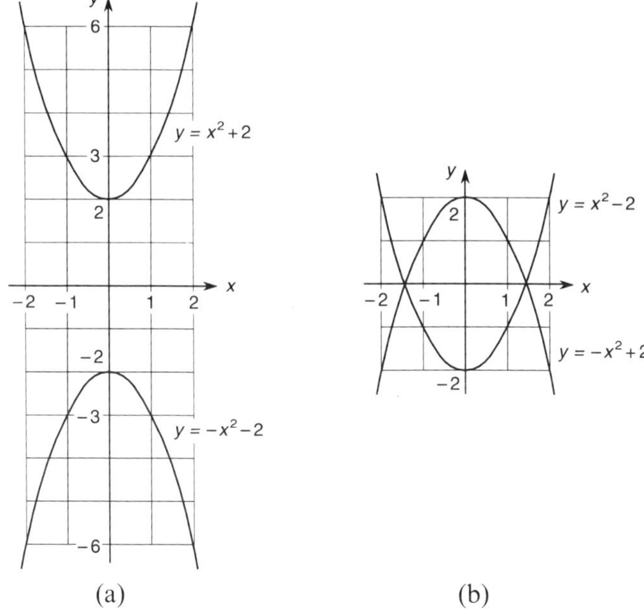

Figure 9.11 Parabolas for which parameter *b* is zero

(b) **The case where *a*, *b* and *c* are finite**; that is $y = ax^2 + bx + c$.

To consider the general effect of parameter b on a quadratic equation, consider the two following equations

$$y = x^2 + 2x - 2$$
$$y = x^2 - 2x - 2$$

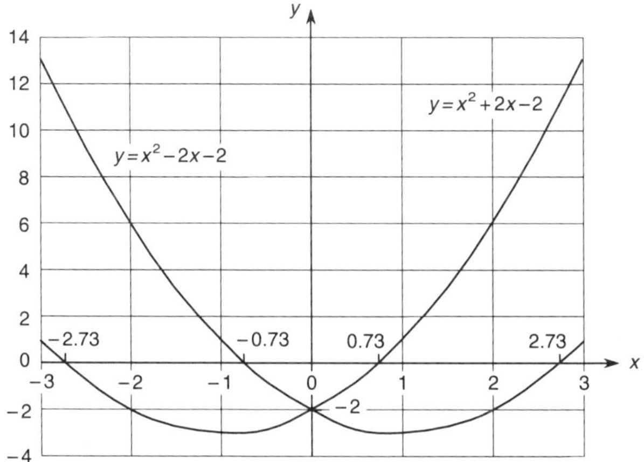

Figure 9.12 The effect of *b* on the position of the parabola

The graphs are plotted in Figure 9.12, and we see that the net effect of parameter b is to shift the graph in the x-direction. The basic curve with $b = 0$ is shown in Figure 9.11(b); when b has a positive value, the turning point of the graph is shifted to the left (see Figure 9.12), and when b has a negative value it is shifted to the right.

Summary

1. A parabola has a turning point.
2. The larger the value of parameter a, the 'sharper' the turning point.
3. A positive value of parameter a results in the curve being concave looking from above, and a negative value of parameter a causes it to be concave from below.
4. Parameter b causes the turning point to be shifted in the x-direction; a positive value causes it to be shifted to the left.
5. The value of parameter c gives the y-intercept of the parabola.
6. If the parabola cuts the x-axis, the points of intersection with the x-axis give the **roots of the equation** (see also sections 4.8 and 9.9). If the curve just touches the x-axis, there are two equal roots to the equation (e.g., $y = x^2 - 6x + 9$). If the curve does not cut the x-axis (see Figure 9.11(a)), the roots are 'imaginary' (see Chapter 11).

9.9 Graphical solution of a quadratic equation

A quadratic equation is formed when $y = 0$ in a quadratic polynomial. That is

$$ax^2 + bx + c = 0$$

The equation can be solved graphically by plotting the graph and noting the values of x for which $y = 0$ (note: a solution is said to be 'imaginary' (see Chapter 11) if the graph does not cut the x-axis).

In general, a quadratic equation has two possible solutions or values of x for which $y = 0$, since the graph normally cuts the x-axis twice (see also Figure 9.12).

The special case where the curve only just touches the x-axis (see, for example, Figure 9.10) appears to give only one result (where the curve touches the x-axis). In fact, there are two solutions and both are identical.

Consider the equations

$$x^2 - 2 = 0 \text{ and } -x^2 + 2 = 0$$

the solution is

$$x = \sqrt{2} = \pm 1.414$$

That is

$$x = +1.414 \text{ or } x = -1.414$$

as shown in Figure 9.11(b).

The equation

$$x^2 + 2x - 2 = 0$$

gives the solutions $x = -2.73$ and $x = 0.73$, whilst the equation

$$x^2 - 2x - 2 = 0$$

gives the solutions $x = -0.73$ and $x = 2.73$ (both graphs are drawn in Figure 9.12).

9.10 Graphical solution of simultaneous equations

The graphical solution of simultaneous equations is obtained by plotting both graphs on the same graph paper, the solution (or solutions) being given by the points where the graphs intersect. The graphical solution of linear simultaneous equations was described in section 9.5. Here we look at more complex problems; *in some cases, the graphical solution is the only method of obtaining a solution*. However, the reader is advised that, at best, a graphical solution gives only an approximate solution since the point(s) of intersection is not always clearly defined.

Worked Example 9.5

Plot the graph of $y_1 = 2x^2 - 6x + 3$, hence solve the equation of $2x^2 - 6x + 3 = 0$. On the same piece of graph paper plot $y_2 = x - 1$ and solve graphically the simultaneous equations

$$2x^2 - 6x + 3 = 0$$
$$x - 1 = 0$$

Solution

TABLE 9.4 Graphical solution of simulataneous equations: Solution to Worked Example 9.5

x	0	1	2	3	4
$2x^2$	0	2	8	18	32
$-6x$	0	-6	-12	-18	-24
3	3	3	3	3	3
y_1	3	-1	-1	3	11
y_2	-1	0	1	2	3

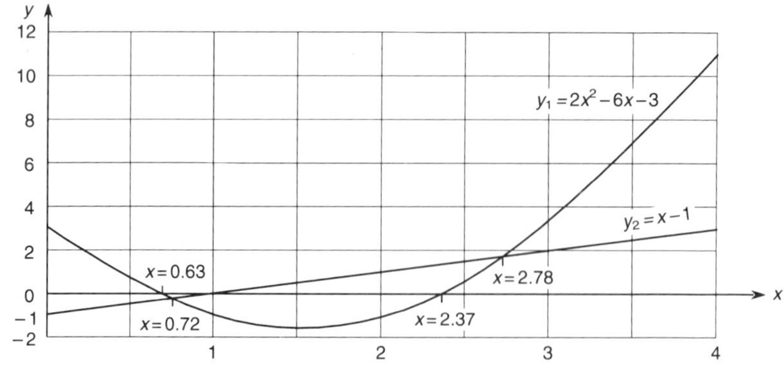

Figure 9.13 Solution to Worked Example 9.5

A table of values for $y_1 = 2x^2 - 6x + 3$ and $y_2 = x - 1$ for the range $x = 0$ to $x = 4$ is given in Table 9.4.

Using the summary in section 9.8, we can conclude for y_1 that, since parameter a in the equation $y_1 = 2x^2 - 6x + 3$ is positive, the curve will be concave looking from above, the negative sign associated with parameter b indicates that the turning point occurs at a positive value of x, and that since parameter $c = 3$, the curve for y_1 intersects the y-axis at $y = 3$. The graph is drawn in Figure 9.13, and a careful inspection shows that the parabola intersects the x-axis at

$$x = 0.63 \text{ and } x = 2.37$$

which are the solutions for $2x^2 - 6x + 3 = 0$.

Next we plot the straight-line graph for y_2. Although the results from Table 9.4 can be used, we can apply the information we already know to draw the graph, that is

$$y_2 = x - 1 = mx + c$$

The graph therefore commences at the y-intercept of $c = -1$, and has a slope of 1.0, so that by the time that $x = 4$, then $y_2 = 3$.

Once again a careful inspection reveals that the graphs for y_1 and y_2 intersect when

$$x = 0.72 \text{ and } x = 2.78$$

These two values give the solution of the simultaneous equations.

There is yet another method at our disposal of solving the simultaneous equations, since we know that not only does $y_1 = 0$ at the intersection of the curves, but also $y_2 = 0$. That is

$$2x^2 - 6x + 3 = 0 = x - 1$$

or

$$2x^2 - 7x + 4 = 0$$

If we plot the graph $y = 2x^2 - 7x + 4$, we will find that its roots are $x = 0.72$ and $x = 2.78$, which agree with the solutions in Figure 9.13.

Worked Example 9.6

Plot the graph $y = x^2 - 4x + 4$, and determine its solution. Also, solve graphically

$$y = x^2 - 4x + 4$$
$$xy = 4$$

Solution

For the equation $y = x^2 - 4x + 4 = ax^2 + bx + c$, we note that (see section 9.8) since a is positive, the parabola is concave looking from above, the turning point occurs when x is positive (parameter b is negative), and the vertical intercept of the curve occurs at $y = 4$ (since $c = 4$). The table of values for y in the range $x = 0$ to $x = 4$ is given in Table 9.5.

TABLE 9.5 Table for solution to Worked Example 9.6

x	0	1	2	3	4
x^2	0	1	4	9	16
$-4x$	0	−4	−8	−12	−16
4	4	4	4	4	4
y	4	1	0	1	4

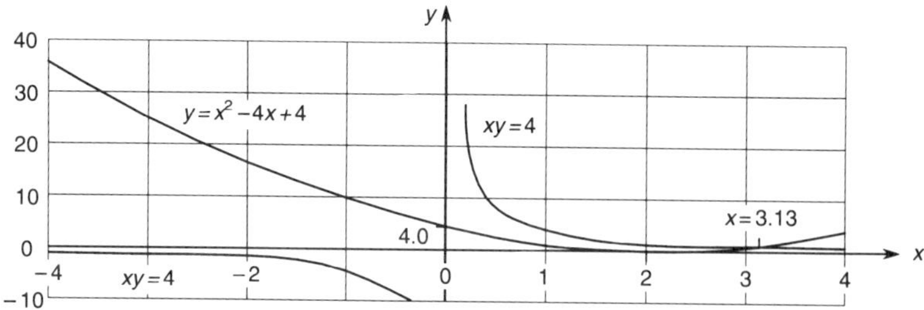

Figure 9.14 Solution to Worked Example 9.6

The graph is plotted in Figure 9.14, and we see that the parabola touches the x-axis at $x = 2$, which is the solution to the equation $x^2 - 4x + 4 = 0$.

From what has been said earlier, the graph of the equation $xy = 4$ is a rectangular hyperbola, which gives curves in the first and third quadrants, as shown in Figure 9.14. From the graph, we see that there is one intersection point which occurs at $x = 3.13$, which is the solution of the simultaneous equations.

This is an example of a problem which is difficult to solve by other than graphical methods.

9.11 The graph of a cubic equation

A **cubic polynomial** is an equation of the third degree, and typical cubic equations include

$$y = ax^3$$

$$y = ax^3 + bx^2$$

$$y = ax^3 + bx^2 + cx$$

$$y = ax^3 + bx^2 + cx + d$$

A **cubic equation** is one in which the polynomial is equated to zero, such as

$$2x^3 - 7x - 3 = 0$$

Typical graphs for cubic expressions are shown in Figure 9.15.

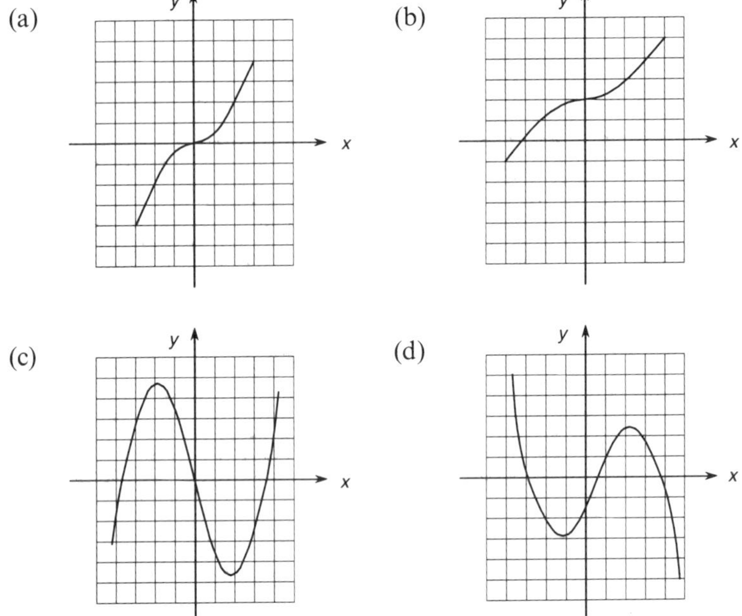

Figure 9.15 Graphs of cubic equations

In general (though not in every case), a cubic graph has two turning points, and the y-intercept is given by the value of parameter d in the expression $y = ax^3 + bx^2 + cx + d$. For example, in the expression $y = 2x^3 - 7x + 3$, the y-intercept occurs at $y = 3$.

The roots of a cubic equation are given by the value(s) of x where the graph cuts the x-axis. Simultaneous equations involving cubic equation(s) can be solved by plotting the equations on the same piece of graph paper, the solution(s) being given by the x-values where the graphs intersect.

9.12 Graph of the law of the form $y = Ax^n$

In earlier sections we have looked at simple cases of a law of the form $y = Ax^n$, i.e., when $n = 1$ (a simple straight-line graph), when $n = 2$ (a quadratic), when $n = 3$ (a cubic) and when $n = -1$ (inverse proportionality).

However, when n is a decimal fraction, such as $n = 2.5$, the graph is a curve whose form we cannot easily identify. In particular, when we obtain experimental results from a device whose law is of the form $y = Ax^n$, and we need to determine both A and n, we must use techniques other than those described hitherto.

In Worked Example 9.7, we will look at a basic method of plotting a graph of the form $y = Ax^n$, and in Worked Example 9.8 we investigate a method of determining A and n from a set of experimental results.

Worked Example 9.7

Draw a graph of the equation $y = 4x^{2.5}$ over the range $x = 0$ to $x = 3$.

Solution

We must first produce a table of results over the specified range of values. This is relatively easy if your calculator has an x^y key but, for the moment, we will assume that this facility is not available to you. However, it is assumed that you either have a table of common logarithms, or you can look them up using a calculator. Since the law is of the form

$$y = Ax^n$$

we can take common logarithms of both sides, giving

$$\begin{aligned}\log y &= \log(Ax^n) = \log x^n + \log A \\ &= n \log x + \log A\end{aligned}$$

The resulting table for $y = 4x^{2.5}$, where $A = 4$ and $n = 2.5$, over the range $x = 0$ to $x = 3$ is given in Table 9.6, and the graph is plotted from these results in Figure 9.16.

TABLE 9.6 Table for solution to Worked Example 9.7

x	0	0.5	1	1.5	2	2.5	3
$\log x$	$-\infty$	−0.301	0	0.1761	0.301	0.3979	0.4771
$2.5 \log x$	$-\infty$	−0.7526	0	0.4402	0.7526	0.9949	1.1928
$\log 4$	0.602	0.602	0.602	0.602	0.602	0.602	0.602
$\log y$	$-\infty$	−0.1506	0.602	1.0422	1.3546	1.5969	1.7948
y	0	0.707	4	11.02	22.62	39.52	62.35

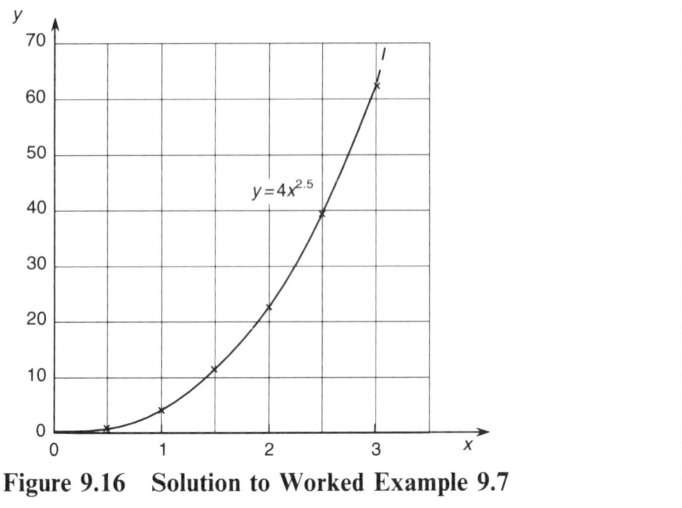

Figure 9.16 Solution to Worked Example 9.7

Worked Example 9.8

The following values of voltage, v, and current, i, were obtained from a test on a semiconductor device

v (V)	1.0	2.0	3.0	4.0	6.0	8.0
i (mA)	0.6	1.48	2.55	3.75	6.5	9.5

Assuming that the law of the device is $i = Av^n$, determine the value of A and n.

Solution

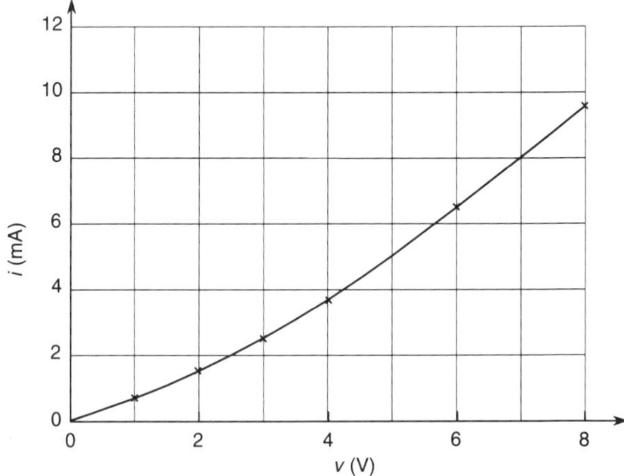

Figure 9.17 Graph for the $v - i$ values in Worked Example 9.8

The graph is plotted in Figure 9.17 and, quite clearly, it is a non-linear curve. Given that the law is of the form $i = Av^n$, we can determine the law using either of two types of graph paper. We can use *linear graph paper* (that is normal squared graph paper), or a *logarithmic scaled graph paper* (that is log-log graph paper).

Use of linear graph paper

As mentioned in Worked Example 9.7, when the law of the graph is of the form $i = Av^n$, we can take common logarithms of both sides and represent the law of the graph in the form

$$\log i = n \log v + \log A$$

Taking logarithms of the values in the table in Worked Example 9.8, we get the following results

$\log v$	0	0.301	0.477	0.602	0.778	0.903
$\log i$	−0.22	0.17	0.407	0.574	0.813	0.98

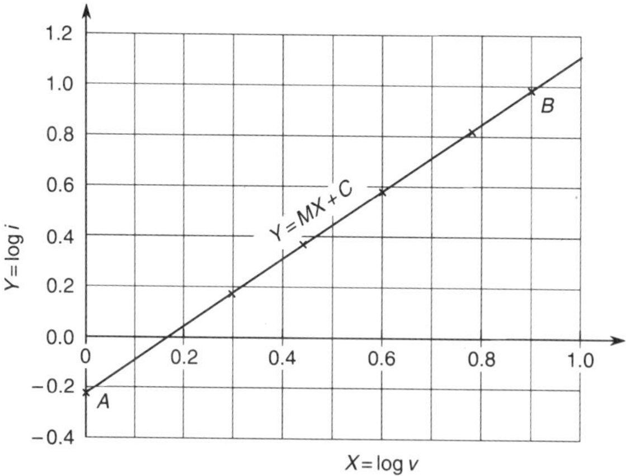

Figure 9.18 Using linear graph paper with logarithmic scales marked on it

When these values are plotted on a piece of linear graph paper, we get the graph in Figure 9.18, and all of the points lie on a straight line (or nearly so!). We can re-write the above equation in the form

$$Y = MX + C$$

which is the equation of a straight line in which M is the gradient and C the vertical intercept. In this case

$$Y = \log i$$
$$M = n$$
$$X = \log v$$
$$C = \log A$$

Clearly, when we plot Y to a base of X (that is $\log i$ to a base of $\log v$), the gradient of the graph is M ($= n$ in the earlier equation), and the Y-axis intercept is C ($= \log A$ in the earlier equation). Taking points A (0, −0.22) and B (0.903, 0.98) in Figure 9.18, we see that the gradient of the graph is

$$M = \frac{0.98 - (-0.22)}{0.903 - 0} = 1.33 = n$$

and the vertical intercept is

$$C = -0.22 = \log A$$

or

$$A = 10^{-0.22} = 0.6$$

That is, the law of the graph is

$$i = 0.6v^{1.33}$$

Use of log-log paper

Special paper is available marked with logarithmic scales, and the use of this paper avoids the need for use to take logarithms of the table of results in Worked Example 9.8.

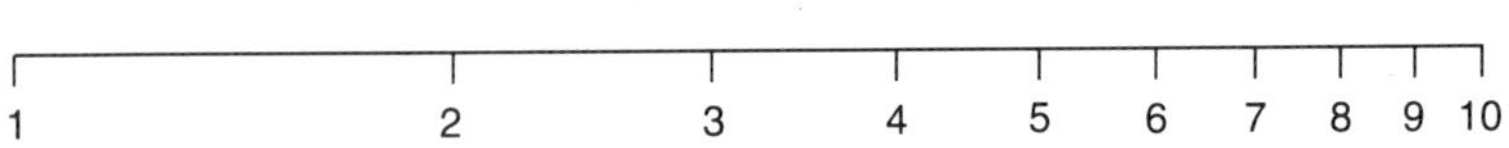

Figure 9.19 Logarithmic scale divisions

A typical logarithmic scale is shown in Figure 9.19, and the distance along the scale is proportional to the logarithm of the value. Thus, if the distance between 1 and 10 in Figure 9.19 is taken as 1 unit, then the value 2 is positioned at $\log 2 = 0.301$ along it, 4 is positioned at $\log 4 = 0.602$ along it, and so on.

The scale markings are from 1 to 9, and the pattern is repeated several times both (in the case of log-log paper) along the x- and y-scales. Each time the scale 1 - 9 appears it is described as **one cycle** or **one decade**. For example, if the scale 1–9 is repeated twice in the x-direction and twice in the y-direction, the graph paper is described as 'Log 2 cycles × 2 cycles'; if it is repeated twice along the x-axis and once along the y-axis it is called 'Log 2 cycles × 1 cycle', etc.

In the case of log-log paper, we write down the *numerical value* from the table in Worked Example 9.8 by the side of the logarithmic scale, the logarithmic scale effectively converting the number into a logarithm. Since the voltage (v) in the table alters in value from 1.0 to 8.0, we only need 1 cycle in the x-direction; the current (i) changes from 0.6 mA, through 1.0 mA to 9.5 mA, and we need 2 cycles in the y-direction to plot the results.

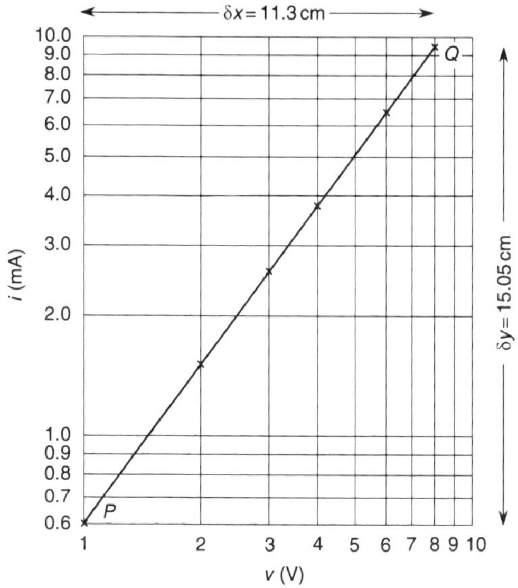

Figure 9.20 Log-log plot, Worked Example 9.8

The graph is plotted in Figure 9.20 directly from the original table of values for v and i. There are two methods of determining the value of A and n for the law $i = Av^n$.

One method is to determine the slope directly from the graph as follows. We see in Figure 9.20 that $\delta x = 11.3$ cm and $\delta y = 15.05$ cm, hence

$$\text{gradient, } n = \delta y/\delta x = 15.05/11.3 = 1.33$$

Remembering that the y-intercept on a normal linear graph is determined at the point where $x = 0$, the equivalent x-axis point on a log-log graph is when $x = 1$ (because $\log 1 = 0$!) Hence the y-intercept on our log-log graph is measured when $x = 1$ and is

$$A = y - \text{intercept} = 0.6$$

That is

$$i = 0.6v^{1.33}$$

which agrees with the result obtained when we plotted the graph using linear graph paper.

The above method is suitable for the determination of A if $x = 1$ is available on the x-scale. If this is not the case, then the method described below can be used.

In the second method, we take any two well-separated values on the straight line. Let us take points P (1, 0.6) and Q (8, 9.5), and write the two equations which satisfy them as follows.

For point P we have

$$0.6 = A \times 1^n$$

and for point Q

$$9.5 = A \times 8^n \tag{9.3}$$

Dividing the second of these by the first gives

$$\frac{9.5}{0.6} = \frac{A \times 8^n}{A \times 1^n} = 8^n$$

or

$$15.83 = 8^n$$

Taking common logarithms of both sides yields

$$\log 15.83 = n \log 8$$

that is

$$n = \log 15.83 / \log 8 = 1.33$$

Substituting this value into (9.3) gives

$$9.5 = A \times 8^{1.33} = 15.89A$$

or

$$A = 9.5/15.89 = 0.6$$

that is

$$i = 0.6v^{1.33}$$

9.13 Law of the form $y = Ax^n + B$

Some types of apparatus have a law of the form $y = Ax^n + B$, where *n is a known value*. For example, the resistance of a tungsten-filament lamp follows a law of the form $R = AV^2 + B$, where V is the voltage applied to the lamp. If we write this type of equation in the form

$$y = AX + B$$

which is a straight line in terms of X and y, we can plot the graph and determine the value of A and B; in this case $X = x^n$. Consider Worked Example 9.9.

Worked Example 9.9

In a test on a new type of semiconductor device, the following values of voltage (v) and current (i) were obtained.

v	1.0	1.5	2.0	2.45	3.0
i	0.75	1.1	1.48	2.04	2.75

It is thought that the law relating v and i is of the form $i = Av^2 + B$. What are the probable values of A and B?

Solution

Since we know the form of the law which relates v and i, we can reduce it to the form

$$i = Av^2 + B = AX + B$$

where $X = v^2$. Accordingly, we list X and i in Table 9.7, and plot X to a base of i in Figure 9.21.

TABLE 9.7 Table for solution to Worked Example 9.9

v	1.0	1.5	2.0	2.45	3.0
X $(= v^2)$	1.0	2.25	4.0	6.0	9.0
i	0.75	1.1	1.48	2.04	2.75

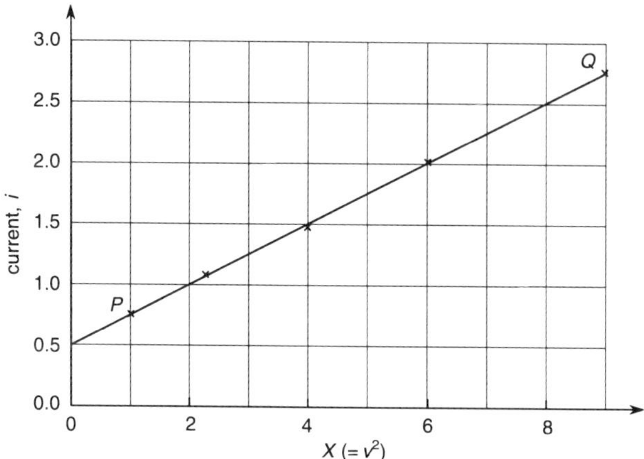

Figure 9.21 Solution to Worked Example 9.9

The results are subject to experimental error, and a suitable straight line is drawn in Figure 9.21. We see that the i-intercept (or y-intercept) at $X = 0$ is $i = 0.5$, so that parameter $B = 0.5$.

The gradient can be calculated from the value of two well-separated points on the line. Let us take points P (1, 0.75) and Q (9, 2.75); the slope is calculated as follows

$$\text{slope, } A = \frac{\delta i}{\delta X} = \frac{i_2 - i_1}{X_2 - X_1} = \frac{2.75 - 0.75}{9 - 1} = \frac{2}{8}$$
$$= 0.25$$

Hence the law of the device is of the form

$$i = 0.25v^2 + 0.5$$

9.14 Plotting and sketching an exponential curve of the form $y = Ae^{-t/\tau}$

An **exponential function** is one containing the expression e^{ax}, where e is the base of Naperian logarithms ($e = 2.71828\ldots$), a is a constant, and x is a variable which, in many electrical problems, is time. Many laws of growth and decay in engineering systems (see also Chapter 14) contain exponential functions, and we need to appreciate the way in which the law controls the response of systems.

Not only do we need to be able to plot these curves accurately, but we also need to be able to visualise and sketch them with some facility. By the end of this chapter, the reader will be able to do this.

Many quantities in electrical and electronic circuits are controlled by exponential laws, including the charge and discharge of capacitors, the rise and decay of current in inductive circuits, etc.

At the moment we will concentrate on the exponential expression

$$y = Ae^{-t/\tau}$$

where A is a constant, t is time, and τ is a **time constant** of a circuit. Since both t and τ have dimensions of time, the ratio t/τ is dimensionless. In electrical and electronic circuits, the value of τ depends on the resistance of a circuit together with the capacitance or the inductance of a circuit. In a resistor-capacitor circuit, the time constant of the circuit is given by

$$\tau = RC \text{ seconds}$$

where R is in ohms, and C is in farads. In a resistor-inductor circuit, the time constant is

$$\tau = L/R$$

where R is in ohms and L in henrys.

Let us look for the moment at the graph for the expression

$$y = 10e^{-0.5t}$$

in which $\tau = 1/0.5 = 2$. If t is in seconds then $\tau = 2\,\text{s}$, if t is measured in minutes then $\tau = 2\,\text{min}$, etc. Let us assume for the moment that $\tau = 2\,\text{s}$. The value of y over a 12 s period of time commencing from $t = 0$ is given in Table 9.8, and the corresponding graph of y plotted to a base of time is shown in Figure 9.22.

TABLE 9.8 Data for the graph of $y = 10e^{-0.5t}$

t	0	2.0	4.0	6.0	8.0	10.0	12.0
$-0.5t$	0	−1.0	−2.0	−3.0	−4.0	−5.0	−6.0
$e^{-0.5t}$	1	0.386	0.135	0.05	0.018	0.007	0.002
y	10	3.68	1.35	0.5	0.18	0.07	0.02

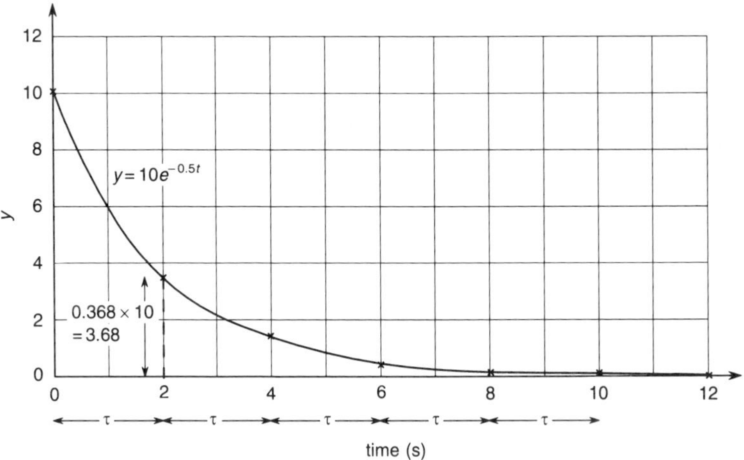

Figure 9.22 Graph of $y = e^{-0.5t}$

Whilst this may seem to be a complex curve, in fact it is a relatively simple curve to sketch because

> **an exponential curve changes by the same proportion for equal time intervals (or equal 'x' intervals).**

For example the curve starts at the value of 10, and diminishes in value to 3.68 after a time interval of τ, i.e., it changes by a factor of 0.368 for each interval of τ. The above rule for exponentially falling curves says that the curve will change by another 0.368 after the next τ seconds. That is, after 2τ seconds from the start of the curve the value of y is

$$10 \times 0.368 \times 0.368 = 1.35$$

and after another τ seconds (i.e., $t = 3\tau$) its value is

$$10 \times 0.368 \times 0.368 \times 0.368 = 0.05, \text{ etc.}$$

In fact, we can define the *time constant* of the system as

the time taken for the value of y to fall to 0.368 of its initial value.

Fortunately, there is an even easier way of being able to sketch the curve, because after a time of approximately 0.7τ the value of y falls to 0.5 of its initial value. Taking τ to be 2 s, then $0.7\tau = 0.7 \times 2 = 1.4$ s; the value of y after the first 1.4 s is therefore

$$10 \times 0.5 = 5$$

In the following 0.7τ interval the value of y falls by a factor of 0.5 again, so that after 2.8 s the value of y is

$$10 \times 0.5 \times 0.5 = 2.5$$

and by $3 \times 0.7\tau = 2.1\tau = 4.2$ s the value of y is

$$10 \times 0.5 \times 0.5 \times 0.5 = 1.25, \text{ etc.}$$

Using this technique, it becomes a very simple procedure to sketch a falling exponential curve, and this is shown in Figure 9.23. In fact, the author uses this technique when sketching exponential curves.

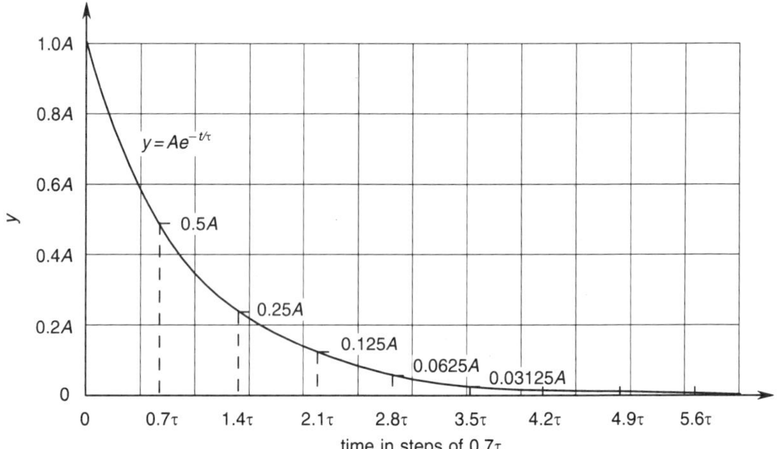

Figure 9.23 A simple method of sketching a decaying exponential curve

9.15 Settling-time of $y = Ae^{-t/\tau}$

A **transient** is a condition which occurs for a very short period of time, usually when a circuit is either switched on or is switched off, and engineers need to know several things about transients in circuits.

Firstly, we need to know how long it takes for the transient to **settle down** or **settle out**. With a falling exponential curve, the transient is said to have settled when the value of y has fallen to about 1 per cent of its initial value, i.e., to about $0.01A$ for the equation $y = Ae^{-t/\tau}$. We can calculate the settling time for the falling exponential transient from the equation

$$0.01A = Ae^{-t/\tau}$$

where t is the time taken for y to fall to $0.01A$. Cancelling A on both sides of the equation gives

$$0.01 = e^{-t/\tau} = 1/e^{t/\tau}$$

that is

$$e^{t/\tau} = 1/0.01 = 100$$

Taking naperian logarithms of both sides of the equation gives

$$\frac{t}{\tau}\ln e = \ln 100 = 4.61$$

but since $\ln e = 1$, then

$$\frac{t}{\tau} = 4.61$$

or

$$t = 4.61\tau$$

That is, the transient has settled out in a time of 4.61τ. Most engineers err on the conservative side and say that **it takes 5τ for the transient to have settled out**. That is, if $\tau = 2$ s, we say that the transient has decayed to an insignificant value after $5 \times 2 = 10$ s.

The period of time taken for the transient to settle out is known as the **transient period**, after which the system enters its **steady-state operating period** (this is illustrated in Figure 9.24).

9.16 Fall-time of $y = Ae^{-t/\tau}$

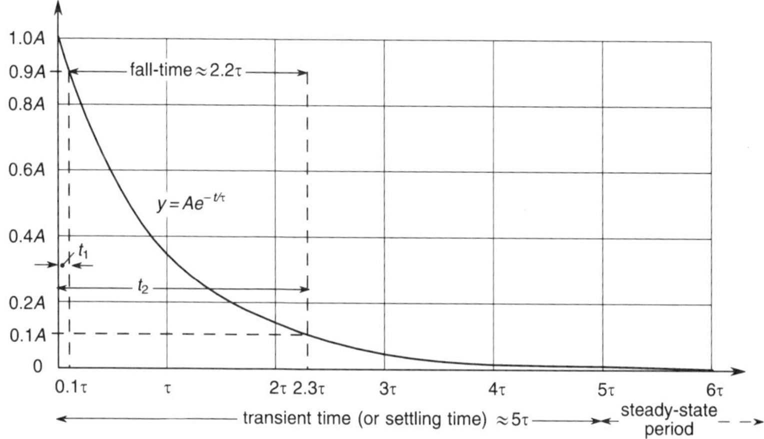

Figure 9.24 The settling-time and fall-time of $y = e^{-t/\tau}$

The **fall-time** of a decaying curve is defined in engineering terminology as **the time taken for y to fall from 90 per cent to 10 per cent of its original value**.

We can determine this period of time by reference to Figure 9.24, in which t_1 is the time taken for y to fall to $0.9A$, and t_2 is the time taken for y to fall from $1.0A$ to $0.1A$. The time taken for y to fall to 0.9 A is determined from the equation

$$0.9A = Ae^{-t_1/\tau}$$

that is

$$0.9 = e^{-t_1/\tau} = 1/e^{t_1/\tau}$$

or

$$e^{t_1/\tau} = 1/0.9 = 1.1111$$

Taking Naperian logarithms of both sides of the equation gives

$$\frac{t_1}{\tau}\ln e = \ln 1.1111 \approx 0.1$$

hence

$$t_1 \approx 0.1\tau$$

The time taken for y to fall from $1.0A$ to $0.1A$ is t_2, where

$$0.1A = Ae^{-t_2/\tau}$$

Solving for t_2 in much the same way we did for t_1 gives

$$t_2 \approx 2.3\tau$$

and the fall-time of the decaying exponential curve is

$$t_f = t_2 - t_1 \approx 2.3\tau - 0.1\tau = 2.2\tau$$

and is shown in Figure 9.24.

Worked Example 9.10

A capacitor is initially charged to 50 V. It discharges into a circuit, the voltage decay follows a law of the form

$$v = 50e^{-t/0.01}$$

Calculate (a) the settling time of the voltage across the capacitor, (b) the fall-time of the capacitor voltage, (c) the capacitor voltage 2 ms after the discharge commences and (d) the time taken for the voltage across the capacitor to fall to 10 V.

Solution

(a) Since the law of the discharge is $v = 50e^{-t/0.01}$, it follows that the circuit time constant is

$$\tau = 0.01 \text{ s or } 10 \times 10^{-3} \text{ s (10 ms)}$$

Since the settling time is about 5τ, then

$$\text{settling time} = 5 \times 10 \text{ ms} = 50 \text{ ms or } 0.05 \text{ s}$$

After this period of time, we can assume that the capacitor is fully discharged.

(b) The fall-time of the capacitor voltage is

$$t_f = 2.2\tau = 2.2 \times 10 \text{ ms} = 22 \text{ ms}$$

This is the time taken for the capacitor voltage to fall from $0.9 \times 50 = 45\,\text{V}$ to $0.1 \times 50 = 5\,\text{V}$.

(c) When $t = 2\,\text{ms}$, the voltage across the capacitor is

$$v = 50e^{-t/\tau} = 50e^{-0.002/0.01} = 50e^{-0.2} = 40.94 \text{ V}$$

(d) Since $v = Ve^{-t/\tau} = V/e^{t/\tau}$, then

$$e^{t/\tau} = V/v = 50/10 = 5$$

Taking Naperian logarithms of both sides of the equation gives

$$\frac{t}{\tau}\ln e = \ln 5 = 1.609$$

but since $\ln e = 1$, then

$$t = 1.609\,\tau = 1.609 \times 10 \text{ ms} = 16.09 \text{ ms}$$

9.17 Plotting and sketching a curve of the form $y = A(1 - e^{-t/\tau})$

The equation $y = A(1 - e^{-t/\tau})$ is typical of an exponential 'growth' curve (see Figure 9.25), such as the rise in voltage across the terminals of a capacitor when it is being charged from a d.c. source, or in the rise of current in an inductor when it is connected to a d.c. supply. Once again, A is a fixed numerical value, $e = 2.71828\ldots$, t is time and τ is the time constant of a circuit.

Let us look at a graph whose equation is

$$y = 10(1 - e^{-t/2}) = 10(1 - e^{-0.5t})$$

where $A = 10$ and $\tau = 2$ (which is usually in seconds). A table corresponding to the time range $t = 0$ to 12 seconds is given in Table 9.9, and the corresponding graph is drawn in Figure 9.25.

TABLE 9.9 Table of results for the graph in Figure 9.25

t	0	2.0	4.0	6.0	8.0	10.0	12.0
$-0.5t$	0	−1.0	−2.0	−3.0	−4.0	−5.0	−6.0
$e^{-0.5t}$	1	0.386	0.135	0.05	0.018	0.007	0.002
$1 - e^{-0.5t}$	0	0.632	0.865	0.95	0.982	0.993	0.998
y	0	6.32	8.65	9.5	8.82	9.93	9.98

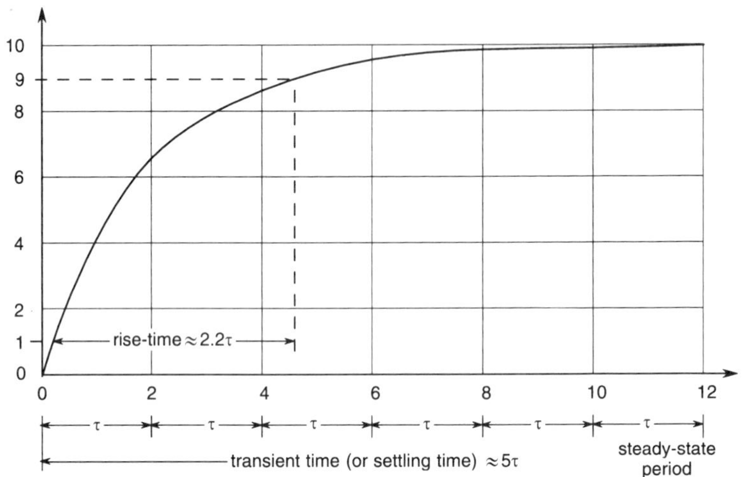

Figure 9.25 The graph of $y = 10(1 - e^{t/\tau})$

It can be seen from the graph that the final value of y approaches 10 as t becomes very large. We can prove this to be the case by putting $t = \infty$ in the equation for y, as follows. If y_∞ is the value of y when $t = \infty$, then

$$\begin{aligned} y_\infty &= 10(1 - e^{-0.5\times\infty}) = 10(1 - e^{-\infty}) \\ &= 10(1 - 1/e^{\infty}) = 10(1 - 0) = 10 \end{aligned}$$

That is, **the final value of the equation $y = A(1-e^{-t/\tau})$ is equal to A.**

Also, we can see from the graph that y rises from zero to 63.2 per cent of its final value in the first period of τ (= 2 s in Table 9.9). As with other exponential curves, **a curve of exponential growth changes by the same proportion during equal time intervals.**

That is, in the first period equal to τ it grows by 63.2 per cent of the final value, in the second period it grows by 63.2 per cent of the difference between its initial value (i.e., $0.632A$) and the final value, and so on.

For example, if $A = 10$ then in the first period of τ it grows to $0.632A$ (= 6.32), in the next period of τ it grows by $0.632(1 - 0.632)A = 0.233A$ so that the value of y at the end of this period is $(0.632 + 0.233)A = 0.865A$ = 8.65 (see $t = 4$ s in Table 9.9). In the next period of τ the value of y grows by $0.632(1 - 0.632)(1 - 0.632)A = 0.085A$, and the value of y when $t = 3\tau$ is $(0.632 + 0.233 + 0.085)A = 0.95A = 9.5$ (see $t = 6$ s in Table 9.9), etc.

Once again, it is possible to simplify the curve sketching process, since the value of y grows by 50 per cent for each 0.7τ period (the reader will find it an interesting exercise to verify this fact). The following table of results shows how this happens

t	y
0	0
0.7τ	$0.5A$
1.4τ	$0.75A$
2.1τ	$0.875A$
2.8τ	$0.9375A$
3.5τ	$0.9688A$
4.2τ	$0.9844A$
4.9τ	$0.9922A$
5.5τ	$0.9961A$

To sketch a growing exponential curve quickly and accurately, it is merely necessary to divide the time base into 0.7τ intervals, and *mark points of 50 per cent of the remaining magnitude between the starting point of the period and the final value.*

Using the engineering assumption that the transient has 'completely' decayed when y has reached 99 per cent of its final value, then we can say that the transient has **settled out** or **settled down** in a period of about 5τ (see the above table of values). This is known as the **settling time** of the transient.

The **rise-time** of the curve is defined as the time taken for it to rise from 10 per cent to 90 per cent of its final value. Analysing the equation shows that it takes a time of about 0.1τ to rise to 10 per cent of its final value, and 2.3τ to rise to 90 per cent. That is, the rise-time of the curve is

$$\text{rise-time, } t_r = 2.3\tau - 0.1\tau = 2.2\tau$$

Worked Example 9.11

The current in an inductor which is suddenly connected to a d.c. supply rises exponentially according to the law $i = 10(1 - e^{-0.1t})$ A, where t is in seconds and i is in amperes. What is (a) the time constant of the circuit, (b) the settling time of the transient, (c) the rise-time of the transient curve, (d) the current in the inductor 4 s after the instant that the supply is connected and (e) the time taken for the current to reach 8 A?

Solution

(a) The equation of the transient is

$$i = 10(1 - e^{-0.1t}) = 10(1 - e^{-t/\tau})$$

That is

$$-0.1t = -t/\tau$$

or

$$0.1 = 1/\tau$$

hence

$$\tau = 10\,\text{s}$$

(b) The settling time of the transient is

$$5\tau = 5 \times 10 = 50\,\text{s}$$

so that steady-state operating conditions are reached after 50 s.

(c) The rise-time of the transient curve is

$$t_r = 2.2\tau = 2.2 \times 10 = 22\,\text{s}$$

(d) The current in the circuit when $t = 4$ s is

$$i = 10(1 - e^{-0.1\times 4}) = 10(1 - e^{-0.4})$$
$$= 10(1 - 0.67) = 3.3\,\text{A}$$

(e) If $i = 8$ A when $t = t_1$, then

$$8 = 10(1 - e^{-0.1t_1})$$

or

$$1 - e^{-0.1t_1} = 8/10 = 0.8$$

giving

$$e^{-0.1t_1} = 1 - 0.8 = 0.2$$

that is

$$e^{0.1t_1} = 1/0.2 = 5$$

Taking natural logarithms of both sides of the equation gives

$$0.1t_1 \ln e = \ln 5 = 1.609$$

but since $\ln e = 1$, then

$$t_1 = 1.609/0.1 = 16.09\,\text{s}$$

Self-test questions

9.1 A straight-line graph passes through points $(-2, -4)$, $(4, 8)$. What is the equation of the graph?

9.2 One straight-line graph passes through the points $(-2, 1)$, $(2, 5)$, and another passes through the points $(-2, -3)$, $(2, 1)$. What is the equation of each graph, and what is the y-intercept in each case?

9.3 Determine the gradient and y-intercept of the following graphs: (a) $x + 3 - 5y = 0$, (b) $x = 7 + 4y$.

9.4 In a test on an electric motor the following results were obtained.

Speed N (rev/min)	300	600	900	1200	1500
V (volts)	61	118	182	241.5	299

Determine the equation relating N and V, making N the dependent variable. Calculate the speed of the motor in rev/s when V is (a) 80 V, (b) 250 V.

9.5 The terminal voltage, V, of an electronic power supply unit is given by $V = E - RI$, where E and R are constants. Under test conditions it is found that when $I = 2$ A then $V = 9.8$ V, and when $I = 10$ A then $V = 9$ V. Plot the graph and determine the value of E and R.

9.6 Solve graphically for x and y between the following simultaneous equations: $y = 6 + 2x$ and $y = 3x - 3$.

9.7 Solve the following quadratic equations graphically: (a) $6x^2 + 11x - 10 = 0$, (b) $6 = 5x^2 - 7x$, (c) $x^2 - 5x = 24$, (d) $3x^2 - 7x = 2$.

9.8 Solve graphically $y = x^2$ and $y = 4x + 15$.

9.9 Plot the graphs of (a) $2x^3 - 9x^2 + 3x + 14 = 0$, (b) $x^3 - 6x + 3 = 0$.

9.10 Two values are related by an equation of the form $y = ax + b$. The following values were obtained for x and y

x	−1	0		2.5	3		9
y			7	13		28	52

Determine the law relating x and y, and also the missing values in the table.

9.11 The breakdown voltage, V kV, of an insulator and its thickness, T mm, are thought to be related by an equation of the form $V = kT^n$, where k and n are constants. If the following values were obtained under test conditions, determine the value of k and n.

T (mm)	4	7	15	22
V (kV)	283	430	762	1016

9.12 The total iron loss, P, of a transformer is related to the frequency, f, by the equation $P = k_1 f + k_2 f^2$. If the following values were obtained on a test on the transformer, determine the value of k_1 and k_2 by plotting P/f to a base of f (this gives a graph of the form $y = mx + c$, where $y = P/f$, $m = k_2$, $x = f$ and $c = k_1$).

f (Hz)	25	50	75	100	125
P (W)	5.65	17.5	35.65	60	90.63

9.13 The pressure, p, and the volume, v, of a gas are connected by the equation $C = pv^n$, where C and n are constants. Given the following values, plot a suitable graph to determine the value of C and n.

v	5	7	9	11	13
p	54.6	34.1	24.0	18.1	14.34

9.14 A voltage pulse of amplitude 5 V is applied to an inductive circuit with a time constant of 5 ms. If the steady-state current in the circuit is 50 mA, draw a curve of the current to a base of time if the equation is given by $i = I(1 - e^{-t/\tau})$, where I is the steady-state current in the circuit. Also determine the current in the coil 1.6 ms after the supply is connected.

9.15 A fully charged capacitor is discharged through a resistor, the time constant of the discharge path being 10 s. The voltage across the capacitor is given by the expression $v_c = Ee^{-t/\tau}$, where E is the initial voltage across the capacitor. Draw the graph of v_c, and determine the time taken for the voltage across the capacitor to fall to (a) 50 per cent, (b) 36.8 per cent and (c) 5 per cent of its initial value.

Summary of important facts

A **graph** shows how one **variable** changes with another. For example, if the equation of a graph is $A = \pi r^2$, r is the **independent variable** and A the **dependent variable**.

Graphs are most frequently drawn on axes which are at right-angles to one another, and points drawn on the graph are defined using **rectangular coordinates** or **cartesian coordinates** relative to the **origin** of the coordinate system. The x-coordinate is called the **abscissa** and the y-coordinate the **ordinate**.

A **straight-line graph** has the equation

$$y = mx + c$$

where m is the **gradient** of the line, and c is the **y-axis intercept** or **vertical intercept**. Many experiments give a graph which is thought to give a straight line, but the results are scattered in a random fashion about the mean position of the line. One method of predicting the equation of the 'best' straight line is the **method of least squares**, and the resulting straight line is known as the **line of regression of *X* on *Y*** or the **line of prediction of *Y***.

Two quantities are said to be **linearly related to one another** if the graph of one variable plotted to the base of the other is a straight line. If the graph passes through the origin, the two quantities are **directly proportional to one another**.

If $xy =$ constant, y is **inversely proportional** to x, and the curve of y to a base of x is a **rectangular hyperbola**.

The graph of the **quadratic equation** $y = ax^2 + bx + c$ is a **parabola**. A parabola has a **turning point** (that is the slope of the graph changes from negative to positive, or vice versa) and, in general

1. the larger the value of parameter a, the 'sharper' the turning point,
2. if parameter a has a positive value, the curve is concave looking from above; if a has a positive value, the curve is concave looking from below,
3. parameter b causes the turning point to be shifted along the x-axis, a positive value shifts the turning point to the left,
4. the value of parameter c gives the y-intercept of the parabola,
5. if the parabola cuts the x-axis, the points of intersection with the x-axis give the **roots of the equation** $ax^2 + bx + c = 0$,
6. if the parabola does not cut the x-axis, the roots are 'imaginary' (see Chapter 11 for details).

The **graphical solution to a pair of simultaneous equations** is given by the point(s) where the graphs intersect when they are plotted on the same graph paper.

A **cubic polynomial** is an equation of the *third degree*, and is of the form $y = ax^3 + bx^2 + cx + d$ and, in general, the graph normally has two turning points. A **cubic equation** is a cubic polynomial in which $y = 0$, i.e., $ax^3 + bx^2 + cx + d = 0$; the solution of a cubic equation is given by the point(s) where the graph cuts the x-axis, and the y-axis intercept is given by $y = d$.

A graph of the form $y = Ax^n$ can be solved by plotting the graph on **logarithmic scaled paper** (or linear graph paper which has logarithmic scales on it).

An **exponential function** describes a function containing e^{ax}, where e is the base of Naperian logarithms ($e = 2.71828\ldots$), and a is a constant. In electrical and electronic engineering, we are frequently concerned with graphs whose equations are either of the form

$$y = Ae^{-t/\tau}$$

or

$$y = A(1 - e^{-t/\tau})$$

where A is a constant, t is time and τ is the **time constant** of a circuit. The first of the above equations gives a graph which *decays exponentially* from an initial value of A at $t = 0$, to a zero when t approaches infinity. The second of the above equations produces a graph which *rises exponentially* from zero at $t = 0$ to a value of A when t approaches infinity.

For both types of curve, the **settling time** of the transient is 5τ; the **fall-time** of the falling exponential curve is 2.2τ, and the **rise-time** of the rising exponential curve is 2.2τ.

10 Vectors and phasors

10.1 Introduction

When defining many physical quantities, such as mass, length, area, volume, etc, we are concerned only with their magnitude. These quantities are known as **scalar quantities**. To define some other physical quantities such as force and velocity we need to know the direction in space in which they act; when we need to know both the magnitude and the direction to define a quantity, we are dealing with a **vector quantity**.

In electrical and electronic engineering we meet with quantities in alternating current theory whose magnitude varies sinusoidally with time. Wheras a vector quantity has a fixed magnitude, an alternating quantity varies continuously with time. Fortunately, engineers have devised a method of converting a sinusoidally varying quantity into a 'fixed' quantity, and these are known as **phasor quantities**.

Fortunately, we can manipulate phasors in much the same way that we can manipulate vectors. However, phasors and vectors should not be confused, since a vector quantity has a direction in 'real' space, whilst a phasor is an electrical engineering concept which converts a sinusoidally varying quantity into something which has magnitude and 'direction' (but not in space!). The way in which this is done is described in this chapter.

By the end of this chapter the reader will be able to

- understand the difference between vectors and phasors,
- add and subtract vectors,
- add and subtract phasors,
- calculate the frequency and angular frequency of sinusoidal waves,
- determine the phase relationship between sinusoidal waves,
- understand phasor diagrams.

10.2 Vector addition and subtraction

(a) Resolution of a vector

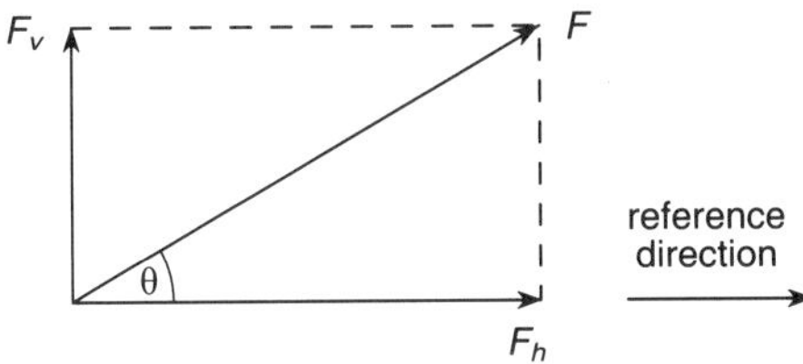

Figure 10.1 Resolving force F into its horizontal and vertical components

A vector can be **resolved** into separate **components** which are at right-angles to one another. Consider force F in Figure 10.1. This can be resolved into two separate components as follows; the component acting in the horizontal direction or **reference direction** is given by

$$F_h = F\cos\theta$$

and the component acting in the vertical direction is

$$F_v = F\sin\theta$$

It follows from Pythagorus's theorem that

$$F = \sqrt{(F_h^2 + F_v^2)}$$

and

$$\tan\theta = \frac{F_v}{F_h}$$

Worked Example 10.1

A force of 200 kN acts on a body at an angle of inclination of 70° to the reference direction. Resolve the force into its reference (horizontal) and quadrature (vertical) components.

Solution

From the above equations, the horizontal component is

$$F_h = F\cos\theta = 200\cos 70^\circ = 68.4\,\text{kN}$$

and the vertical component is

$$F_v = F\sin\theta = 200\sin 70^\circ = 187.9\,\text{kN}$$

Check: $\sqrt{(F_h^2 + F_v^2)} = \sqrt{(68.4^2 + 187.9^2)} = 199.96\,\text{kN}$
The small error of 0.04 kN in the final calculation is due to 'rounding' the values of F_h and F_v to one decimal place.

(b) Addition of vectors

If several vectors act on a body, **the resolved components of the resultant is equal to the sum of the resolved components of the individual vectors**. The magnitude of the sum of the vectors can be obtained by applying Pythagorus's theorem to the result (see Worked Example 10.2).

Worked Example 10.2

Three tugs A, B and C tow an oil platform, and apply the following forces to it

tug A: 18 MN at 10° N of E
tug B: 15 MN at 40° N of E
tug C: 12 MN at 35° S of E

Determine the magnitude and direction of the resultant force acting on the rig.

Solution

The problem can be solved either graphically or mathematically. However, it should be pointed out that, at best, the graphical solution will only be an approximate solution.

Mathematical solution

Using East as the reference direction, we will resolve the forces applied by the tugs in an Easterly (reference direction) and in a North–South (quadrature) direction as follows.

(i) Tug A: The force applied in the Easterly (reference) direction is

$$F_{hA} = 18\cos 10^\circ = 17.73\,\text{MN}$$

and the Northerly (vertically upwards) force is

$$F_{vA} = 18\sin 10^\circ = 3.13\,\text{MN}$$

(ii) Tug B: The force applied in the Easterly (reference) direction is

$$F_{hB} = 15\cos 40^\circ = 11.49\,\text{MN}$$

and the Northerly (vertically upwards) force is

$$F_{vB} = 15\sin 40^\circ = 9.64\,\text{MN}$$

(iii) Tug C: The force applied in the Easterly (reference) direction is

$$F_{hC} = 12\cos 35^\circ = 9.83\,\text{MN}$$

and the Southerly (vertically downwards) force is

$$F_{vC} = 12\sin 35^\circ = 6.88\,\text{MN}$$

In fact, we often consider all forces in the same plane to act in the same direction. That is, force F_{vC} can be thought of as producing a force acting in a Northerly (i.e., vertically upwards) direction. In this case, we consider the angle of action of this force as being -35° relative to the East. This results in the following for tug C:

$$\text{Force acting towards the East} = 12\cos(-35^\circ) = 9.83\,\text{MN}$$

$$\text{Force acting towards the North} = 12\sin(-35^\circ) = -6.88\,\text{MN}$$

The net result of the calculation is the same in both cases. The resultant force acting on the oil rig is

$$\begin{aligned}\text{Force acting towards the East} &= F_{hA} + F_{hB} + F_{hC}\\ &= 17.73 + 11.49 + 9.83\\ &= 39.05\,\text{MN}\end{aligned}$$

$$\begin{aligned}\text{Force acting towards the North} &= F_{vA} + F_{vB} + F_{vC}\\ &= 3.13 + 9.64 + (-6.88)\\ &= 5.89\,\text{MN}\end{aligned}$$

Hence the magnitude of the total force acting on the rig is

$$F = \sqrt{(39.05^2 + 5.89^2)} = 39.49\,\text{MN}$$

The direction of the force relative to the reference direction (East) can be calculated from the following

$$\tan\theta = \frac{\text{vertical (North) force}}{\text{horizontal (East) force}} = \frac{5.89}{39.05} = 0.1508$$

Hence

$$\theta = \arctan 0.1509 = 8.58^\circ \text{ N of E}$$

Graphical solution

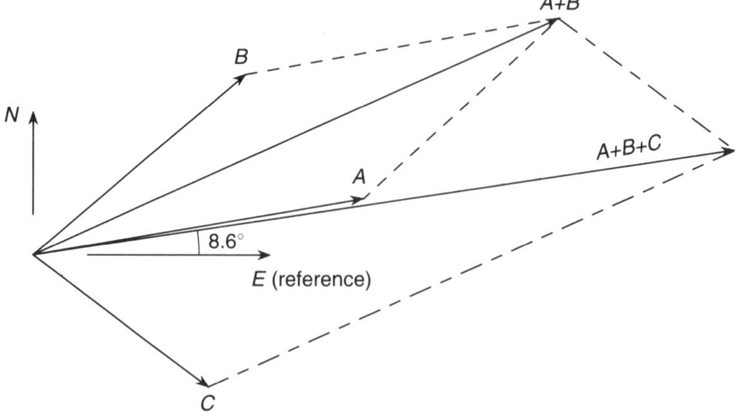

Figure 10.2 Solution to Worked Example 10.2

One method of solving the problem graphically is to add the forces together in pairs as follows. Initially we add the force produced by two of the tugs, say A and B, using the parallelogram of forces to get the force $(A + B)$ in Figure 10.2.

Next we add the vector corresponding to tug C to the force $(A + B)$, giving not only the magnitude of the resultant force $(A + B + C)$ on the oil rig, but also its direction.

It should be pointed out that the forces A, B and C must accurately be drawn to scale and in the correct direction. Any lack of care in doing this means that the answer will be in error.

(c) Subtraction of vectors

To subtract one vector from another, we add the negative value of the vector being subtracted (the subtrahend) to the number it is being subtracted from (the minuend). That is

$$\begin{aligned}\text{vector difference} &= \text{vector } A - \text{vector } B \\ &= \text{vector } A + (-\text{vector } B)\end{aligned}$$

Worked Example 10.3

Two forces act on the frame of a transformer, and the first force has a magnitude of 10 kN acting at an angle of 60° to the reference direction. If the resultant force on the frame is 12 kN at an angle of 15° to the reference direction, determine the magnitude and direction of the second force.

Solution

There are three forces (which are all vector quantities) in this problem, one of which we do not know (we will call this force B). The first force (force A) has a magnitude of 10 kN acting at an angle of 60°, and the resultant force (force R) has a magnitude of 12 kN acting at an angle of 15°. The vector equation connecting the three forces is

$$\text{resultant force} = \text{force } A + \text{force } B$$

that is the vectors are related by

$$\begin{aligned}\text{force } B &= \text{resultant} - \text{force } A \\ &= \text{resultant} + (-\text{force } A)\end{aligned}$$

That is, force B is the vector difference between the resultant force and force A.

Graphical solution

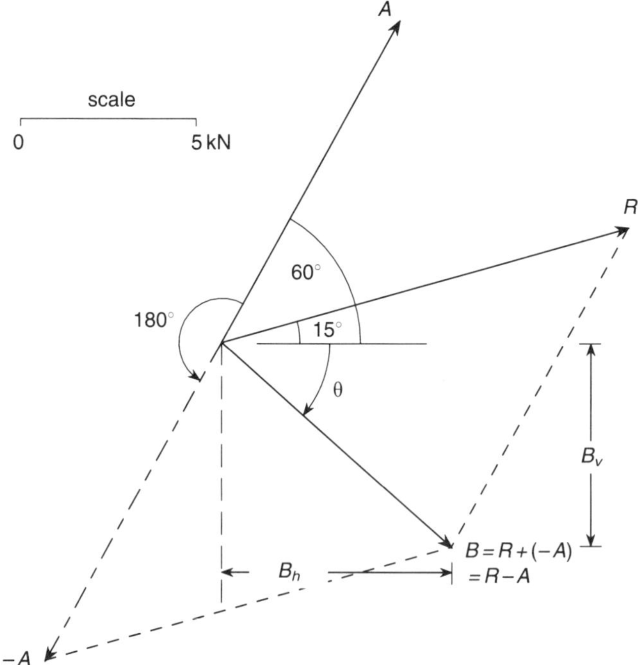

Figure 10.3 Solution to Worked Example 10.3

Force A and the resultant force (force R) are shown in Figure 10.3. Initially we draw (−force A) by rotating force A through 180° (or −180°), and then we *add* (−force A) to the resultant force R to give

$$\begin{aligned} \text{force } B &= \text{force } R + \text{force } (-A) \\ &= \text{force } R - \text{force } A \end{aligned}$$

From Figure 10.3, we measure force B to be 8.65 kN, and its angle of action, θ, is judged to be −40°.

Mathematical solution

Initially we determine the horizontal and vertical components of force as follows.

Force A

$$\text{horizontal component, } A_h = A\cos 60^\circ = 10\cos 60^\circ = 5\,\text{kN}$$

$$\text{vertical component, } A_v = A\sin 60^\circ = 10\sin 60^\circ = 8.66\,\text{kN}$$

Force R

The horizontal and vertical components of the resultant force are

$$\text{horizontal component, } R_h = R\cos 15^\circ = 12\cos 15^\circ = 11.59\,\text{kN}$$

$$\text{vertical component, } R_v = R\sin 15^\circ = 12\sin 15^\circ = 3.1\,\text{kN}$$

Force B

Hence (see Figure 10.3), the horizontal component of force B is

$$B_h = R_h + (-A_h) = 11.59 + (-5) = 6.59\,\text{kN}$$

and the vertical component of force B is

$$B_v = R_v + (-A_v) = 3.1 + (-8.66) = -5.56\,\text{kN}$$

The magnitude of force B is therefore

$$B = \sqrt{(B_h{}^2 + B_v{}^2)} = \sqrt{(6.59^2 + (-5.56^2))} = 8.62\,\text{kN}$$

and angle θ (see Figure 10.3) is calculated from

$$\tan\theta = B_v/B_h = -5.56/6.59 = -0.844$$

hence

$$\theta = \arctan(-0.844) = -40.2^\circ$$

10.3 Phasor representation

The reader will recollect that sinusoidal waves were discussed in Chapter 6, and is reminded that a sinewave is the graph of the vertical displacement of the tip of a line which rotates at a constant speed in an anticlockwise direction. The length of the rotating line is the maximum value of the sinewave, and the speed of the rotating line in rad/s corresponds to the angular frequency of the wave.

A **phasor** is associated with a sinusoidal wave, and is an engineering 'tool' which enables us to describe the magnitude and angle of the line producing the wave at a particular point in time. The point to note about a sinewave is that its value varies continuously, and the phasor notation allows us to 'fix' its magnitude and angle at a point in time (note: a vector defines, say, a force in *space*, whereas a phasor describes, say, a sinusoidal voltage in *time*).

Electrical engineers refer to the **effective value** or **r.m.s. value (root-mean-square value)** – see Chapter 13 for details – of a sinusoidal wave, which is the equivalent d.c. value of the alternating wave so far as heating is concerned. Where the case of a *sinusoidal wave* is concerned, the r.m.s. value of the wave is

$$\text{r.m.s. value} = \frac{\text{maximum value}}{\sqrt{2}}$$
$$= 0.7071 \times \text{maximum value}$$

The reader should note very carefully that the figure of 0.7071 **applies only to a sinusoidal wave**, and does not apply to other waves, i.e., a square wave and a triangular wave have their own r.m.s. 'multiplying factor'.

We can therefore say for a sinewave of peak value V_m its r.m.s. value or effective value is

$$V_{\text{rms}} = 0.7071\, V_m$$

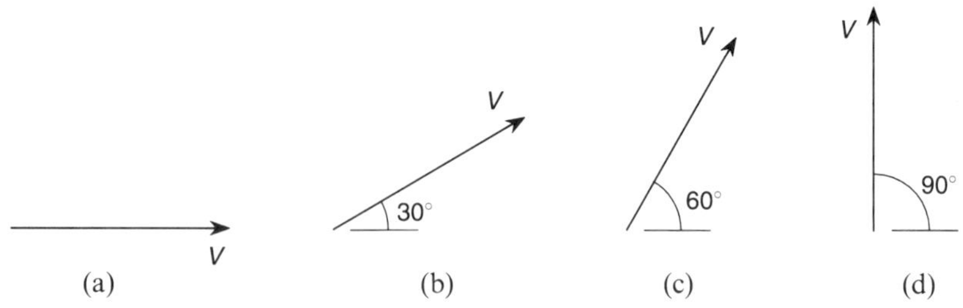

Figure 10.4 Phasor diagram representing a sine wave at (a) $\theta = 0°$, (b) $\theta = 30°$, (c) $\theta = 60°$, (d) $\theta = 90°$

The r.m.s. value is quoted when we refer to the 'value' of an alternating wave. For example, a 250 V sinewave has a maximum value of

$$250 \times \sqrt{2} = 353.6\,\text{V}$$

A sinusoidal current represented by the expression $i = I_m \sin \omega t$ has an r.m.s. voltage of

$$I_{\text{rms}} = 0.7071 I_m$$

To represent a sinewave in phasor form, we simply 'freeze' the wave at a particular point in time (or at a particular phase angle), and draw a line *equal in length to its r.m.s. value at that angle.* This is illustrated in Figure 10.4 corresponding to an angle of (a) 0°, (b) 30°, (c) 60° and (d) 90°. Also, the length (V) of the phasor is equal to the r.m.s. value of the wave.

10.4 Phase relationship between sinewaves

The sinewaves drawn out by the rotating lines V_m and I_m in Figure 10.5(a) commence at the same point, and simultaneously pass through zero at the end of each cycle. That is, the two sinewaves are **in phase with one another**.

Two sinusoidal waves of the same frequency are said to be **out of phase with one another** if they commence at different times. In particular (see Figure 10.5(b)), if i commences before v we say that ***i* leads *v* by angle ϕ_1**.

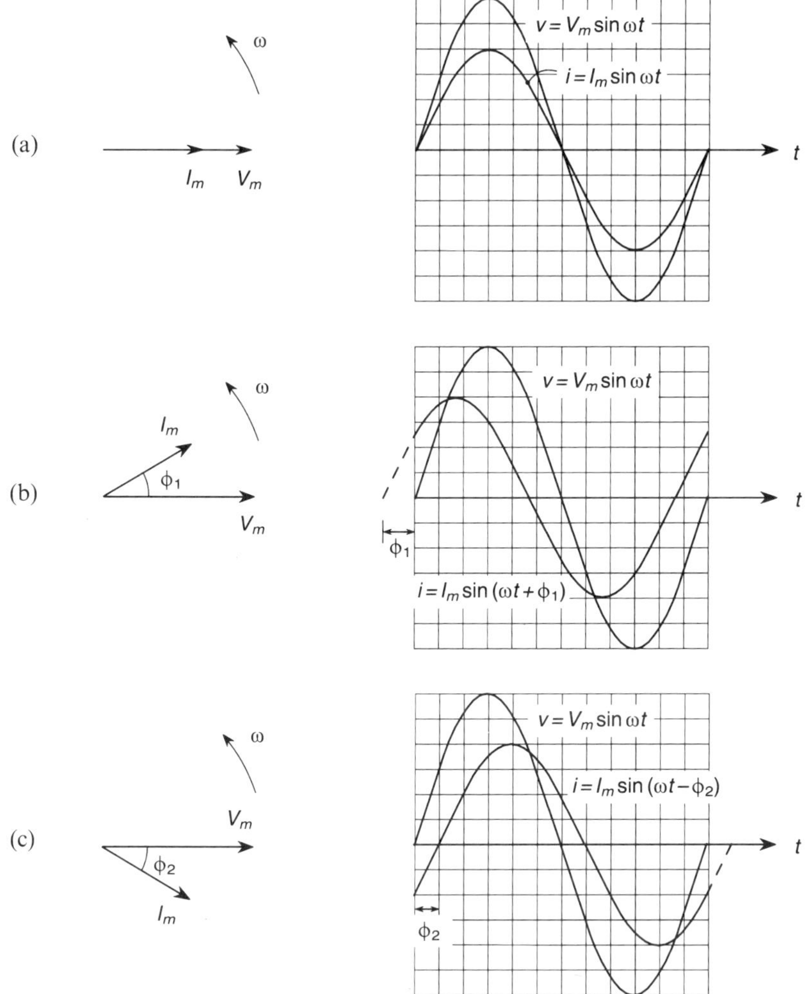

Figure 10.5 (a) *v* and *i* are in phase with one another, (b) *i* leads *v* by ϕ, (c) *v* leads *i* by ϕ

Angle ϕ_1 is known as the **phase angle** between the two waves. In this case there are two possible ways of describing the phase angle. The first is to say that *i leads v by* ϕ_1; the second is to say that *v lags behind i by* ϕ_1. Engineers tend to think of the voltage as being the 'reference quantity' and, in this case, we generally prefer to use the former expression.

If *v* commences its cycle before *i* (see Figure 10.5(c)), we can say that *v leads i by* ϕ_2 or, alternatively, *i lags behind v by* ϕ_2 (oncc again, an engineer may prefer to use the latter statement).

In all three waveforms in Figure 10.5, the voltage waveform starts from zero when $t = 0$ so that, in all three cases we may say that

$$v = V_m \sin \omega t$$

Also, when v and i are in phase with one another (Figure 10.5(a)), we can write

$$i = I_m \sin \omega t$$

When the current leads the voltage by ϕ_1 (Figure 10.5(b)), we can write

$$i = I_m \sin(\omega t + \phi_1)$$

and when i lags behind v by ϕ_2 (Figure 10.5(c)) we can write

$$i = I_m \sin(\omega t - \phi_2)$$

Worked Example 10.4

What is the phase relationship between the following:
(a) $v_1 = 10 \sin \omega t$ and $v_2 = 20 \sin(\omega t - \pi/6)$,
(b) $i = 15 \sin \omega t$ and $v = 4 \cos \omega t$,
(c) $i_1 = 15 \sin(\omega t + 30°)$ and $i_2 = 20 \sin(\omega t - \pi/3)$.

Solution

Some of the phase angles in the problem are given in radians and some in degrees. To simplify matters, we will convert all phase angles to degrees, bearing in mind that $360° \equiv 2\pi$ rad, or 1 rad $\equiv 57.3°$.

(a) Since the phase shift associated with v_1 is zero, we may say that $v_1 = 10 \sin(\omega t + 0°)$. The phase shift associated with v_2 is $-\pi/6$ rad or $-30°$, so that $v_2 = 20 \sin(\omega t - 30°)$. That is

v_2 lags 30° behind v_1 (or v_1 leads v_2 by 30°).

(b) Here the phase shift associated with i is zero, and the waveform for v follows a cosine curve. Since we already know that $\cos\theta = \sin(\theta + 90°)$ (see Chapter 6), then we may write

$$v = \sin(\omega t + 90°)$$

Comparing the expressions for v and i, we see that

v leads i by 90° (or i lags behind v by 90°)

(c) In this case the phase angle associated with i_1 is $+30°$, and that associated with i_2 is $-\pi/3$ or $-60°$. That is

i_1 leads i_2 by 90° (or i_2 lags behind i_1 by 90°)

10.5 Phasor diagrams

A **phasor diagram** shows the line representing the r.m.s. value of sinusoidal waves, together with an associated phase angle. There are many possible phasor diagrams for a given waveform combination, depending on the point in the waveform diagram where we draw the phasor diagram; bearing this fact in mind, each phasor diagram is equivalent so far as magnitude and phase angle is concerned. This is explained in more detail below.

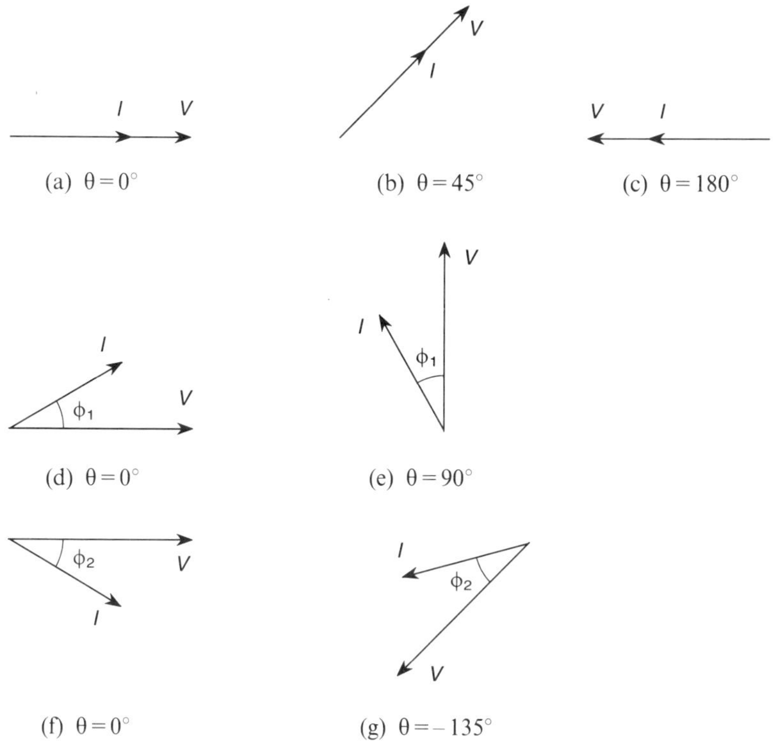

Figure 10.6 (a), (b), (c) possible phasor diagrams representing Figure 10.5(a); (d), (e) possible phasor diagrams representing Figure 10.5(b); (f), (g) possible phasor diagrams representing 10.5(c)

In Figure 10.6 we draw a range of phasor diagrams which will represent the waveform diagrams in Figure 10.5.

If we compare the phasor diagram in Figure 10.6(a) with the waveforms in Figure 10.5(a), we see that the phasors for the voltage and current have been drawn for $\omega t = 0$ (or $\theta = 0$), the phasors merely being the rotating lines in Figure 10.5(a) reduced by a factor of 0.7071 so that they represent the r.m.s. value of the respective wave. Also, the line has been 'frozen' at $t = 0$ or $\omega t = 0$.

If we allow time to progress in Figure 10.5(a) until $\omega t = \pi/4$ or $\theta = 45^\circ$, and 'freeze' the phasors in time once again, we get the phasor diagram in Figure 10.6(b). To all intents and purposes, the phasor diagrams in Figures 10.6(a) and 10.6(b) *are equivalent to one another*, because other events in the circuit, i.e., the voltage across the circuit elements and the current in the circuit have also progressed by the same amount of time. The reader should note that although the phasor diagrams are equivalent to one another, *they are not equal to one another* since they represent events at different times in the circuit.

Next, if we allow time to progress so that $\omega t = \pi$ rad or $\theta = 180^\circ$, we get the phasor diagram in Figure 10.6(c). Once again, we can regard the phasor diagrams in Figures 10.6(a), (b) and (c) as being equivalent to one another. The reader will note that, in all cases, V and I are in phase with one another, and the r.m.s. value of V is always the same, and the r.m.s. value of I is always the same.

Similarly, we see that phasor diagrams (d) and (e) in Figure 10.6 represent the waveform diagram in Figure 10.5(b) at different points in time. Phasor diagrams (f) and (g) in Figure 10.6 also represent the waveform in Figure 10.5(c) at different points in the cycle.

10.6 Addition and subtraction of phasors

As with vectors, phasors can be added or subtracted either graphically or mathematically, both methods being based on the parallelogram addition (or subtraction) technique. Again, it should be pointed out that graphical methods are less accurate than numerical calculations. Also, when adding or subtracting phasors *graphically*, we can only deal with one pair of phasors at a time.

Worked Example 10.5

Two alternating currents enter a node in a circuit, the magnitude and phase angle of the currents being, respectively

$I_1 = 10\,\text{A}$ at -10° to the reference direction,

$I_2 = 20\,\text{A}$ at 15° to the reference direction.

Determine the magnitude and phase angle of the current entering the node.

Solution

We will solve this problem both graphically and by calculation as follows.

Graphical solution

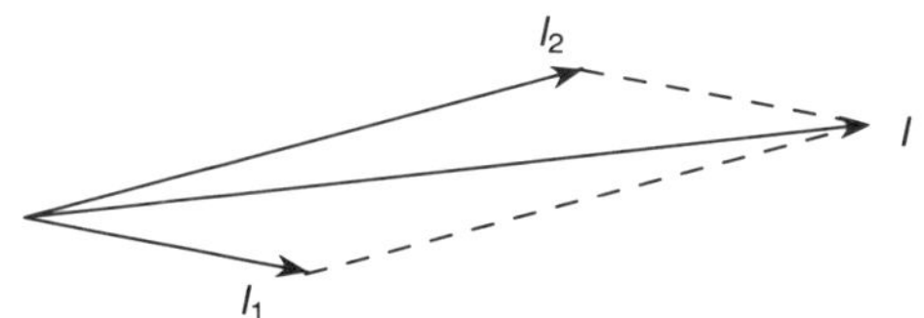

Figure 10.7 Solution of Worked Example 10.5

The two phasors I_1 and I_2 are drawn to scale in Figure 10.7, and the parallelogram completed by dotted lines. The total current, I, is given by the diagonal of the parallelogram, and is measured to be 29.5 A at a phase angle of about 6.5° relative to the reference direction.

The parallelogram must be drawn to give the largest possible diagram, and the length and phase angle of I must be measured very carefully. Although this method may appear to be quick and easy to obtain, in reality it takes just as long as the calculation, and is rather less accurate!

Solution by calculation

The resolved components of the two currents are calculated below. The horizontal or reference component of I_1 is

$$I_{1h} = 10\cos(-10^\circ) = 9.85\,\text{A}$$

and the vertical or quadrature component of I_1 is

$$I_{1v} = 10\sin(-10^\circ) = -1.74\,\text{A}$$

For I_2 the resolved components are

$$I_{2h} = 20\cos 15^\circ = 19.32\,\text{A}$$

$$I_{2v} = 20\sin 15^\circ = 5.18\,\text{A}$$

The horizontal or reference component of the total current, I, entering the node is

$$I_h = I_{1h} + I_{2h} = 9.85 + 19.32 = 29.17\,\text{A}$$

and the vertical component of I is

$$I_v = I_{1v} + I_{2v} = -1.74 + 5.18 = 3.44\,\text{A}$$

hence the magnitude of the total current is

$$I = \surd(29.17^2 + 3.44^2) = 29.37\,\text{A}$$

and its phase angle with relative to the reference direction is

$$\phi = \arctan(I_v/I_h) = \arctan(3.44/29.17)$$
$$- 6.73^\circ$$

Worked Example 10.6

In a three-phase system, the magnitude of the red line to neutral voltage, V_{RN}, is 200 V and its phase angle relative to the reference direction is zero. The magnitude of the yellow line to neutral voltage is 200 V and its phase angle relative to the reference direction is 120°. If the voltage of the red line with respect to the yellow line is given by the *phasor difference*

$$V_{RY} = V_{RN} - V_{YN}$$

determine the magnitude and the phase angle of V_{RY}.

Solution

Once again, we will obtain the result both graphically and by calculation.

Graphical solution

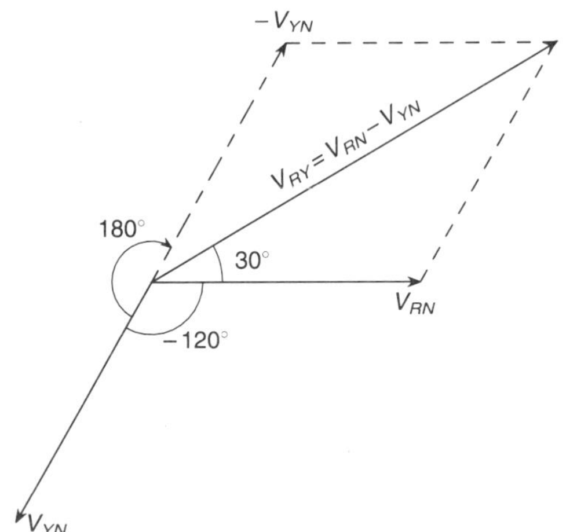

Figure 10.8 Solution of Worked Example 10.6

As with vectors, to subtract one value (the subtrahend) from another value (the minuend), we obtain the 'negative' of the subtrahend (V_{YN}) by rotating it through 180°, and add it to the minuend (V_{RN}). In this case we draw the phasor for V_{YN} (200 V at an angle of $-120°$), and then rotate it through 180° (or $-180°$) to form $-V_{YN}$ as shown in the chain-dotted line in Figure 10.8.

Next, using the conventional parallelogram method, we add V_{RN} to $-V_{YN}$ to give the required voltage V_{RY}. The magnitude of V_{RY} is measured to be 344 V at an angle of 30° relative to the reference direction, that is at $+30°$ to V_{RN}. That is

V_{RY} leads V_{RN} by 30° (or V_{RN} lags behind V_{RY} by 30°)

Solution by calculation

Once again, we must resolve each phasor into its horizontal (reference) component, and its vertical (quadrature) component, and determine the total value of the resolved components. From these values, we can evaluate the magnitude and the phase angle of the resultant voltage.

For V_{RN}

The magnitude of V_{RN} is 200 V and its phase angle relative to the reference direction is 0°, hence

$$\text{horizontal component, } V_{RNh} = 200\cos 0° = 200\,\text{V}$$
$$\text{vertical component, } V_{RNv} = 200\sin 0° = 0\,V$$

For V_{YN}

The magnitude of V_{YN} is 200 V and its phase angle relative to the reference direction is −120°, hence

$$\text{horizontal component, } V_{YNh} = 200\cos(-120°) = -100\,\text{V}$$
$$\text{vertical component, } V_{YNv} = 200\sin(-120°) = -173.2\,\text{V}$$

For V_{RY}

The total horizontal component of V_{RY} is

$$\text{horizontal component, } V_{RYh} = V_{RNh} - V_{YNh} = 200 - (-100) = 300\,\text{V}$$
$$\text{vertical component, } V_{RYv} = V_{RNv} - V_{YNv} = 0 - (-173.2) = 173.2\,\text{V}$$

hence the magnitude of V_{RY} is

$$V_{RY} = \surd(V_{RYh}^2 + V_{RYv}^2) = \surd(300^2 + 173.2^2) = 346.4\,\text{V}$$

and its phase angle relative to the reference direction is

$$\phi = \arctan(V_{RYv}/V_{RYh}) = \arctan(173.2/300) = \arctan 0.577 = 30°$$

That is, V_{RY} has an r.m.s. value of 346.4 V, and leads V_{RN} (which is in the reference direction) by 30°.

10.7 Problems involving more than two vectors or phasors

Many problems in engineering involve several vectors or phasors. For example, in a mechanical problem there may be several forces acting on a structure, and electrical engineers may be concerned with calculating the sum of several phasor voltages or currents.

As mentioned earlier, when dealing with *graphical solutions*, only two vectors or phasors can be dealt with at a time. However, when dealing with the mathematical solution, we can *add together* a large number of resolved components *which act in the same direction*. That is, the addition of a large number of resolved components is quicker and more accurate than graphical methods.

When subtracting vectors or phasors, we can only subtract one vector or phasor from another at a time.

Self-test questions

10.1 A force of 20 kN acts on a body at an inclination of 50° to the reference direction, and another force of 30 kN acts at an angle of −120° relative to the reference direction. Determine (a) the resultant resolved components of the total force and (b) the total force acting on the body and its direction relative to the reference direction.

10.2 If an additional force of 25 kN at an angle of −60° relative to the reference direction acts on the body in question 10.1, determine the new value of total force and its direction acting on the body.

10.3 The r.m.s. value of a sinusoidal current is 25 A, and its periodic time is 45 ms. Determine an expression for the instantaneous current, and calculate its value after (a) 5 ms, (b) 15 ms, (c) 25 ms and (d) 40 ms.

10.4 Determine the frequency and periodic time of a voltage sinewave having a peak value of 10 V, and which has an instantaneous value of 5 V at 10 ms after the commencement of the wave.

10.5 Calculate the sum of the following currents

$$i_1 = 20 \sin \omega t$$
$$i_2 = 10 \sin(\omega t + \pi/6)$$
$$i_3 = 15 \cos \omega t$$
$$i_4 = 10 \sin(\omega t - \pi/6)$$
$$i_5 = 25 \cos(\omega t + 2\pi/3)$$

The sum should be represented in the form $I_m \sin(\omega t \pm \phi)$.

10.6 Voltages V_{AB} and V_{BC} of magnitude 50 V and 75 V, respectively, have a phase difference of 60° between them. The two voltages are connected in series so that the voltage V_{AC} is given by $V_{AC} = V_{AB} + V_{BC}$. Determine the magnitude of V_{AC} and its phase angle with respect to V_{BC}.

10.7 The e.m.f. applied to two series-connected elements is given by $e = 100 \sin \omega t$, and the voltage across one of the elements is $89.44 \sin(\omega t + 0.4637)$. Determine the magnitude and phase angle of the voltage across the second element.

10.8 Two currents are given by $i_1 = 50 \sin(100\pi t)$ A and $i_2 = 25 \sin(100\pi t + \pi/6)$ A, where t is in seconds. Plot a graph showing i_1 and i_2 to a base of time over the range $t = 0$ to $t = 40$ ms. If the two currents flow into a node in a circuit, plot the resultant waveform of $i_1 + i_2$ on the same graph. Determine also the expression for the instantaneous current flowing into the node.

10.9 A parallel circuit has three branches, the instantaneous current in each of the branches is

$$i_1 = 10 \sin(\omega t + \pi/3)\ \text{A}$$
$$i_2 = 5 \cos \omega t\ \text{A}$$
$$i_3 = 8 \sin(\omega t - 45°)\ \text{A}$$

Determine the expression for the instantaneous current, i, drawn by the circuit given that $i = i_1 + i_2 + i_3$, and evaluate the r.m.s. value of the current in each branch, and the r.m.s. current drawn from the supply.

10.10 The total voltage applied to a series circuit is given by $v = v_1 + v_2 + v_3$, where

$$v = 195 \sin(\omega t - 9.3°)$$
$$v_1 = 100 \sin \omega t$$
$$v_2 = 100 \sin(\omega t + 80°)$$

Determine an expression for v_3.

Summary of important facts

A **vector quantity** has both magnitude and direction *in space*. A **phasor quantity** defines a sinusoid which continually changes in magnitude; the magnitude of the phasor corresponds to the **root-mean-square (r.m.s.) value** of the sinusoid, and has a **phase angle** relative to a **reference direction** (usually the horizontal direction on the phasor diagram).

Vector addition or **phasor addition** can either be carried out **graphically** (by constructing a parallelogram of the vector or phasor quantities), or by **adding the resolved components** of the vectors or phasors. If V_h is the total horizontal component, and V_v is the total vertical component then, by Pythagorus's theorem, the **magnitude** of the resultant is

$$V_T = \sqrt{(V_h^2 + V_v^2)}$$

and its **phase angle** is

$$\phi = \arctan(V_v/V_h)$$

Vector subtraction or **phasor subtraction** is carried out by *adding* the negative value of the vector or phasor to be subtracted (the *subtrahend*) to the vector or phasor it is subtracted from (the *minuend*). If for example, we wish to subtract V_2 from V_1, then V_2 is the subtrahend and V_1 the minuend. The difference V_E is given by

$$V_E = V_1 - V_2 = V_1 + (-V_2)$$

Given that we know V_2 as a phasor (or vector), it is merely necessary to rotate it through 180° to obtain $-V_2$.

A **phasor diagram** shows lines representing the r.m.s. value of sinusoidal waves, together with their associated phase angles.

11 Complex numbers

11.1 Introduction

In Chapter 10 we discussed the way in which a phasor was represented in terms of its rectangular co-ordinates, i.e., measurements in the horizontal (reference) and vertical (quadrature) directions. When dealing with the addition or subtraction of phasors we saw that, mathematically, the process is quite straightforward when we know the rectangular co-ordinates of the phasor. Fortunately, the process has been made even more convenient for us when we use the method of **complex numbers**, as outlined below.

The reader should not confuse the word *complex* with the word *complicated*, since the techniques we use only involve fairly straightforward trigonometry of right-angled triangles. In its engineering terms, a complex number is one having both *magnitude and direction*, i.e., a complex number represents a line drawn at some angle to a reference direction.

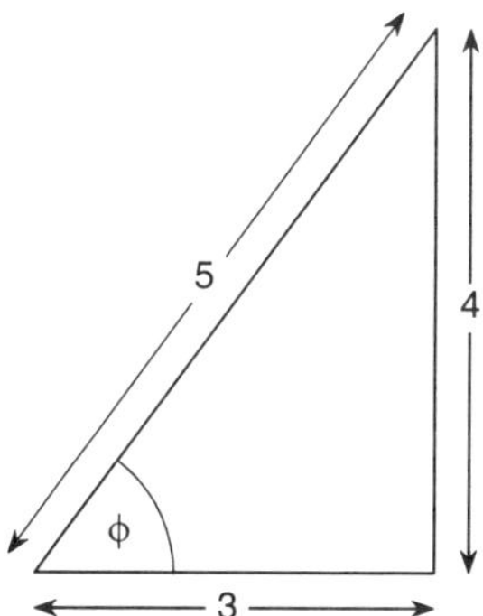

Figure 11.1 Representation of a complex number

Consider the line of length 5 units in Figure 11.1, which has a horizontal component of 3 and a vertical component of 4. The line can be described in terms of a complex number (since it has both magnitude and direction) as follows

$$\begin{matrix}\text{complex}\\\text{number}\end{matrix} = \begin{matrix}\text{horizontal}\\\text{component of 3}\end{matrix} + \begin{matrix}\text{vertical}\\\text{component of 4}\end{matrix}$$

However, this is a rather verbose description, and we simplify it by replacing the expression 'vertical component of' by the letter 'j' or the letter 'i'; mathematicians use the letter 'i' but, because 'i' represents current in electrical engineering, engineers use the letter 'j'.

Using this notation to represent the complex number given above we have, for Figure 11.1

$$\text{complex number} = 3 + j4$$

This form is known as the **rectangular form (or cartesian form) of representation of a complex number**, and in section 11.4 we will meet an alternative form known as the *polar form* of representation.

Clearly, by Pythagorus's theorem, the magnitude of the complex number is

$$\text{magnitude} = \sqrt{(3^2 + 4^2)} = 5$$

and the angle ϕ is

$$\phi = \arctan(4/3) = 53.13^\circ$$

We describe the horizontal component of the complex value as the **real part** of the complex number, and the vertical part of the complex number as the **imaginary part**. This is, of course, a rather superficial division because both components are as 'real' as one another (or as 'imaginary' as one another!). Nonetheless, this notation has been developed, and we are stuck with it.

Moreover, the imaginary part of a complex number can be thought of as being in the form

$$\text{imaginary part} = \text{imaginary operator} \times \text{a real value}$$

For example, the imaginary part of the complex value given above is $j4$, where 'j' is the **imaginary operator**, and 4 is a real value.

To distinguish between a 'normal' number and a complex number, we write complex values in **bold upright characters** (as in this chapter). For example, if $\mathbf{Z}$ is a complex value, then

$$\mathbf{Z} = \text{real part} + (j \times \text{imaginary part})$$

and we can write

$$\text{real part of } \mathbf{Z} = \text{Re } \mathbf{Z} = \text{Re}\,(3 + j4) = 3$$

and

$$\text{imaginary part of } \mathbf{Z} = \text{Im } \mathbf{Z} = \text{Im}\,(3 + j4) = 4$$

where Re and Im are understood, respectively, to mean 'the real part of' and 'the imaginary part of'. In the case of the imaginary part of the number above, we are only looking at the imaginary part of the number, and the complex operator j is dropped.

By the end of this chapter the reader will be able to

- understand what is meant by a 'complex' number,
- appreciate the difference between the 'real part' and the 'imaginary part' of a complex number,
- use the imaginary operator j,
- draw Argand diagrams,

- appreciate the difference between polar and rectangular forms of complex numbers, and convert from one form to another,
- represent the impedance of a circuit in complex form,
- add, subtract, multiply and divide complex numbers,
- determine the conjugate of a complex number,
- perform electrical circuit calculations.

11.2 More about imaginary numbers

Consider the quadratic equation $x^2 + x + 1 = 0$. If we solve the equation using the quadratic formulae (see Chapter 4) we get

$$x = \frac{-1 \pm \sqrt{(1^2 - [4 \times 1 \times 1])}}{2 \times 1} = \frac{-1 \pm \sqrt{(1-4)}}{2}$$
$$= \frac{-1 \pm \sqrt{(-3)}}{2}$$

Since the square of either a positive number or a negative number is itself a positive number, it follows that *a negative number cannot have a 'real' square root*. We can therefore write down

$$\sqrt{(-3)} = \sqrt{((-1) \times 3)} = \sqrt{(-1)} \times \sqrt{3} = \sqrt{(-1)} \times 1.732$$

and, once again, we can describe $\sqrt{(-1)}$ as the *imaginary operator*, so that

$$\sqrt{(-3)} = j1.732$$

Clearly, we can write

$$\mathbf{x} = \frac{-1 \pm j3}{2} = -\frac{1}{2} + j\frac{3}{2} \text{ or } -\frac{1}{2} - j\frac{3}{2}$$

The reader will observe that **x** is written in bold because it is a complex value. We can therefore see that

$$j = \sqrt{(-1)}$$
$$j^2 = (\sqrt{(-1)})^2 = -1$$
$$j^3 = j^2 \times j = -j$$
$$j^4 = j^2 \times j^2 = -1 \times (-1) = 1, \text{ etc.}$$

11.3 The Argand diagram

A complex value can be drawn on an **Argand diagram** (although it was named after Jean Robert Argand, the method was first suggested in 1797 by Caspar Wessel), in which the horizontal direction on the diagram is known as the *real direction*, and the vertical direction is known as the *imaginary direction* (see Figure 11.2).

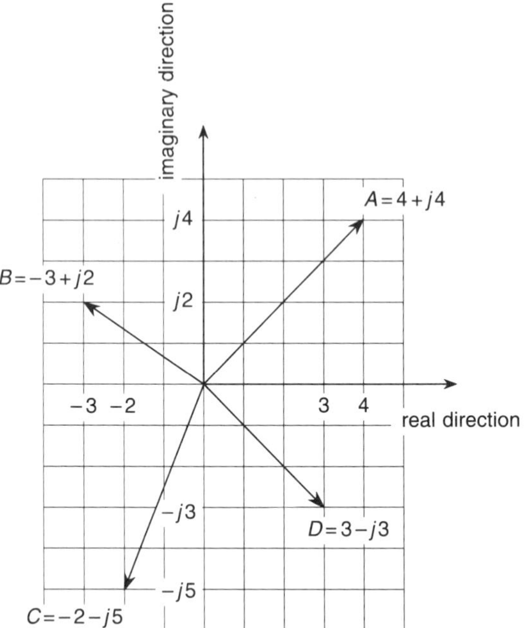

Figure 11.2 The Argand diagram

The Argand diagram is drawn in what is known as the **complex plane** because it has a 'real' axis and an 'imaginary' axis. The four complex values represented in Figure 11.2 are

$$\mathbf{A} = 4 + j4$$
$$\mathbf{B} = -3 + j2$$
$$\mathbf{C} = -2 - j5$$
$$\mathbf{D} = 3 - j3$$

11.4 The polar form of a complex number

An alternative method of representing a complex number is known at the **polar form** of the number, in which the complex number is represented by its magnitude or **modulus**, and its angle or **argument** with respect to a reference direction.

Both the rectangular form and the polar form have their own advantages, and these will be explained as the chapter unfolds.

Consider the complex value in Figure 11.1, which is represented in rectangular form by

$$\mathbf{Z} = 3 + j4$$

The modulus or magnitude of the number is 5 (see Figure 11.1), and we write* this as

$$Z = 5$$

The angle, ϕ, that Z makes with the reference direction is obtained by simple trigonometry as follows.

$$\phi = \arctan(4/3) = 53.13^\circ$$

The complex number $3 + j4$ can therefore be represented in polar form as follows

$$\mathbf{Z} = Z\angle\phi$$

that is

$$\mathbf{Z} = 5\angle 53.13^\circ$$

11.5 Relationship between rectangular and polar complex numbers

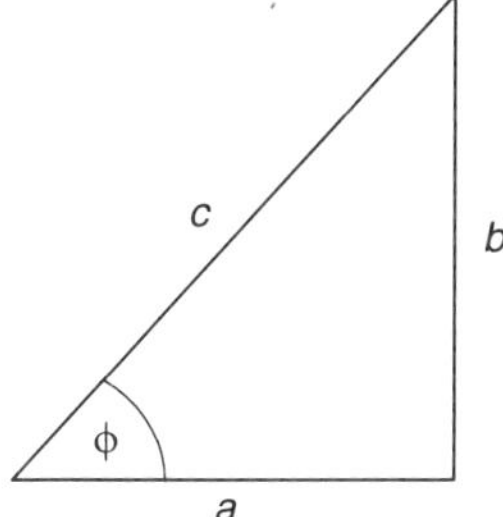

Figure 11.3 Relationship between rectangular and polar forms of a complex number

Referring to Figure 11.3, we see that the complex value **c** can be written in either of the following forms.

$$\mathbf{c} = a + jb$$

or

$$\mathbf{c} = c\angle\phi$$

where the relationship between the two is obtained from Figure 11.3, that is

$$c = \sqrt{(a^2 + b^2)} \text{ and } \phi = \arctan(b/a)$$

or

$$a = c\cos\phi \text{ and } b = c\sin\phi$$

* Since the modulus is simply the 'size' of the complex value, and does not involve 'direction', we write it in normal print and not in bold.

Any reader having a calculator with rectangular to polar conversion, and polar to rectangular conversion on it will find these features invaluable for complex number calculations. However, the reader is reminded that these features are merely an aid to the solution of problems, and they do not 'teach' you how to do the conversion.

After studying Worked Example 11.1, the reader will be able to show that the rectangular complex values in Figure 11.2 are represented in polar form as follows

$$A = 5.66\angle 45^\circ,\ B = 3.61\angle 146.3^\circ$$
$$C = 5.39\angle -111.8^\circ,\ D = 4.24\angle -45^\circ$$

Worked Example 11.1

(a) Determine the modulus and argument of the following complex numbers: (i) $3 + j5$, (ii) $-4 - j6$.

(b) Determine the rectangular complex form of the following complex numbers: (i) $4\angle 50^\circ$, (ii) $5\angle -120^\circ$.

Solution

(a) Referring to Figure 11.3, we see that if $\mathbf{c} = a + jb$, then $c = \sqrt{(a^2 + b^2)}$ and $\phi = \arctan(b/a)$.

(i) In this case, $a = 3$ and $b = 5$, hence

$$c = \sqrt{(3^2 + 5^2)} = 5.83$$

and

$$\phi = \arctan(5/3) = 59.04^\circ$$

That is

$$3 + j5 \equiv 5.83\angle 59.04^\circ$$

(ii) Here $a = -4$ and $b = -6$, therefore

$$c = \sqrt{((-4)^2 + (-6)^2)} = 7.75$$

and

$$\phi = \arctan((-6)/(-4)) = \arctan 1.5$$

It should be pointed out here that, since both a and b have negative values, the angle is in the third quadrant. However, if we are using a calculator, it will show that (using $a = -4$ and $b = -6$) the angle appears to be 56.3°. We must use our knowledge of mathematics to realise that the angle ϕ is in the third quadrant and is given by

$$\phi = 56.3^\circ + 180^\circ = 226.3^\circ \text{ (or } -123.7^\circ)$$

hence

$$-4 - j6 \equiv 7.75\angle 226.3^\circ$$

(b) Here we use the relationships

$$a = c\cos\phi \text{ and } b = c\sin\phi$$

(i) For the complex value $4\angle 50°$, $c = 4$ and $\phi = 50°$, hence

$$a = 4\cos 50° = 4 \times 0.6428 = 2.5712$$

and

$$b = 4\sin 50° = 4 \times 0.766 = 3.064$$

hence

$$4\angle 50° \equiv 2.5712 + j3.064$$

(ii) Here $c = 5$ and $\phi = -120°$, giving

$$a = 5\cos(-120°) = 5 \times (-0.5) = -2.5$$

and

$$b = 5\sin(-120°) = 5 \times (-0.866) = -4.33$$

that is

$$5\angle -120° \equiv -2.5 - j4.33$$

11.6 Representation of electrical impedance in complex form

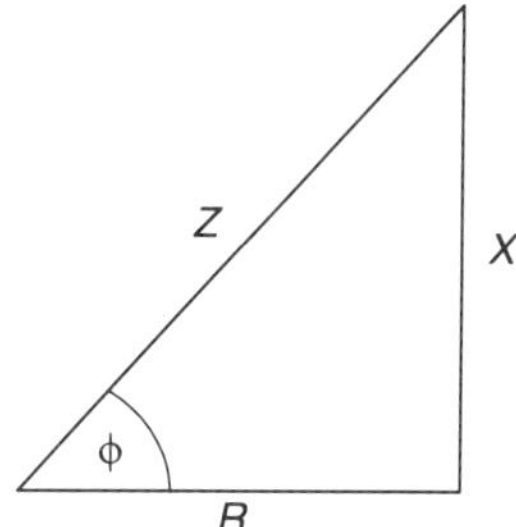

Figure 11.4 Impedance triangle of a series inductive circuit

A typical **impedance triangle** of a series circuit is shown in Figure 11.4, where R is the *resistance*, X the *reactance*, Z the *impedance* and ϕ the *phase angle* of the circuit. From the knowledge we already have of complex numbers, we can say that

$$\mathbf{Z} = R + jX \text{ and } \phi = \arctan(X/R)$$

also

$$\mathbf{Z} = Z\angle\phi$$

where $Z = \sqrt{(R^2 + X^2)}$

If, for example, $R = 10\Omega$ and $X = 5\Omega$ (note: since X has a positive value, the circuit is inductive!), then

$$\mathbf{Z} = 10 + j5\Omega$$

The modulus of the impedance is

$$Z = \sqrt{(R^2 + X^2)} = \sqrt{(10^2 + 5^2)} = 11.18\Omega$$

and the phase angle of the circuit is

$$\phi = \arctan(X/R) = \arctan(5/10) = 26.57°$$

That is

$$\mathbf{Z} = 11.18\angle 26.57°\Omega$$

Note: If X was a capacitive reactance of 5Ω, then the impedance of the circuit would be

$$\mathbf{Z} = 10 - j5\Omega = 11.18\angle - 26.57°\Omega$$

11.7 Addition and subtraction of complex numbers

The reader should note that:

> **Complex numbers must be converted into their rectangular form before they are added together or subtracted from one another.**

Polar complex numbers cannot be added together or subtracted from one another. The polar to rectangular complex number conversion key on a calculator is very useful in this situation.

Complex numbers (in their rectangular form) are *added together* by separately adding the real parts and the imaginary parts. For example, if $\mathbf{Z_1} = R_1 + jX_1$, $\mathbf{Z_2} = R_2 + jX_2$, and $\mathbf{Z_3} = R_3 + jX_3$, then

$$\mathbf{Z_1} + \mathbf{Z_2} + \mathbf{Z_3} = (R_1 + R_2 + R_3) + j(X_1 + X_2 + X_3)$$

Two complex numbers are *subtracted from one another* by subtracting separately the real parts and the imaginary parts of the numbers (note: although many complex numbers can be added together, we can only subtract one complex number from another). For example, if $\mathbf{V_1} = A + jB$ and $\mathbf{V_2} = C + jD$, then

$$\mathbf{V_1} - \mathbf{V_2} = (A - C) + j(B - D)$$

Worked Example 11.2

Two complex voltages $\mathbf{V_1} = 10 + j6\,\text{V}$ and $\mathbf{V_2} = 8\angle - 10°\,\text{V}$ are connected in series with one another, the resultant voltage being applied to two series-connected impedances of value $\mathbf{Z_1} = 3 + j5\,\Omega$ and $\mathbf{Z_2} = 2 - j4\,\Omega$ (the former has an inductive reactance, and the latter having a capacitive reactance). Determine the total voltage applied to the circuit, and the complex impedance of the circuit.

Solution

To add the two voltages together we must, initially, convert $\mathbf{V_2}$ into its rectangular form as follows. The real component of $\mathbf{V_2}$ is

$$\text{Re}\,\mathbf{V_2} = \text{Re}\,(8\angle -10^\circ) = 8\cos(-10^\circ) = 7.88\text{ V}$$

and its imaginary part is

$$\text{Im}\,\mathbf{V_2} = \text{Im}\,(8\angle -10^\circ) = 8\sin(-10^\circ) = -1.39\text{ V}$$

That is

$$\mathbf{V_2} = 7.88 - j1.39\text{ V}$$

and the total voltage applied to the circuit is

$$\begin{aligned}\mathbf{V_T} &= \mathbf{V_1} + \mathbf{V_2} = (10 + j6) + (7.88 - j1.39)\\ &= (10 + 7.88) + j(6 - 1.39) = 17.88 + j4.61\text{ V}\end{aligned}$$

Now, the modulus or magnitude of $\mathbf{V_T}$ is

$$V_T = \sqrt{(17.88^2 + 4.61^2)} = 18.46\text{ V}$$

and the phase angle ϕ_T of the total voltage is

$$\phi_T = \arctan(4.61/17.88) = 14.46^\circ$$

or

$$\mathbf{V_T} = V_T\angle\phi_T = 18.46\angle 14.46^\circ\text{ V}$$

The reader should note that engineers prefer to use the polar notation because, in practice, most of the instruments we use measure polar quantities. For example, we use voltmeters and ammeters to measure the modulus of voltage and current, respectively, and we use oscilloscopes to measure phase angles. Only a few specialised instruments give rectangular complex values.

The total impedance of the circuit is

$$\begin{aligned}\mathbf{Z_T} &= \mathbf{Z_1} + \mathbf{Z_2} = (3 + j5) + (2 - j4)\\ &= (3 + 2) + j(5 - 4) = 5 + j1\ \Omega\end{aligned}$$

From this we see that the phase angle of the circuit is

$$\phi = \arctan(1/5) = 11.31^\circ$$

and the magnitude of the total impedance is

$$Z_T = \sqrt{(5^2 + 1^2)} = 5.099\ \Omega$$

or

$$\mathbf{Z_T} = Z_T\angle\phi = 5.099\angle 11.31^\circ\ \Omega$$

Worked Example 11.3

Two complex voltages $\mathbf{V}_1$ and $\mathbf{V}_2$ are connected in series, and the total voltage is $\mathbf{V}_T = 15\angle 80^\circ$ V. If $\mathbf{V}_1 = 7.1 + j7.1$ V, determine the value of $\mathbf{V}_2$.

Solution

Since the two voltages are connected in series, then

$$\mathbf{V}_T = \mathbf{V}_1 + \mathbf{V}_2$$

or

$$\mathbf{V}_2 = \mathbf{V}_T - \mathbf{V}_1$$

To perform the subtraction, both voltages must be in their rectangular form, and we must convert $\mathbf{V}_T$ into its rectangular form as follows.

$$\text{Re}\,\mathbf{V}_T = 15\cos 80^\circ = 2.6 \text{ V}$$

and

$$\text{Im}\,\mathbf{V}_T = 15\sin 80^\circ = 14.77 \text{ V}$$

That is

$$\mathbf{V}_T = 2.6 + j14.77 \text{ V}$$

From the above equation

$$\begin{aligned}\mathbf{V}_2 = \mathbf{V}_T - \mathbf{V}_1 &= (2.6 + j14.77) - (7.1 + j7.1)\\ &= (2.6 - 7.1) + j(14.77 - j7.1)\\ &= -4.5 + j7.67V\end{aligned}$$

When converted to its polar form (which is left as an exercise for the reader) this becomes

$$\mathbf{V}_2 = 8.89\angle 120.4^\circ \text{ V}$$

11.8 Multiplication of complex numbers

Although it is possible to multiply complex numbers in their rectangular form, **all values should (preferably) be converted into their polar form**.

The reason for suggesting the use of polar complex numbers is that multiplication is more difficult (and error-prone) when using the rectangular form. The rectangular to polar complex number conversion key on a calculator is very useful in this situation.

Multiplication using polar complex values

If the complex current in a circuit is given by $\mathbf{I} = I\angle\theta$ and the impedance of the circuit is $\mathbf{Z} = Z\angle\phi$, then the complex voltage across the circuit is

$$\mathbf{V} = \mathbf{IZ} = I\angle\theta \times Z\angle\phi = IZ\angle(\theta + \phi)$$

That is, when we multiply polar complex numbers together, we multiply the magnitude values and add the angles.

Multiplication using rectangular complex values

If the values are given in rectangular complex form, we can use the usual algebraic methods to carry out the multiplication, as shown below. If $\mathbf{I} = a + jb$ and $\mathbf{Z} = c + jd$, then

$$\begin{aligned}\mathbf{V} = \mathbf{IZ} &= (a + jb)(c + jd) = ac + jad + jbc + j^2bd \\ &= ac + jad + jbc - bd = (ac - bd) + j(ad + bc)\end{aligned}$$

From the above, the reader will appreciate that multiplication using rectangular complex values is quite a slow process, and is error-prone.

Worked Example 11.4

The impedance of an a.c. circuit is given by $\mathbf{Z} = 3 + j6\,\Omega$, and the current in the circuit is $5\angle 30^\circ$ A. Determine the complex value of the voltage applied to the circuit.

Solution

Initially we will convert the impedance into its polar form as shown below. The modulus of the impedance is

$$Z = \sqrt{(3^2 + 6^2)} = 6.71\ \Omega$$

and its phase angle is

$$\phi = \arctan(6/3) = 63.43^\circ$$

that is

$$\mathbf{Z} = 6.71\angle 63.43^\circ\ \Omega$$

From Ohm's law, the voltage applied to the circuit is

$$\begin{aligned}\mathbf{V_S} = \mathbf{IZ} &= 5\angle 30^\circ \times 6.71\angle 63.43^\circ \\ &= 5 \times 6.71\angle(30^\circ + 63.43^\circ) = 33.55\angle 93.43^\circ\ \text{V}\end{aligned}$$

Alternatively, we can carry out the calculation using the rectangular complex version of the numbers as follows. The rectangular complex version of the current is

$$\text{Re}\,\mathbf{I} = 5\cos 30^\circ = 4.33\ \text{A}$$
$$\text{Im}\,\mathbf{I} = 5\sin 30^\circ = 2.5\ \text{A}$$

that is

$$\mathbf{I} = 4.33 + j2.5\ \text{A}$$

Hence

$$\begin{aligned}\mathbf{V}_S = \mathbf{IZ} &= (4.33 + j2.5)(3 + j6)\\ &= 12.99 + j7.5 + j25.98 + j^2 15\\ &= (12.99 - 15) + j(7.5 + 25.98)\\ &= -2.01 + j33.48\ \text{V}\end{aligned}$$

The reader should verify that the two values of $\mathbf{V}_S$ are equivalent.

11.9 The conjugate of a complex number

Before moving on to the division of complex numbers, we need to know about the **conjugate** of a complex number.

The conjugate of a complex number is obtained by changing the sign of the imaginary part of the complex rectangular value, or by changing the sign of the angle of a complex polar value.

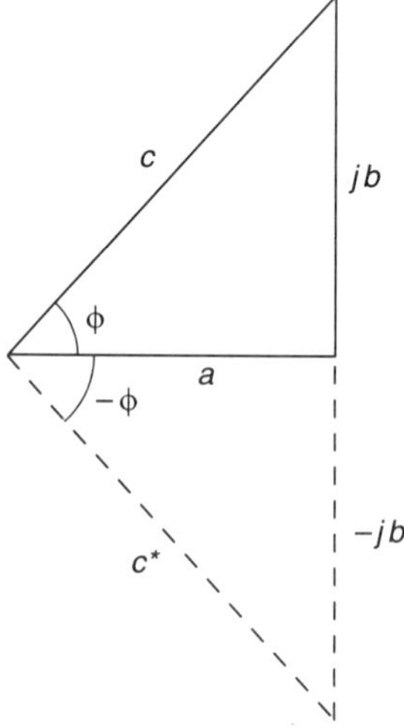

Figure 11.5 Conjugate of a complex number

Referring to Figure 11.5, we see that the rectangular complex value represented by c in the figure is

$$\mathbf{c} = a + jb$$

so that its conjugate (written as $\mathbf{c}^*$) is

$$\mathbf{c}^* = a - jb$$

where $\mathbf{c}^*$ is shown in the dotted line in Figure 11.5. We can also see that if we reverse the mathematical sign of the complex part of the number, then the mathematical sign of ϕ also changes. That is $+\phi$ becomes $-\phi$ in the conjugate. That is if

$$\mathbf{c} = c\angle\phi$$

then

$$\mathbf{c}^* = c\angle -\phi$$

Hence if $c = 3 + j4 \equiv 5\angle 53.13^\circ$, then

$$\mathbf{c}^* = 3 - j4 \equiv 5\angle -53.13^\circ$$

A complex number and its conjugate form a **conjugate pair**, and the *product of a conjugate pair is a real number*. For example, if $\mathbf{c} = a + jb$, then

$$\begin{aligned}\mathbf{c} \times \mathbf{c}^* &= (a + jb)(a - jb) = a^2 + jab - jab - j^2b \\ &= (a^2 + b^2) + j(ab - ab) = a^2 + b^2\end{aligned}$$

or

$$\mathbf{c} \times \mathbf{c}^* = c\angle\phi \times c\angle -\phi = c^2\angle(\phi - \phi) = c^2$$

Note: since $c = \sqrt{(a^2 + b^2)}$ then $c^2 = a^2 + b^2$.

11.10 Division of complex numbers

Division of complex numbers can be carried out using either polar or rectangular complex values, *but polar complex values are quicker and less error-prone*.

Division using polar complex values

If $\mathbf{V}$ is a complex voltage applied to an a.c. circuit, and $\mathbf{Z}$ is the complex impedance of the circuit, where $\mathbf{V} = V\angle\theta_1$ and $\mathbf{Z} = Z\angle\theta_2$, then from Ohm's law the current in the circuit is

$$\mathbf{I} = \frac{\mathbf{V}}{\mathbf{Z}} = \frac{V\angle\theta_1}{Z\angle\theta_2} = \frac{V}{Z}\angle(\theta_1 - \theta_2)$$

That is, **when we divide one polar complex number by another, we divide the magnitudes and subtract the angles, in the manner shown above.**

For example if $\mathbf{V} = 250\angle 10^\circ$ and $\mathbf{Z} = 10\angle 25^\circ$, then

$$\mathbf{I} = \frac{\mathbf{V}}{\mathbf{Z}} = \frac{250\angle 10^\circ}{10\angle 25^\circ} = 25\angle(10 - 25)^\circ = 25\angle(-15^\circ) \text{ A}$$

Division using rectangular complex values

Suppose that $\mathbf{V} = a + jb$ and $\mathbf{Z} = c + jd$, then the complex current in the circuit is

$$\mathbf{I} = \frac{\mathbf{V}}{\mathbf{Z}} = \frac{a + jb}{c + jd}$$

In this case we can convert the denominator to a 'real' number having no complex part simply by multiplying the denominator by its conjugate. To keep the equation balanced, we must also multiply the numerator by the conjugate of the denominator.

The process of multiplying the denominator by its conjugate is known as **rationalising the denominator**.

That is

$$\mathbf{I} = \frac{\mathbf{V}}{\mathbf{Z}} = \frac{\mathbf{VZ}^*}{\mathbf{ZZ}^*} = \frac{(a + jb)(c - jd)}{(c + jd)(c - jd)}$$

$$= \frac{ac - jad + jbc - j^2bd}{c^2 - jdc + jdc - j^2d} = \frac{(ac + bd) + j(bc - ad)}{c^2 + d^2}$$

For example if $\mathbf{V} = 3 + j4$ volts and $\mathbf{Z} = 6 - j8\ \Omega$, then

$$\mathbf{I} = \frac{\mathbf{V}}{\mathbf{Z}} = \frac{3 + j4}{6 - j8} = \frac{\mathbf{VZ}^*}{\mathbf{ZZ}^*} = \frac{(3 + j4)(6 + j8)}{(6 - j8)(6 + j8)}$$

$$= \frac{18 + j24 + j24 + j^2 32}{6^2 + 8^2} = \frac{(18 - 32) + j(24 + 24)}{100}$$

$$= -0.14 + j0.48 \text{ A}$$

11.11 a.c. electric circuit calculations

In this section we look at the solution of a series circuit and a parallel circuit.

A series a.c. circuit

Figure 11.6 shows a series a.c. circuit in which $\mathbf{Z}_1$ and $\mathbf{Z}_2$ are complex impedances of value

$$\mathbf{Z}_1 = 10 + j6\ \Omega$$

$$\mathbf{Z}_2 = 8\angle -30^\circ\ \Omega$$

and the supply voltage is

$$\mathbf{V}_S = 200\angle 50^\circ \text{ V}$$

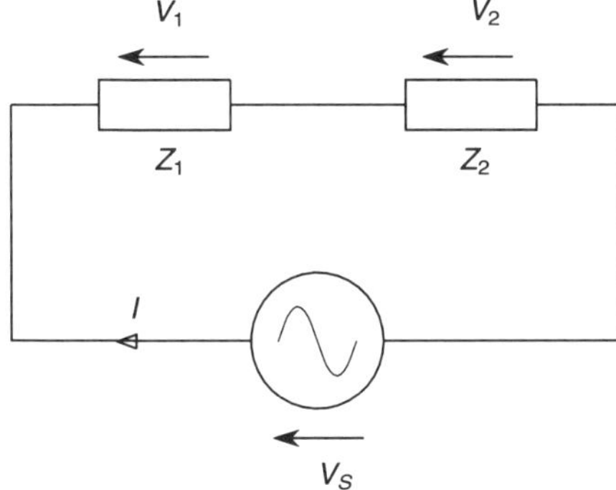

Figure 11.6 A series a.c. circuit

We will calculate the complex value of the total impedance of the circuit, the current in the circuit, and the voltage across each impedance in the circuit.

The process involved is much the same as for any circuit analysis problem of this type in that, after determining the total impedance of the circuit, we use Ohm's law to calculate the current. Once the current is known, we apply Ohm's law once again to calculate the voltage across each impedance.

In order to determine the total impedance of the circuit, we must add the complex impedances together, and to do this we need to express the impedance values in rectangular form. We already have $\mathbf{Z_1}$ in this form, and

$$\begin{aligned}\mathbf{Z_2} &= 8\angle -30^\circ = 8\cos 30^\circ - j8\sin 30^\circ \\ &= 6.982 - j4\,\Omega\end{aligned}$$

The above calculation illustrates the usefulness of a polar-to-rectangular conversion key on a calculator. The total impedance of the circuit is

$$\begin{aligned}\mathbf{Z_T} &= \mathbf{Z_1} + \mathbf{Z_2} = (10 + j6) + (6.982 - j4) \\ &= 16.928 + j2\,\Omega\end{aligned}$$

In order to calculate the current, we must divide the complex voltage by the complex impedance of the circuit, and this is best done using the polar form of the complex values. Hence

$$\begin{aligned}\mathbf{Z_T} &= \sqrt{(16.928^2 + 2^2)}\angle\arctan(2/16.928) \\ &= 17.05\angle 6.74^\circ\,\Omega\end{aligned}$$

The complex value of $\mathbf{Z_T}$ tells us that the circuit has an inductive impedance (since ϕ is positive), and that the current lags behind the voltage by 6.74°, i.e., the angle of the current relative to the reference direction is $(50 - 6.74)^\circ = 43.26^\circ$.

From Ohm's law

$$\mathbf{I} = \frac{\mathbf{V_S}}{\mathbf{Z_T}} = \frac{200\angle 50^\circ}{17.05\angle 6.74^\circ} = 11.73\angle 43.26^\circ \text{ A}$$

To calculate the voltage across each impedance we use the equation $\mathbf{V} = \mathbf{IZ}$. Since we are multiplying complex numbers together, both $\mathbf{I}$ and $\mathbf{Z}$ need to be in polar form, and

$$\mathbf{Z}_1 = 10 + j6 = \sqrt{(10^2 + 6^2)}\angle\arctan(6/10)$$
$$= 11.66\angle 30.96°\ \Omega$$

hence the voltage across $\mathbf{Z}_1$ is

$$\mathbf{V}_1 = \mathbf{IZ}_1 = 11.73\angle 43.26° \times 11.66\angle 30.96°$$
$$= 136.77\angle 74.22°\ \text{V}$$

and

$$\mathbf{V}_2 = \mathbf{IZ}_2 = 11.73\angle 43.26° \times 8\angle -30°$$
$$= 93.84\angle 13.26\ \text{V}$$

The reader will find it an interesting exercise to verify that the sum of $\mathbf{V}_1$ and $\mathbf{V}_2$ is equal to $\mathbf{V}_S$.

The phasor diagram for the circuit is shown in Figure 11.7.

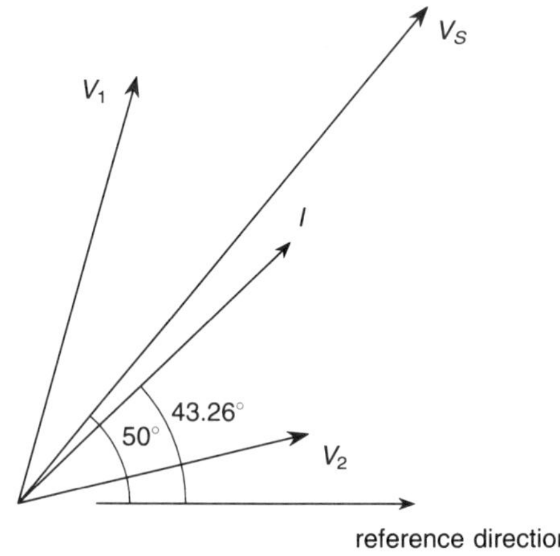

Figure 11.7 Phasor diagram for the series circuit calculation

A parallel a.c. circuit

A typical two-branch parallel a.c. circuit is shown in Figure 11.8 in which

$$\mathbf{Z}_1 = 10 - j6\ \Omega$$
$$\mathbf{Z}_2 = 12\angle 30°\ \Omega$$
$$\mathbf{I}_1 = 4\angle 20°\ \text{A}$$

Using complex numbers, we will determine the impedance of the parallel circuit, the current in $\mathbf{Z}_2$, the voltage $\mathbf{V}_S$ across the circuit, and the total current $\mathbf{I}$ drawn by the circuit.

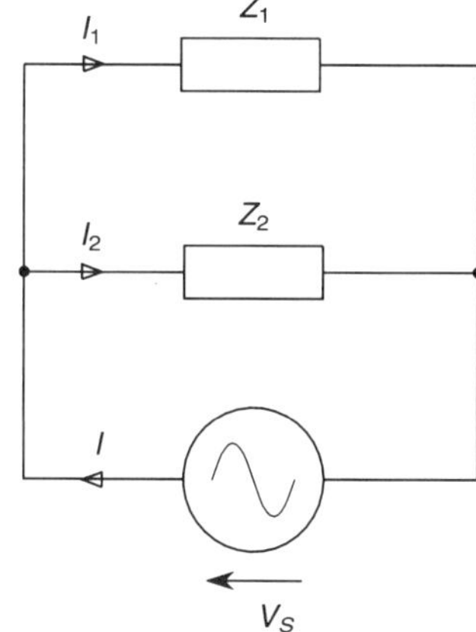

Figure 11.8 A parallel a.c. circuit

The effective impedance, $\mathbf{Z}_T$, of the parallel circuit is given by

$$\mathbf{Z}_T = \mathbf{Z}_1\mathbf{Z}_2/(\mathbf{Z}_1 + \mathbf{Z}_2)$$

That is, we need to multiply and to add $\mathbf{Z}_1$ and $\mathbf{Z}_2$, so that we need the impedances both in rectangular and polar form! Initially we will convert $\mathbf{Z}_1$ into its polar form as follows.

$$\begin{aligned}\mathbf{Z}_1 &= 10 - j6 \equiv \sqrt{(10^2 + (-6^2))}\arctan(-6/10)\\ &= 11.662\angle -30.96^\circ\ \Omega\end{aligned}$$

and we convert $\mathbf{Z}_2$ into rectangular form.

$$\begin{aligned}\mathbf{Z}_2 &= 12\angle 30^\circ = 12\cos 30^\circ + j12\sin 30^\circ\\ &= 10.392 + j6\end{aligned}$$

The effective impedance of the parallel circuit is therefore

$$\begin{aligned}\mathbf{Z}_T &= \mathbf{Z}_1\mathbf{Z}_2/(\mathbf{Z}_1 + \mathbf{Z}_2)\\ &\frac{11.662\angle -30.96^\circ \times 12\angle 30^\circ}{(10 - j6) + (10.392 + j6)} = \frac{139.94\angle -0.96^\circ}{20.392\angle 0^\circ}\\ &= 6.862\angle -0.96^\circ\end{aligned}$$

The voltage across the parallel circuit is calculated below

$$\begin{aligned}\mathbf{V}_S &= \mathbf{I}_1\mathbf{Z}_1 = 4\angle 20^\circ \times 11.662\angle -30.96^\circ\\ &= 46.65\angle -10.96^\circ\ \text{V}\end{aligned}$$

The current flowing in $\mathbf{Z}_2$ is calculated using Ohm's law as follows.

$$\mathbf{I}_2 = \frac{\mathbf{V}_S}{\mathbf{Z}_2} = \frac{46.65\angle -10.96^\circ}{12\angle 30^\circ} = 3.89\angle -40.96^\circ\ \text{A}$$

and the total current drawn by the circuit is

$$\mathbf{I} = \frac{\mathbf{V}_S}{\mathbf{Z}_T} = \frac{46.65\angle -10.96^\circ}{6.862\angle -0.96^\circ} = 6.8\angle -10^\circ\ \text{A}$$

The reader will find it a useful exercise to verify that

$$\mathbf{I} = \mathbf{I}_1 + \mathbf{I}_2$$

The phasor diagram for the circuit is shown in Figure 11.9.

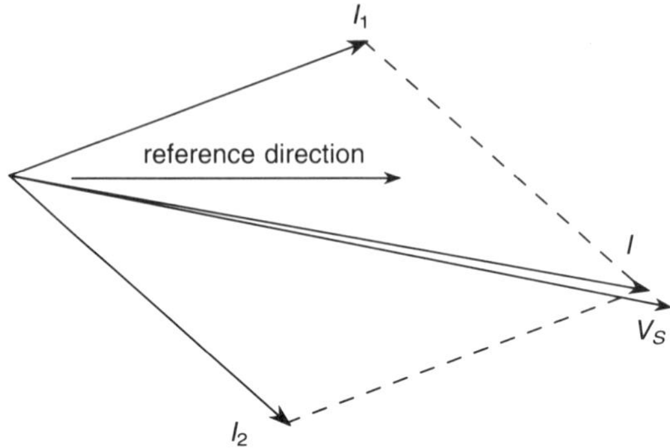

Figure 11.9 Phasor diagram for the parallel circuit calculation

Self-test questions

11.1 Draw an Argand diagram showing the following complex values (a) $4 + j5$, (b) $10\angle 30°$, (c) $-5 + j2$, (d) $7\angle 120°$, (e) $-6 - j7$, (f) $6\angle 200°$, (g) $7 - j4$, (h) $4\angle -40°$.

11.2 Without using a calculator with a rectangular-to-polar conversion key, convert the following rectangular complex values into their equivalent polar values (a) $-7 - j8$, (b) $7 + j4$, (c) $4 - j7$, (d) $-4 + j3$.

11.3 Without using a calculator with a polar-to-rectangular conversion key, convert the following polar complex values into their equivalent rectangular complex values: (a) $8\angle -140°$, (b) $6\angle 120°$, (c) $3\angle -78°$, (d) $6.5\angle 85.2°$.

11.4 Add the following complex values, and convert the result into both polar and rectangular form (a) $(2 + j5) + (3 + j8)$, (b) $(-5 + j6) + 7\angle 45°$, (c) $15\angle 30° + 9\angle -120°$.

11.5 Subtract the following complex values (a) $(2 + j5) - (3 + j8)$, (b) $(-5 + j6) - 7\angle 45°$, (c) $15\angle 30° - 9\angle -120°$.

11.6 Multiply the following complex numbers
(a) $10\angle 20° \times 30\angle 0.8\,\text{rad}$, (b) $(-2 - j3) \times 8.2\angle 2.0\,\text{rad}$
(c) $(3 + j4) \times (-5 - j6)$.

11.7 Divide the following complex values: (a) $10\angle 20°/30\angle 0.8\,\text{rad}$, (b) $(-2 - j3)/8.2\angle 2.0\,\text{rad}$, (c) $(3 + j4)/(-5 - j6)$.

11.8 Two voltages are connected in series to an a.c. circuit whose impedance is $(3 + j4)\,\Omega$. Calculate the current in the circuit if $\mathbf{V}_1 = 8 + j2\,\text{V}$ and $\mathbf{V}_2 = 8\angle -50°\,\text{V}$.

11.9 Voltages of $\mathbf{V}_1 = 35.36\angle 0^\circ$ V and $\mathbf{V}_2 = 35.36\angle 90^\circ$ are connected in series to a circuit whose impedance is $\mathbf{Z} = R + j(X_L - X_C)$, where R is a resistance of $10\,\Omega$, X_L an inductive reactance of $20\,\Omega$, and X_C a capacitive reactance of $130\,\Omega$. Determine (a) the total voltage applied to the circuit, (b) the complex impedance of the circuit, and (c) the current in the circuit.

11.10 A voltage of $110\angle 45^\circ$ V is applied to three elements in series whose impedances are, respectively, $\mathbf{Z}_1 = 3 + j6\,\Omega$, $\mathbf{Z}_2 = 4\angle 0^\circ$ and $\mathbf{Z}_3 = 8 - j2\,\Omega$. Determine (a) the total impedance of the circuit, (b) the current in the circuit and (c) the complex voltage across each impedance.

Summary of important facts

A **real number** is one simply having a value, and lies in the 'reference' direction. An **imaginary number** is a real number in association with a **complex operator** (j or i), which implies a 'direction' at right-angles to the **reference direction**. A **complex number** is the sum of a real number and an imaginary number, and can be drawn on an **Argand diagram**.

The complex operator j can be written $j = \sqrt{(-1)}$, and

$$j^2 = -1$$

$$j^3 = -j$$

$$j^4 = 1, \text{ etc.}$$

The **rectangular or cartesian form of a complex number** is written as

$$\mathbf{Z} = a + jb$$

where 'a' is the real part of the number, and 'jb' is the imaginary part of the number. The **polar form of a complex number** is written as

$$\mathbf{Z} = r\angle\theta$$

where r is the **modulus** or magnitude of the number, and θ the **argument** or angle. Rectangular and polar complex values are related as follows.

$$r = \sqrt{(a^2 + b^2)}$$

$$\theta = \arctan(b/a)$$

where

$$a = r\cos\theta$$

$$b = r\sin\theta$$

The *rectangular form* of complex numbers can be **added** by separately adding the real and imaginary parts, and can be **subtracted** by separately subtracting the real and imaginary parts. If $\mathbf{Z_1} = a + jb$ and $\mathbf{Z_2} = c + jd$, then

$$\mathbf{Z_1} + \mathbf{Z_2} = (a + c) + j(b + d)$$

and

$$\mathbf{Z_1} - \mathbf{Z_2} = (a - c) + j(b - d)$$

Multiplication and **division** of complex numbers is best carried out using *polar complex values* (see below for details of division using rectangular complex numbers). If $\mathbf{A} = r_1\angle\theta_1$ and $\mathbf{B} = r_2\angle\theta_2$, then

$$\mathbf{AB} = r_1 r_2 \angle(\theta_1 + \theta_2)$$

and if $\mathbf{C} = r_3\angle\theta_3$ and $\mathbf{D} = r_4\angle\theta_4$, then

$$\frac{\mathbf{C}}{\mathbf{D}} = \frac{r_3}{r_4}\angle(\theta_3 - \theta_4)$$

The **conjugate** of a complex number is obtained by changing the sign of the imaginary part of a rectangular complex number, or by changing the sign of the angle of a polar complex number. That is if a complex number is

$$\mathbf{Z} = \mathbf{a} + \mathbf{jb} \equiv \mathbf{r}\angle\theta$$

then the conjugate of the complex number is

$$\mathbf{Z}^* = a - jb \equiv r\angle - \theta$$

A complex number and its conjugate form a **conjugate pair**, and the product of a conjugate pair is a real number. In the above case

$$\mathbf{ZZ}^* = (a + jb)(a - jb) = a^2 + b^2$$

and

$$\mathbf{ZZ}^* = r\angle\theta \times r\angle - \theta = r^2$$

Division of complex numbers using rectangular complex values is carried out by **rationalising the denominator** of the equation, in which both the denominator and the numerator are multiplied by the conjugate of the denominator. If $\mathbf{A} = a + jb$ and $\mathbf{B} = c + jd$, then

$$\frac{\mathbf{A}}{\mathbf{B}} = \frac{\mathbf{AB}^*}{\mathbf{BB}^*} = \frac{(a + jb)(c - jd)}{(c + jd)(c - jd)}$$

$$= \frac{(ac + bd) + j(bc - ad)}{c^2 + d^2}$$

12 Differentiation

12.1 Introduction

The **differential calculus** is a method used to determine the *rate of change* of one quantity with respect to another. For example, the speed of an object is the rate of movement of the object with respect to time; provided that we know the equation for the movement of the object, we can determine its velocity at any point in time by differentiating the equation. Differential calculus is of great interest in all branches of engineering, and we will take a gentle approach to the topic.

By the end of this chapter the reader will be able to

- understand the concept of a function,
- understand more about the gradient and slope of a graph,
- differentiate from first principles,
- differentiate higher-order functions,
- differentiate $y = an^x$
- differentiate the sum of a number of functions,
- determine the second derivative of a function,
- determine the maximum values, the minimum values and turning points on a graph,
- understand and be able to apply the maximum power transfer theorem to electrical and electronic circuits,
- differentiate a function of a function,
- differentiate the product of two functions,
- differentiate a quotient,
- use a table of standard derivatives.

12.2 The concept of a 'function'

We have referred occasionally to the word 'function' several times without having to fully understand it. For example, in the equation $y = 6x^2 + 4x + 10$, the value of y depends on the value of x, and we say that *y is a function of x*. Also, the resistance of a length of wire depends on the length of the wire, so that the resistance is a function of its length. We can therefore define a function as follows:

> **When two quantities are related so that the value of the dependent variable is related to the independent variable, then the dependent variable is said to be a function of the independent variable.**

In the case of the equation $y = 6x^2 + 4x + 10$, x is the independent variable and y is the dependent variable, so that any change in x produces an x change in y. The symbol $\boldsymbol{f(x)}$ is used to denote 'a function of x' and, in the case of the above equation, we can say that

$$y = 6x^2 + 4x + 10$$

or

$$f(x) = 6x^2 + 4x + 10$$

Sometimes capital F is used in place of f, and we may say

$$F(x) = 6x^2 + 4x + 10$$

If the independent variable is time, t, as in the following equation

$$v = V_m \sin(\omega t + \phi)$$

then we may say $v = f(t)$, or

$$f(t) = V_m \sin(\omega t + \phi)$$

When the independent variable has a particular value, we may write it down inside a pair of brackets to give an answer to the expression. For example, if $f(x) = 2x + 3$, then

$$f(0) = (2 \times 0) + 3 = 3$$
$$f(2) = (2 \times 2) + 3 = 7$$
$$f(-1) = (2 \times (-1)) + 3 = 1, \text{ etc}$$

12.3 Notation for a small change in a variable

When dealing with functions, we adopt a special notation to indicate a small change in the value of the variable (note: the change may either be an increase or a decrease). If we consider the movement of an object, a change in its movement can be denoted by δx (δ is the lower case Greek letter delta or 'd'), and the corresponding amount of time during which the change occurs is δt.

We can say that if two variables x and y are related so that y is a function of x, then a change δx in x produces a corresponding (but not equal) change δy in y. For example, if $y = 3x^2 + 5x + 10$, then when $x = 4$ then

$$y = (3 \times 4^2) + (5 \times 4) + 10 = 78$$

If there is a change δx in x, then the change δy in y can be calculated from

$$y + \delta y = 3(x + \delta x)^2 + 5(x + \delta x) + 10$$

If $\delta x = 0.1$ then

$$y + \delta y = 3(4 + 0.1)^2 + 5(4 + 0.1) + 10 = 80.93$$

that is

$$\delta y = 80.93 - y = 80.93 - 78 = 2.93$$

12.4 Gradient and slope of a graph

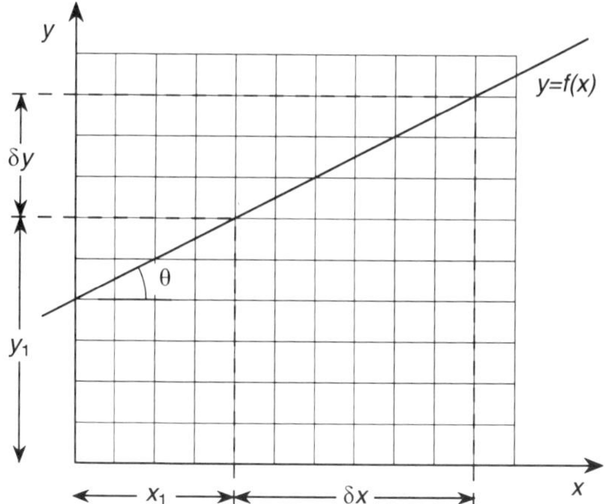

Figure 12.1 The gradient and slope of a line

Consider the straight-line graph in figure 12.1, in which y is a function of x. We see that a change δx in the variable x produces a change δy in the variable y.

The ratio $\dfrac{\delta y}{\delta x}$ is known as the **gradient** of the line. The line makes angle θ with the x-axis, so that $\dfrac{\delta y}{\delta x}$ is the tangent of angle θ, hence the gradient of the line is **the tangent of the angle made with the positive direction x-axis**. Angle θ is known as the **slope of the line** and, on occasions, it may be described (although not strictly correctly) as the gradient of the line.

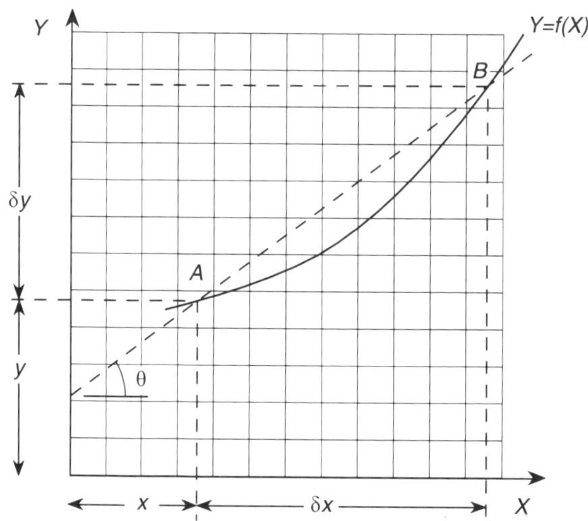

Figure 12.2 The gradient of a curve

Defining the gradient of a curve is a little more difficult than in the case of a straight line (see figure 12.2). The co-ordinates of point A on the graph are (x, y) and the co-ordinates of point B are $(x + \delta x, y + \delta y)$, and the gradient of the line joining A and B is

$$\frac{\delta y}{\delta x} = \tan \theta$$

This is, of course, the gradient of the line joining A to B, but is not necessarily the gradient of the curve either at A or at B.

The only way we can determine the gradient at a point on the curve is to make δx (and therefore δy) progressively smaller until δx is zero (or nearly so!). We describe this by saying that $\delta x \to 0$. To illustrate our point, consider the curve defined by $y = x^2$; we will attempt to determine the slope of the curve when $x = 4$. Initially, we will consider a change in x of $\delta x = 1$, and calculate the slope of the graph. When $x = 4$, the value of y is

$$y = x^2 = 42 = 16$$

and

$$y + \delta y = (x + \delta x)^2 = (4 + 1)^2 = 25$$

so that $\delta y = 25 - y = 25 - 16 = 9$, giving a gradient of

$$\frac{\delta y}{\delta x} = \frac{9}{1} = 9$$

TABLE 12.1 Estimation of the gradient of $y = x^2$ when $x = 4$

Value of x	δx	$x + \delta x$	$(x + \delta x)^2$	δy	$\frac{\delta y}{\delta x}$
4	1.0	5.0	25.0	9.0	9.0
4	0.5	4.5	20.25	4.25	8.5
4	0.1	4.1	16.81	0.81	8.1
4	0.01	4.01	16.0801	0.0801	8.01
4	0.001	4.001	16.008001	0.008001	8.001

In Table 12.1 we gradually reduce δx from 1.0 to 0.001, and see how the estimated value of the gradient changes. Clearly we see that, as δx gets smaller and smaller, the gradient approaches the value 8. That is

$$\frac{\delta y}{\delta x} \to 8 \text{ as } \delta x \to 0$$

If the process in Table 12.1 is carried out for a value other than $x = 4$, the gradient tends to a final value other than 8. Try it for $x = 2$ and $x = -3$.

The limiting value of $\delta y / \delta x$ as δx approaches zero is written as

$$\frac{dy}{dx}$$

(pronounced 'dy by dx') and is known as the **first derivative** or **differential coefficient** of y with respect to x. Alternative symbols are Dx, $\dot{x}$ and $f'(x)$.

The process of **differentiation** is one of determining the gradient of the tangent to a graph; the reader should appreciate that $\frac{dy}{dx}$ means that the equation has been **differentiated once with respect to x**.

12.5 Differentiation from first principles

Consider the equation $y = x^2$. If x changes by δx, then y will change by δy according to the relationship

$$y + \delta y = (x + \delta x)^2 = x^2 + 2x\delta x + (\delta x)^2$$

Since $y = x^2$, we can subtract y from the left-hand side of the equation and x^2 from the right-hand side, and the equation will remain balanced to give the following

$$\delta y = 2x\delta x + (\delta x)^2$$

or

$$\frac{\delta y}{\delta x} = 2x + \delta x$$

Now

$$\frac{dy}{dx} = \frac{\delta y}{\delta x} \text{ as } \delta x \text{ tends to zero}$$

Writing $\delta x = 0$ in the above expression gives

$$\frac{dy}{dx} = 2x$$

That is, the **first derivative** of the curve $y = x^2$ is equal to $2x$ for any value of x! Looking at Table 12.1 shows that, when $x = 4$, the gradient tends to $2x = 8$ as δx tends to zero. This confirms the above calculation; the reader should reproduce this table for values other than $x = 4$.

Worked Example 12.1

Determine the first derivative for the equation of a straight-line graph, i.e.

$$y = mx + c$$

where m is the gradient of the graph, and c is the y-axis intercept.

Solution

When x increases by δx then

$$y + \delta y - m(x + \delta x) + c = mx + m\delta x + c$$

Subtracting y from the left-hand side of the equation, and $(mx + c)$ from the right-hand side leaves

$$\delta y = m\delta x$$

or

$$\frac{\delta y}{\delta x} = m$$

Clearly, the graph is a straight line, and has a gradient of m. It follows that, as δx tends to zero, then

$$\frac{dy}{dx} = m$$

That is, the first derivative of $y = mx + c$ is

$$\frac{dy}{dx} = m$$

The reader may like to show that

(a) if $y = 4x + 6$ then $\dfrac{dy}{dx} = 4$

(b) if $y = 4x - 6$ then $\dfrac{dy}{dx} = 4$,

(c) if $y = -3x + 6$ then $\dfrac{dy}{dx} = -3$.

12.6 Differentiating higher-order functions

The general rule for differentiating higher-order functions follows that given above. We will take a look at some higher-order functions in Worked Examples 12.2 and 12.3, and the general solution is given in Table 12.3 in section 12.17.

Worked Example 12.2

Determine an expression for dy/dx for the equation $y = ax^2 + b$.

Solution

When x increases by δx we have

$$\begin{aligned} y + \delta y &= a(x + \delta x)^2 + b \\ &= a(x^2 + 2x\delta x + (\delta x)^2) + b \\ &= ax^2 + 2ax\delta x + a(\delta x)^2 + b \end{aligned}$$

Subtracting y from the left-hand side of the equation and $(ax^2 + b)$ from the right-hand side leaves

$$\delta y = 2ax\delta x + a(\delta x)^2$$

or

$$\frac{\delta y}{\delta x} = 2ax + a\delta x$$

When δx tends to zero we see that

$$\frac{dy}{dx} = 2ax$$

In fact we have already seen for this equation that when $a = 1$, i.e., $y = x^2$, then

$$\frac{dy}{dx} = 2x$$

The reader may like to show that

(a) if $y = 4x^2 + 3$ then $\dfrac{dy}{dx} = 8x$,

(b) if $y = 4x^2 - 3$ then $\dfrac{dy}{dx} = 8x$,

(c) if $y = -2x^2 + 8$ then $\dfrac{dy}{dx} = -4x$.

Worked Example 12.3

Determine an expression for dy/dx for the equation $y = ax^3 + b$.

Solution

If x in the above expression increases by δx then

$$\begin{aligned} y + \delta y &= a(x + \delta x)^3 + b \\ &= a(x^3 + 3x^2\delta x + 3x(\delta x)^2 + (\delta x)^3) + b \\ &= ax^3 + 3ax^2\delta x + 3ax(\delta x)^2 + a(\delta x)^3 + b \end{aligned}$$

Subtracting y from the left-hand side of the equation and $(ax^3 + b)$ from the right-hand side gives

$$\delta y = 3ax^2\delta x + 3ax(\delta x)^2 + a(\delta x)^3$$

hence

$$\frac{\delta y}{\delta x} = 3ax^2 + 3ax\delta x + a(\delta x)^2$$

In the limit when δx tends to zero we get

$$\frac{dy}{dx} = 3ax^2$$

The reader may like to show that

(a) if $y = 4x^3 + 8$, then $\frac{dy}{dx} = (3 \times 4)x^2 = 12x^2$,

(b) if $y = 4x^3 - 8$, then $\frac{dy}{dx} = (3 \times 4)x^2 = 12x^2$,

(c) if $y = -2x^3 + 6$, then $\frac{dy}{dx} = (3 \times (-2))x^2$
$= -6x^2$

12.7 Differentiating the general case of $y = ax^n$

We will not attempt to analyse this equation in detail, but will draw general conclusions from the following.

(1) If $y = ax + b$, then $\frac{dy}{dx} = a$.

(2) If $y = ax^2 + b$, then $\frac{dy}{dx} = 2ax$.

(3) If $y = ax^3 + b$, then $\frac{dy}{dx} = 3ax^2$.

We can therefore conclude that

$$\textbf{if } \boldsymbol{y = ax^n + b}\textbf{, then } \boldsymbol{\frac{dy}{dx} = nax^{n-1}}$$

For example

$$\text{If } y = 5x^2 - 3, \text{ then } \frac{dy}{dx} = 2 \times 5 \times x^{2-1} = 10x.$$

$$\text{If } y = 9x^3 + 7, \text{ then } \frac{dy}{dx} = 3 \times 9x^{3-1} = 27x^2.$$

$$\text{If } y = x^4/5, \text{ then } \frac{dy}{dx} = \frac{4 \times x^{4-1}}{5} = 0.8x^3.$$

12.8 Differentiating a constant

In the expression $y = 4$, clearly y has a constant and unchanging value, so that its rate of change is zero. That is

$$\frac{dy}{dx} = \frac{d(4)}{dx} = 0$$

That is

the derivative of a constant is zero.

12.9 Differentiating a sum of functions

In the case of a sum of functions of the following form

$$y = ax^2 + bx + c$$

then, when x changes by δx, we have

$$\begin{aligned} y + \delta x &= a(x + \delta x)^2 + b(x + \delta x) + c \\ &= (ax^2 + 2ax\delta x + a(\delta x)^2) + (bx + b\delta x) + c \end{aligned}$$

Subtracting y from the left-hand side of the equation and $(ax^2 + bx + c)$ from the right-hand side, we get

$$\delta y = 2ax\delta x + a(\delta x)^2 + b\delta x$$

or

$$\frac{\delta y}{\delta x} = 2ax + a\delta x + b$$

As δx tends towards zero we get

$$\frac{dy}{dx} = 2ax + b$$

We note here that $2ax$ is the differential coefficient of ax^2, b is the differential coefficient of bx, and the differential coefficient of the constant c is zero. That is

the differential coefficient of a sum of functions is the sum of the individual differential coefficients.

Worked Example 12.4

Determine the differential coefficient of the following
(a) $y = 2x^4 - 4x - 6$, (b) $s = ut + \frac{1}{2}at^2$, (c) $y = x^3 + 2/\sqrt{x}$,
(d) $v = u^{1.5} - 1/(2u^{3.5})$.

Solution

(a) $\dfrac{dy}{dx} = (4 \times 2x^{4-1}) - (1 \times 4x^{1-1}) = 8x^3 - 4$

(b) $\dfrac{ds}{dt} = (1 \times ut^{1-1}) + (2 \times \dfrac{1}{2}at^{2-1}) = u + at$

(c) In this case $y = x^3 + 2x^{-1/2}$, hence

$$\frac{dy}{dx} = (3 \times x^{3-1}) + (-\frac{1}{2} \times 2x^{(-0.5-1)})$$
$$= 3x^2 - x^{-1.5} = 3x^2 - 1/x^{1.5}$$

(d) This equation is rewritten in the form $v = u^{1.5} - \frac{1}{2}u^{-3.5}$, hence

$$\frac{dv}{du} = (1.5 \times u^{1.5-1}) - ((-3.5) \times \frac{1}{2}u^{(-3.5-1)})$$
$$= 1.5u^{0.5} + 1.75u^{-4.5} = 1.5\sqrt{u} + \frac{1.75}{u^{4.5}}$$

Worked Example 12.5

Determine the first derivative of the graphs (a) $y = 2x^2 - 1.5x + 1$ and (b) $y = x^3 + x^2 + 1$ when (i) $x = 3$, (ii) $x = -2$.

Solution

(a) The equation of the curve is $y = 2x^2 - 1.5x + 1$, and its differential is

$$\frac{dy}{dx} = 4x - 1.5$$

(i) When $x = 3$ then

$$\frac{dy}{dx} = (4 \times 3) - 1.5 = 10.5$$

(ii) When $x = -2$ then

$$\frac{dy}{dx} = (4 \times (-2)) - 1.5 = -9.5$$

(b) The equation of the curve is $y = x^3 + x^2 + 1$, and its differential is

$$\frac{dy}{dx} = 3x^2 + 2x$$

(i) When $x = 3$ then

$$\frac{dy}{dx} = (3 \times 3^2) + (2 \times 3) = 33$$

(ii) When $x = -2$ then

$$\frac{dy}{dx} = (4 \times (-2)^2) + (2 \times (-2)) = 8$$

12.10 The second derivative of a function

If the linear distance, s, moved by an object is given by $s = 10t + 2t^2$, where t is time, then the velocity of the object is

$$v = \frac{ds}{dt} = 10 + 4t$$

and its acceleration, a, is the rate of change of the velocity, and is given by

$$a = \frac{dv}{dt} = \frac{d(10 + 4t)}{dt} = 4$$

That is, the acceleration is obtained by **twice differentiating the distance moved**. This is expressed mathematically as

$$a = \frac{d^2s}{dt^2}$$

which is pronounced 'd two s by dt squared', and is the **second derivative** of s.

In functional notation, the second derivative of $f(x)$ is written $f''(x)$.

Worked Example 12.6

A body moves in a straight line according to the equation

$$S = 3t^2 - 2t + 5$$

where S is the distance moved in metres and t is time in seconds. Determine (a) the distance moved (δS) between $t = 4$ s and $t = 4.1$ s, (b) the velocity when $t = 4$ s and (c) its acceleration.

Solution

(a) If t changes by δt, the increment in movement, δS, can be calculated from

$$S + \delta S = 3(t + \delta t)^2 - 2(t + \delta t) + 5$$
$$= 3t^2 + 6t\delta t + 3(\delta t)^2 - 2t - 2\delta t + 5$$

Subtracting S from the left-hand side of the equation and $(3t^2 - 2t + 5)$ from the right-hand side leaves the equation unchanged, as follows

$$\delta S = 6t\delta t + 3(\delta t)^2 - 2\delta t$$
$$= (6 \times 4 \times 0.1) + (3 \times 0.1^2) - (2 \times 0.1)$$
$$= 2.23 \text{ m}$$

Alternatively, the value of S can be calculated from the original equation both for $t = 4$ s and $t = 4.1$ s, and the distance moved is the difference between the two values.

(b) The velocity of the body is

$$v = \frac{ds}{dt} = \frac{d(3t^2 - 2t + 5)}{dt} = 6t - 2$$

when $t = 4$ s

$$v = (6 \times 4) - 2 = 22 \text{ m/s}$$

(c) The acceleration of the body is

$$a = \frac{dv}{dt} = \frac{d(6t - 2)}{dt} = 6 \text{ m/s}^2$$

12.11 Stationary points on a graph

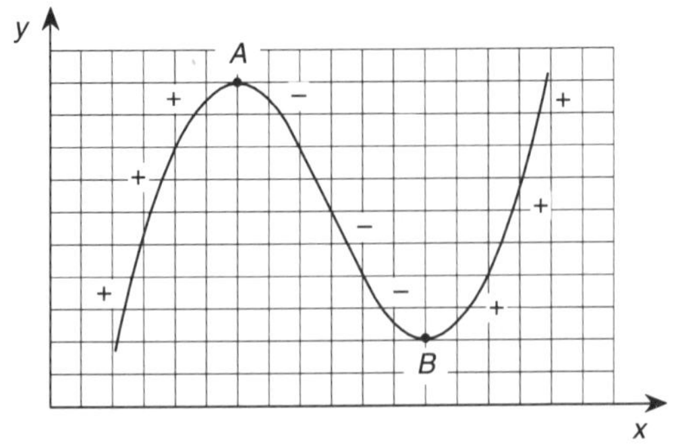

Figure 12.3 Stationary points on a curve; '+' means a positive gradient, '–' means a negative gradient

Consider the graph in Figure 12.3; the gradient of the graph is positive for both high and low values of x, and is negative between them, and is zero at points A and B. We say that the graph has **turning points** at A and B, at which point the first derivative, $f'(x)$, is zero.

12.12 Introduction to turning points

A turning point on a graph is defined as a point where the sign of the gradient of the graph changes from positive to negative (or from negative to positive).

We are particularly interested in two types of turning points, namely maximum points (the plural is **maxima**) and minimum points (the plural is **minima**).

A **maximum point** occurs where the gradient changes from a positive value to a negative value, and the tangent to the curve at that point is parallel to the x-axis (see point A in Figure 12.3). A **minimum point** occurs where the gradient changes from a negative value to a positive value, and the tangent to the curve at that point is parallel to the x-axis (see point B in Figure 12.3).

12.13 Determination of maxima and minima

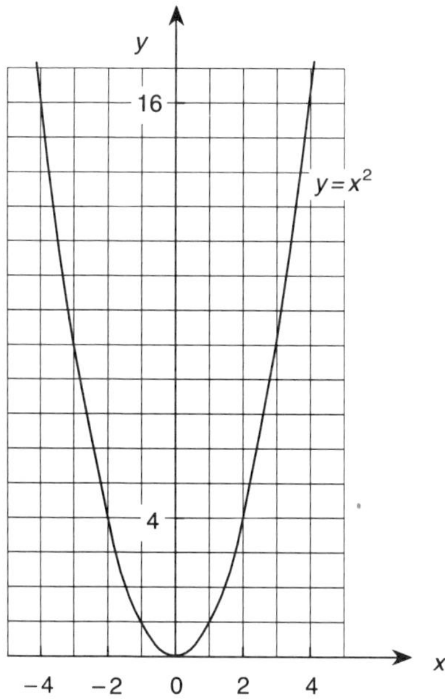

Figure 12.4 The graph of $y = x^2$

We have already said that the slope of a curve is zero at a maximum or a minimum point. Consider the curve $y = x^2$ in Figure 12.4; the first derivative of the equation is

$$\frac{dy}{dx} = 2x$$

Clearly, when x has a positive value the gradient of the curve is positive, and when x is negative the gradient of the curve is negative, and when x is zero, the gradient of the curve is zero. That is, there is a stationary point at $x = 0$. Moreover, since the gradient of the curve changes from negative to positive as it passes through zero, it follows that there is a *minimum point* when $x = 0$.

However, what we need is a mathematical method of telling us whether the turning point is a maximum or a minimum.

In the case of a curve having a minimum point (see, for example, Figure 12.4), the gradient of the curve increases as the value of x passes through the turning point, i.e. the gradient changes from a negative value to a positive value. That is to say

> **the rate of change of the gradient of the curve is positive at a minimum point,**

or

> **at a minimum point, $\frac{d^2y}{dx^2}$ is positive.**

Let us take a further look at the curve for $y = x^2$. In this case

$$\frac{dy}{dx} = 2x$$

and

$$\frac{d^2y}{dx^2} = 2$$

Since d^2y/dx^2 is positive, it follows that the curve has a *minimum point*.

Let us take a look at the curve for the equation $y = -x^2$, which is plotted in Figure 12.5. The first derivative of this equation is

$$\frac{dy}{dx} = -2x$$

Hence, for negative values of x the gradient is positive, and for positive values of x the gradient is negative. That is, the curve has a maximum point.

The second derivative of the equation is

$$\frac{d^2y}{dx^2} = \frac{d(-2x)}{dx} = -2$$

From this we see that

> **at a maximum point, $\frac{d^2y}{dx^2}$ is negative.**

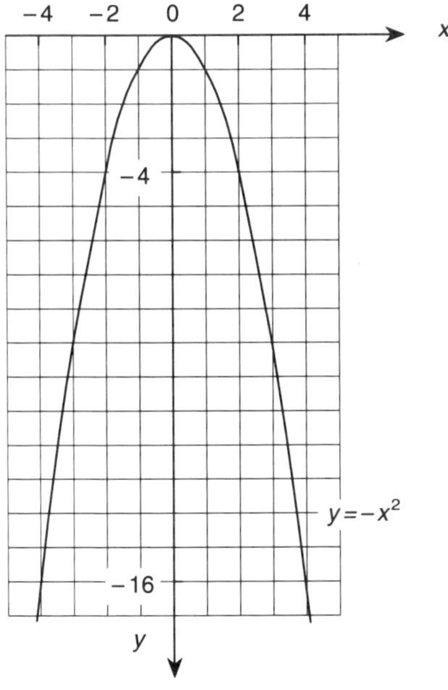

Figure 12.5 The graph of $y = -x^2$

Summary

	Minimum point	*Maximum point*
$y = f(x)$	Decreasing before Increasing after	Increasing before Decreasing after
$\frac{dy}{dx}$	Negative before Positive after (hence increasing)	Positive before Negative after (hence decreasing)
$\frac{d^2y}{dx^2}$	Positive	Negative

Worked Example 12.7

Determine the value of x and y at the turning point of the graph of $y = 6x^2 + 11x - 10$. Show mathematically whether the turning point is a maximum or a minimum.

Solution

Initially we will make a few comments which are based on the work in previous chapters. It was shown in Chapter 9, for an expression of the form $y = ax^2 + bx + c = 6x^2 + 11x - 10$ that (1) the graph has a turning point; (2) since parameter a (= 6) is positive the graph is concave looking from above i.e., it has a minimum point; (3) since parameter b (= 11) is positive, the turning point is shifted to the left of $x = 0$, i.e., the minimum point occurs when x is negative; and (4) the value of parameter c (= −10) is equal to the y-intercept of the graph. Moreover, using the mathematical method of solving the quadratic equation, we find that the curve cuts the x-axis at $x = -2.5$ and $x = 0.6667$. With this information, the reader is practically in a position to sketch the shape of the curve.

The first differential of the equation with respect to x is

$$\frac{dy}{dx} = \frac{d(6x^2 + 11x - 10)}{dx} = 12x + 11$$

The turning point in the curve occurs when

$$\frac{dy}{dx} = 0 = 12x + 11$$

or at

$$x = \frac{11}{12} = -0.917$$

when the value of y is

$$\begin{aligned} y &= 6x^2 + 11x - 10 \\ &= 6(-0.917)^2 + 11(-0.917) - 10 = -15.04 \end{aligned}$$

Also

$$\frac{d^2y}{dx^2} = \frac{d}{dx}(12x + 11) = 12$$

Since this value is positive, the graph has a minimum point.

Worked Example 12.8

Determine the turning points of the curve defined by the equation $y = 2x^3 - 7x - 3$. State also which of the turning points is a minimum and which a maximum.

Solution

We can observe that when $x = 0$, then

$$y = 2x^3 - 7x - 3 = (2 \times 0^3) - (7 \times 0) - 3 = -3$$

That is, the y-intercept is at $y = -3$. The first derivative of the equation is

$$\frac{dy}{dx} = \frac{d(2x^3 - 7x - 3)}{dx} = 6x^2 - 7$$

Hence turning points occur when

$$\frac{dy}{dx} = 0 = 6x^2 - 7$$

or when

$$x^2 = 7/6$$

that is

$$x = \sqrt{(7/6)} = \pm 1.08$$

That is, there is one turning point at $x = -1.08$ and another at $x = +1.08$.

The second derivative of the equation is

$$\frac{d^2y}{dx^2} = \frac{d(6x^2 - 7)}{dx} = 12x$$

When $x = -1.08$, then the value of the second derivative is $12x = 12 \times (-1.08) = -12.96$. Since d^2y/dx^2 is negative at this point, it follows that the curve has a *maximum* at $x = -1.08$.

The value of y at the maximum point is

$$y = 2x^3 - 7x - 3 = 2(-1.08)^3 - 7(-1.08) - 3 = 2.04$$

When $x = +1.08$, then the value of the second derivative is $12x = 12 \times 1.08 = 12.96$. Since d^2y/dx^2 is positive at this point, it follows that the curve has a *minimum* at $x = 1.08$.

The value of y at the minimum point is

$$y = 2x^3 - 7x - 3 = 2(1.08)^3 - 7(1.08) - 3 = -8.04$$

12.14 Differentiating a function of a function

If $y = (x^2 + 3)^5$, we can let $z = x^2 + 3$, so that this complex function above reduces to

$$y = z^5$$

Hence, y is a function of z, and z is a function of x. We therefore say that

y is function of a function of x.

If we differentiate the above expression for y with respect to z, we get

$$\frac{dy}{dz} = 5z^4$$

and

$$\frac{dz}{dx} = \frac{d(x^2+3)}{dx} = 2x$$

It therefore follows that

$$\frac{dy}{dx} = \frac{dy}{dz}\cdot\frac{dz}{dx} = 5z^4 \times 2x = 5(x^2+3)^4 \times 2x$$
$$= 10x(x^2+3)^4$$

The rule

$$\boldsymbol{\frac{dy}{dx} = \frac{dy}{dz}\cdot\frac{dz}{dx}}$$

is known as the **function of a function rule** and applies to all functions of functions.

Worked Example 12.9

Determine dy/dx for (a) $y = (x^3 - 6x + 3)^2$, (b) $y = (3x^4 - 4x^2 + x - 6)^5$.

Solution

(a) In this case we let $z = x^3 - 6x + 3$, that is $y = z^2$, hence

$$\frac{dy}{dz} = 2z$$

and

$$\frac{dz}{dx} = 3x^2 - 6$$

Therefore

$$\frac{dy}{dx} = \frac{dy}{dz}\cdot\frac{dz}{dx} = 2z(3x^2 - 6)$$
$$= 2(x^3 - 6x + 3)(3x^2 - 6)$$

(b) Here $z = 3x^4 - 4x^2 + x - 6$ and $y = z^5$, hence

$$\frac{dy}{dz} = 5z^4$$

and

$$\frac{dz}{dx} = 12x^3 - 8x + 1$$

Therefore

$$\frac{dy}{dx} = \frac{dy}{dz} \cdot \frac{dz}{dx} = 5z^4(12x^3 - 8x + 1)$$

$$= 5(3x^4 - 4x^2 + x - 6)^4(12x^3 - 8x + 1)$$

12.15 Differential of a product

If $y = uv$, where u and v are both functions of x, then, as x changes to $x + \delta x$, it follows that u changes in value to $(u + \delta u)$, and v changes in value to $(v + \delta v)$, and y becomes $(y + \delta y)$. That is

$$y + \delta y = (u + \delta u)(v + \delta v)$$

$$= uv + v\delta u + u\delta v + \delta u\delta v$$

Subtracting y from the left-hand side of the equation and uv from the right-hand side maintains equilibrium between the two sides, giving

$$\delta y = v\delta u + u\delta v + \delta u\delta v$$

and dividing throughout the equation by δx leaves us with

$$\frac{\delta y}{\delta x} = v\frac{\delta u}{\delta x} + u\frac{\delta v}{\delta x} + \frac{\delta u\delta v}{\delta x}$$

In the limit that δx tends to zero the above equation becomes

$$\frac{dy}{dx} = v\frac{du}{dx} + u\frac{dv}{dx}$$

or

$$\boldsymbol{\frac{d(uv)}{dx} = v\frac{du}{dx} + u\frac{dv}{dx}}$$

This expression is the **differential coefficient of the product uv.**

Worked Example 12.10

Differentiate the following equations with respect to x: (a) $y = x^{\frac{1}{2}}(x^2 + 4x - 2)$, (b) $y = 3x^2/(1 - x)$.

Solution

(a) In this case we will let $u = x^{\frac{1}{2}}$ and $v = x^2 + 4x - 2$, hence

$$\frac{dy}{dx} = \frac{du}{dx} + \frac{dv}{dx}$$

$$= (x^2 + 4x - 2) \times \frac{1}{2}x^{0.5-1} + x^{\frac{1}{2}} \times (2x + 4)$$

$$= \frac{1}{2}x^{-0.5}(x^2 + 4x - 2) + x^{0.5}(2x + 4)$$

(b) Although this expression contains a quotient (see also section 12.16), we can treat it as a product as follows.

$$y = 3x^2/(1 - x) = 3x^2(1 - x)^{-1} = uv$$

where $u = 3x^2$ and $v = (1 - x)^{-1}$. The derivative of u with respect to x is

$$\frac{du}{dx} = \frac{d(3x^2)}{dx} = 6x$$

and, in this case we must treat v as a function of a function. If we let $z = 1 - x$, so that $v = z^{-1}$, it follows that

$$\frac{dv}{dx} = \frac{dy}{dz}\cdot\frac{dz}{dx} = -z^{-2} \times (-1) = z^{-2} = \frac{1}{(1 - x)^2}$$

Using the derivative product rule

$$\frac{dy}{dx} = v\frac{du}{dx} + u\frac{dv}{dx}$$

$$= ((1 - x)^{-1} \times 6x) + \frac{3x^2}{(1 - x)^2}$$

$$= \frac{6x}{(1 - x)} + \frac{3x^2}{(1 - x)^2} = \frac{6x(1 - x) + 3x^2}{(1 - x)^2}$$

$$= \frac{6x - 6x^2 + 3x^2}{(1 - x)^2} = \frac{3x(2 - x)}{(1 - x)^2}$$

12.16 Differential coefficient of a quotient

Consider the expression

$$y = \frac{u}{v}$$

where u and v are functions of x. If a change δx in x causes u to change to $(u + \delta u)$, and v to change to $(v + \delta v)$, then

$$y + \delta y = \frac{u + \delta u}{v + \delta v}$$

or

$$\delta y = \frac{u + \delta u}{v + \delta v} - y = \frac{u + \delta u}{v + \delta v} - \frac{u}{v}$$

$$= \frac{(u + \delta u)v - u(v + \delta v)}{(v + \delta v)v} = \frac{uv + v\delta u - uv - u\delta v}{(v + \delta v)v} = \frac{v\delta u - u\delta v}{(v + \delta v)v}$$

Dividing throughout by δx gives

$$\frac{\delta y}{\delta x} = \frac{v\dfrac{\delta u}{\delta x} - u\dfrac{\delta v}{\delta x}}{(v + \delta v)v}$$

As δx tends to zero, $(v + \delta v)$ tends to v, so that the denominator term becomes v^2, and **the differential coefficient of the quotient u/v is**

$$\frac{dy}{dx} = \frac{v\dfrac{du}{dx} - u\dfrac{dv}{dx}}{v^2}$$

Worked Example 12.11

Determine the differential coefficient of (a) $\dfrac{x^2 + 3x + 4}{2x + 1}$, (b) $\dfrac{3x^2}{1 - x}$

Solution

(a) In this case $u = x^2 + 3x + 4$ and $v = 2x + 1$, hence

$$\frac{du}{dx} = 2x + 3 \text{ and } \frac{dv}{dx} = 2, \text{ therefore}$$

$$\frac{dy}{dx} = \frac{v\dfrac{du}{dx} - u\dfrac{dv}{dx}}{v^2}$$

$$= \frac{(2x + 1)(2x + 3) - (x^2 + 3x + 4) \times 2}{(2x + 1)^2}$$

The reader will find it an interesting exercise to show that the above expression can be simplified to

$$\frac{dy}{dx} = \frac{2x^2 + 2x - 5}{(2x + 1)^2}$$

(b) In this case we let $u = 3x^2$ and $v = (1 - x)$, and

$$\frac{du}{dx} = 6x \text{ and } \frac{dv}{dx} = -1, \text{ hence}$$

$$\frac{dy}{dx} = \frac{v\dfrac{du}{dx} - u\dfrac{dv}{dx}}{v^2}$$

$$= \frac{(1 - x)6x - 3x^2 \times (-1)}{(1 - x)^2}$$

$$= \frac{3x(2 - x)}{(1 - x)^2}$$

The reader should compare this with the solution of Worked Example 12.10(b).

Worked Example 12.12

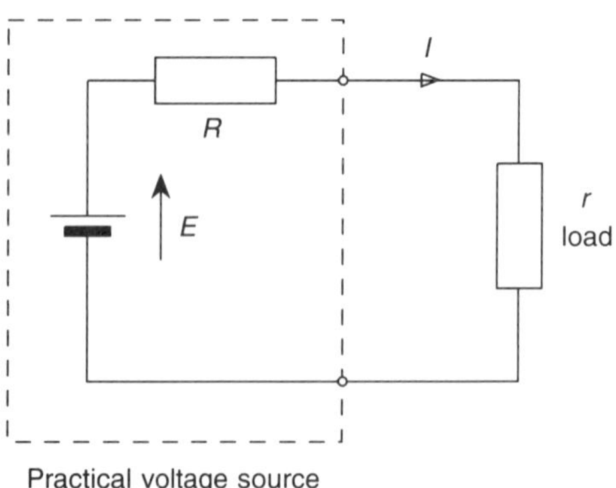

Figure 12.6 Worked Example 12.12

A practical electrical power source can be regarded as an ideal voltage source of e.m.f. E, in series with an internal resistance R, as shown in Figure 12.6. If a resistive load, r, is connected to the terminals of the source, determine the value of r *which consumes the maximum power* from the source.

Solution

This is a practical situation that every electronic engineer meets daily because, when connecting a load to a power source (which may be, for example, connecting a loudspeaker to an electronic amplifier), he must decide what the resistance of the load must be if maximum power is to be extracted from the source.

From Ohm's law, the current in the circuit is

$$I = E/(R + r)$$

and the power, P, consumed by the load is

$$P = I^2 r = \frac{E^2 r}{(R + r)^2}$$

In this problem we shall look at the way in which the value of r affects the power it consumes. Clearly, r can have any value between zero and infinity.

When $r = 0$, no voltage is developed across the load (even though the current is very high), and *the power consumed by the load is zero*. When $r = \infty$, no current flows in the load and, once again, *no power is developed in the load*. Clearly, in practice, power is developed in the load, and it is the function of this exercise to determine the condition for maximum power consumption.

Figure 12.7 Graph showing the curve for power consumption in a resistive circuit as the resistance changes in value

A graph showing how the power consumed varies with load resistance is plotted in Figure 12.7. Most colleges have a laboratory experiment in which this graph is plotted, and is used to verify the **maximum power transfer theorem**, which is taught in all courses in electrical engineering principles.

It was shown in section 12.12 that a maximum occurs when the gradient of the dP/dr graph in Figure 12.7 is zero. Writing down the equation for power once more we get

$$P = \frac{E^2 r}{(R + r)^2} = \frac{u}{v}$$

where $u = E^2 r$ and $v = (R + r)^2$. In this case we can easily see that $du/dr = E^2$ but, in order to determine dv/dr we must write $z = (R + r)$, and $v = z^2$. Using the function of a function notation (where R is a fixed value) we see that

$$\frac{dv}{dr} = \frac{dv}{dz}\frac{dz}{dr} = 2z \times 1 = 2z = 2(R + r)$$

From the differential of a quotient rule we get

$$\frac{dP}{dr} = \frac{v\dfrac{du}{dr} - u\dfrac{dv}{dr}}{v^2}$$

$$= \frac{((R + r)^2 \times E^2) - (E^2 r \times 2(R + r))}{(R + r)^4}$$

The power in the load is a maximum when $dP/dr = 0$, which occurs when the numerator of the above equation is zero, that is when

$$(R + r)^2 E^2 = E^2 r \times 2(R + r)$$

or when

$$R + r = 2r$$

hence maximum power is consumed when

$$r - R$$

that is to say, the load resistance is equal to the internal resistance of the source. This is verified by the results in Table 12.2, which lists the power consumed when the load has resistance values of (a) $r = R/2$, (b) $r = R$ and (c) $r = 2R$. The results are calculated using the equation

$$P = E^2 r/(R + r)$$

TABLE 12.2 Solution to Worked Example 12.12

Load resistance	$r = R/2$	$r = R$	$r = 2R$
Power consumed	$0.222E^2/R$	$0.25E^2/R$	$0.222E^2/R$

The reader will find it of value to plot the curve in the region of $r = R$ in some detail.

12.17 Standard derivatives

TABLE 12.3 A list of standard derivatives

y	$\dfrac{dy}{dx}$
x^n	nx^{n-1}
ax^n	anx^{n-1}
$\sin x$	$\cos x$
$\sin ax$	$a \cos ax$
$\sin(ax + b)$	$a \cos(ax + b)$
$\cos x$	$-\sin x$
$\cos ax$	$-a \sin ax$
$\cos(ax + b)$	$-a \sin(ax + b)$
$e^k x$	$ke^k x$
$ae^k x$	$ake^k x$
$\ln x$	$1/x$
$\ln(ax + b)$	$a/(ax + b)$

The subject of differential calculus covers a vast range of topics and, at this point, a number of equations of importance are listed in Table 12.3, in which a, b, k and n are constants. Worked Examples 12.13–12.16 illustrate the use of many of the standard derivatives.

Worked Example 12.13

Differentiate the following with respect to x: (a) $y = \sin 5x$, (b) $y = \sin^3 x$, (c) $y = \cos^2 4x$.

Solution

(a) From Table 12.3 we see that

$$\frac{d}{dx}(\sin ax) = a\cos ax,$$

hence

$$\frac{dy}{dx} = 5\cos 5x$$

(b) The expression in this case is a function of a function, and we write $z = \sin x$, and $y = z^3$, hence

$$\frac{dy}{dx} = \frac{dy}{dz}\frac{dz}{dx} = 3z^2\cos x = 3\sin^2 x.\cos x$$

(c) In this case we may write $z = \cos 4x$, and $y = z^2$, so that

$$\frac{dy}{dx} = \frac{dy}{dz}\frac{dz}{dx} = 2z(-4\sin 4x) = -8\cos 4x.\sin 4x$$

Worked Example 12.14

The e.m.f., e, induced in inductor L is given by

$$e = L\frac{di}{dt}$$

If $i = I_m \sin \omega t$, where I_m is the maximum current, and ω is the angular frequency of the supply, determine an expression for e.

Solution

Since $i = I_m \sin \omega t$, then

$$\frac{di}{dt} = I_m \times \omega\cos\omega t$$

or

$$e = L\frac{di}{dt} = \omega L I_m \cos\omega t = X_L I_m \cos\omega t$$

where $X_L = \omega L$ is known as the **inductive reactance** of the inductor, and has the dimensions of ohms.

Worked Example 12.15

Differentiate the following: (a) $y = x^2 \sin x$, (b) $y = 4x^3 \cos 3x$, (c) $y = (6 \sin 2t)/t^2$.

Solution

(a) This is a product term of the type $y = uv$, where $u = x^2$ and $v = \sin x$, hence

$$\frac{dy}{dx} = v\frac{du}{dx} + u\frac{dv}{dx}$$
$$= (\sin x \times 2x) + (x^2 \cos x) = 2x \sin x + x^2 \cos x$$

(b) Again, this is another product term with $u = 4x^3$ and $v = \cos 3x$, therefore

$$\frac{dy}{dx} = (\cos 3x \times 12x^2) + (4x^3 \times (-3 \sin 3x))$$
$$= 12x^2 \cos 3x - 12x^3 \sin 3x$$
$$= 12x^2(cos 3x - x \sin 3x)$$

(c) This expression is a quotient term of the type $y = u/v$, where $u = 6 \sin 2t$ and $v = t^2$, hence

$$\frac{dy}{dt} = \frac{v\dfrac{du}{dt} - u\dfrac{dv}{dt}}{v^2}$$
$$= \frac{(t^2 \times (6 \times 2 \cos 2t)) - (6 \sin 2t \times 2t)}{t^4}$$
$$= \frac{12t^2 \cos 2t - 12t \sin 2t}{t^4}$$
$$= \frac{12}{t^3}(t \cos 2t - \sin 2t)$$

Worked Example 12.16

Differentiate (a) $y = e^{3x} \sin^2 x$, (b) $y = \ln x / \cos^2 x$.

Solution

(a) Here we have a product term $y = uv$, where $u = e^{3x}$ and $v = \sin^2 x$. In this case

$$\frac{du}{dx} = 3e^{3x}$$

We must treat v as a function of a function where $z = \sin x$ and $v = z^2$, hence

$$\frac{dv}{dx} = \frac{dv}{dz}\frac{dz}{dx} = 2z \times \cos x = 2 \sin x . \cos x$$

Therefore

$$\frac{dy}{dx} = v\frac{du}{dx} + u\frac{dv}{dx}$$
$$= (\sin^2 x \times 3e^{3x}) + (e^{3x} \times 2 \sin x . \cos x)$$
$$= e^{3x} \sin x(3 \sin x + 2 \cos x)$$

(b) We can write

$$y = \frac{\ln x}{\cos^2 x} = \frac{u}{v}$$

Once again, v is a function of a function, and the reader should be able to show that

$$\frac{dv}{dx} = -2 \cos x . \sin x$$

hence

$$\frac{dy}{dx} = \frac{v\dfrac{du}{dx} - u\dfrac{dv}{dx}}{v^2}$$
$$= \frac{(\cos^2 x \times 1/x) - \ln x \times (-2 \cos x . \sin x)}{\cos^4 x}$$
$$= \left[\frac{1}{x}\cos^2 x + 2 \ln x . \cos x . \sin x\right] / (\cos^4 x)$$

Self-test questions

12.1 Explain what is meant by a 'function'.

12.2 From first principles, differentiate: (a) $y = 5x - 3$, (b) $d = 6t^4 + t^3$, (c) $s = 4t^2 - 3t + 6$, (d) $y = 1/x^2$.

12.3 Differentiate by inspection (a) $y = 4x^3 - 6x + 1$, (b) $f(x) = 5\sqrt{x}$, (c) $l = 5m^4 + 6m^2 - 3m + 2$, (d) $y = 5.6x^{2.2} + 8x^{-1} - 5\sqrt{x}$, (e) $y = 0.6x^{2.4}$.

12.4 If

$$y = \frac{x^3}{3} + \frac{5x^2}{2} - 6x + 4,$$

determine the number of stationary points on the graph, and state which is a maximum and which a minimum.

12.5 If $y = 4x^3 - 48x^2 + 144x$, determine the turning points on the graph, and calculate the value of x and y at each turning point.

12.6 Plot the graph for $y = -x^2 + 5x - 7$ over the range $x = 0$ to $x = 5$, and determine the gradient of the graph when x has the value (a) 1.5, (b) 2.5, (c) 3.5. What is the value of y at each of these points?

Using calculus, show that the graph has one turning point, and state whether this is a minimum or a maximum point.

12.7 When designing an electrical system, the following equation was obtained

$$y = (2x + 1) + 1/(2x + 1)$$

Determine the values of x which make y either a maximum or a minimum.

12.8 Differentiate the following equations with respect to x (a) $y = 4x \sin x$, (b) $y = e^{-x}$ in x^2, (c) $y = \sin x . \cos x$.

Summary of important facts

When two quantities are related to one another, so that a change in the independent variable produces a specific change in the dependent variable, then the dependent variable is said to be a **function** of the independent variable. For example, if $A = \pi r^2$, then A is a function of r.

The **gradient** of a straight-line graph is the tangent of the angle the line makes with the x-axis.

Differentiation is the process of determining the tangent to a graph at a point, and

$$\frac{dy}{dx}$$

means that the equation has been **differentiated once**;

$$\frac{d^2y}{dx^2}$$

is the **second differential** of the equation to the curve.

The **differential coefficient of a sum of functions** is the sum of the individual differential coefficients.

A **stationary point** on a graph occurs when

$$\frac{dy}{dx} = 0,$$

and a **turning point** occurs when the gradient of a graph changes from positive to negative (or vice-versa). At a **maximum point** the slope changes from positive to negative, and at a **minimum point** the slope changes from negative to positive. The *second differential* at a minimum point has a positive value, and at a maximum point it is negative.

If $y = \cos^2 x$, we can write $z = \cos x$, and $y = z^2$. In this case we describe y as a **function of a function of x**. A function of a function is differentiated using the following rule.

$$\frac{dy}{dx} = \frac{dy}{dz} \cdot \frac{dz}{dx}$$

If $y = uv$, where u and v are functions of x, then

$$\frac{dy}{dx} = v\frac{du}{dx} + u\frac{dv}{dx}$$

and if $y = \frac{u}{v}$, then

$$\frac{dy}{dx} = \frac{v\frac{du}{dx} - u\frac{dv}{dx}}{v^2}$$

13 Integration

13.1 Introduction

Integration is the reverse of differentiation. That is, if we know the derivative of an equation, integration allows us to obtain the original equation.

Also, integration is a process of summation or adding parts together, and it allows us to determine the area under a curve or graph. Engineers frequently need to know the average value and the 'effective' value of a waveform in an electrical circuit; the process of integration allows us to calculate it.

A knowledge of the processes involved in integration gives us a sound grasp of many theoretical principles of electrical and electronic engineering.

By the end of this chapter the reader will be able to

- understand what is meant by an 'indefinite' integral and the arbitrary constant of integration,
- determine the value of the arbitrary constant of integration,
- integrate the sum of differentials,
- integrate trigonometrical functions,
- determine the value of a definite integral and calculate the area under a curve,
- determine a 'volume of revolution',
- compute the mean value and the root-mean-square (r.m.s.) value of an alternating waveform.

13.2 Indefinite integrals and the arbitrary constant of integration

If we consider the equation

$$y = \frac{x^4}{4}$$

it follows from Chapter 12 that

$$\frac{dy}{dx} = 4 \times \frac{x^{4-1}}{4} = x^3$$

or

$$dy = x^3\,dx$$

It would seem reasonable at this point to suggest that, if we integrated the above equation, we should be able to predict that $y = x^4/4$.

However, if we consider the function

$$y = \frac{x^4}{4} + 6$$

then the work in Chapter 12 also tells us that

$$\frac{dy}{dx} = x^3$$

Clearly it is not possible, on face value, to commence with the expression $dy = x^3\,dx$ and return to the original equation since we have at least two possible solutions, namely

$$y = \frac{x^4}{4} \text{ and } y = \frac{x^4}{4} + 6$$

In fact, there are an infinite number of possible solutions because the differential coefficient of any constant in the equation is zero!

An integral without any specified limits, such as the examples given above, is known as an **indefinite integral**, and its solution **must contain an arbitrary constant of integration** in the answer (sometimes known as the *constant of integration* or *arbitrary constant*). We will use letter K for this constant. Thus the integral of $x^3.dx$ is

$$y = \frac{x^4}{4} + K$$

where the value of K is determined by inserting known values of x and y into the above equation.

In electrical and electronic circuits, the 'known conditions' usually occur at the instant when the circuit is connected to (or is disconnected from) the supply, and are described as the **boundary conditions**.

Although integration is simply 'differentiation in reverse', we can use the list of standard integrals in Table 13.1, which is based on the list of standard derivatives (Table 12.3) in Chapter 12. The reader will note that the process of integration is represented by the elongated '*s*' symbol, $\int$.

For example, if $dy = x^3.dx$, we can use Table 13.1 to say that

$$y = \int x^3.dx = \frac{1 \times x^{(3+1)}}{3+1} + K = \frac{x^4}{4} + K$$

where K is the constant of integration. Also if $dy = 5\sqrt{x}.dx$ then

$$y = \int 5\sqrt{x}.dx = \int 5x^{\frac{1}{2}}.dx = \frac{5x^{(\frac{1}{2}+1)}}{\frac{1}{2}+1} + K$$

$$= \frac{10}{3}x^{1.5} + K$$

TABLE 13.1 List of standard integrals

Note: K is the constant of integration.

Function	*Integral*
a	$ax + K$
ax^n	$\frac{ax^{n+1}}{n+1} + K \quad (n \neq 1)$
$\sin ax$	$-\frac{1}{a}\cos ax + K$
$\sin(ax + b)$	$-\frac{1}{a}\cos(ax + b) + K$
$\cos ax$	$\frac{1}{a}\sin ax + K$
$\cos(ax + b)$	$\frac{1}{a}\sin(ax + b) + K$
ae^{kx}	$\frac{a}{k}e^{kx} + K$
$\frac{1}{x}$	$\ln x + K$
$\frac{1}{ax + b}$	$\frac{1}{a}\ln(ax + b) + K$

and if $dy = \frac{4}{x^5}.dx = 4x^{-5}.dx$, then

$$y = \int 4x^{-5}.dx = \frac{4x^{(-5+1)}}{-5+1} + K = -x^{-4} + K = \frac{-1}{x^4} + K$$

The reader should note that the integral of x^n in the first row of Table 13.1 **does not apply when $n = -1$**. We will return to this in section 13.3.

The accuracy of an integration can be tested by differentiating the integral, which should give the original expression.

(a) Determining the value of the arbitrary constant of integration

Using two of the above examples, we will determine the value of the constant of integration for each.

Suppose, in the equation $dy = x^3.dx$ (corresponding to the equation $y = \frac{x^4}{4} + K$), the boundary conditions are $y = 12$ when $x = 2$; to determine the value of K, we simply insert these values into the equation for y, that is we insert them in the equation

$$y = \frac{x^4}{4} + K$$

This gives

$$12 = \frac{2^4}{4} + K = \frac{16}{4} + K = 4 + K$$

hence

$$K = 12 - 4 = 8$$

The complete equation is, therefore

$$y = \frac{x^4}{4} + 8$$

Also if, in the equation $dy = (4/x^5).dx$ (or $y = (-1/x^4) + K$), we know that $y = 0.988$ when $x = 3$, then

$$0.988 = -\frac{1}{3^4} + K = -0.012 + K$$

or

$$K = 0.988 + 0.012 = 1$$

and the complete equation is

$$y = -\frac{1}{x^4} + 1$$

13.3 Integrating x^n when $n = -1$

If $n = -1$ in the equation $dy = x^n.dx$, then the integral is

$$\int x^{-1}.dx = \int \frac{dx}{x}$$

If we simply apply the rule in the first row of Table 13.1 we would get

$$\int x^{-1}.dx = \frac{x^{(-1+1)}}{-1+1} + K = \frac{x^0}{0} = \frac{1}{0} + K = \infty + K$$

Clearly we cannot apply this rule in the case where $n = -1$. In fact, it is shown in the seventh row of Table 13.1 that

$$\int \frac{dx}{x} = \ln x + K$$

The reader should carefully note this fact.

When integrating an expression with x in the denominator, the reader should investigate the possibility that the integral may be logarithmic. If, for example, we wish to evaluate

$$\int \frac{dx}{3x + 2}$$

we can let $Y = 3x + 2$, so that $\dfrac{dY}{dx} = 3$, or $dx = dY/3$, and we may re-write the above equation in the form

$$\int \frac{dY/3}{Y} = \frac{1}{3}\int \frac{dY}{Y} = \frac{1}{3}\ln Y + K = \frac{1}{3}\ln(3x+2) + K$$

In fact, this is expressed in row eight of Table 13.1 when we say that

$$\int \frac{dx}{ax+b} = \frac{1}{a}\ln(ax+b) + K$$

Clearly, in cases like these, *we make the numerator of the equation equal to the derivative of the denominator* (see examples (g) and (h) in Worked Example 13.1).

Worked Example 13.1

Integrate the following functions with respect to x: (a) x^2, (b) $\sqrt{x}$, (c) $x^{-\frac{1}{2}}$, (d) $4x^6$, (e) $5x^{-2/3}$, (f) $2.5x^{0.8}$, (g) $1/(3x+1)$, (h) $x^2/(x^3+2)$.

Solution

(a) $$\int x^2.dx = \frac{x^{(2+1)}}{2+1} + K = \frac{x^3}{3} + K$$

(b) $$\int \sqrt{x}.dx = \int x^{0.5}.dx = \frac{x^{(0.5+1)}}{1+0.5} + K = \frac{x^{1.5}}{1.5} + K$$

(c) $$\int x^{-\frac{1}{2}}.dx = \frac{x^{(-\frac{1}{2}+1)}}{-\frac{1}{2}+1} + K = \frac{x^{\frac{1}{2}}}{\frac{1}{2}} + K = 2\sqrt{x} + K$$

(d) $$\int 4x^6.dx = \frac{4x^{(6+1)}}{6+1} + K = \frac{4}{7}x^7 + K$$

(e) $$\int 5x^{-2/3}.dx = \frac{5x^{(1-2/3)}}{1-2/3} + K = \frac{5}{1/3}x^{1/3} + K = 15x^{1/3} + K$$

(f) $$\int 2.5x^{0.8} = \frac{2.5x^{(0.8+1)}}{0.8+1} + K = 1.389x^{1.8} + K$$

(g) In this case we let $Y = 3x+1$, or $dY/dx = 3$, hence $dx = dY/3$, therefore

$$\int \frac{dx}{3x+1} = \frac{1}{3}\int \frac{dY}{Y} = \frac{1}{3}\ln Y + K = \frac{1}{3}\ln(3x+1) + K$$

(h) Here we let $Y = x^3+2$, or $dY = 3x^2.dx$, therefore $x^2.dx = dY/3$, hence

$$\int \frac{x^2}{x^3+2}\,dx = \frac{1}{3}\int \frac{dY}{Y} = \frac{1}{3}\ln Y + K$$

$$= \frac{1}{3}\ln(x^3+2) + K$$

13.4 Integrating a sum of differentials

The integral of a sum of differential is the sum of the separate integrals; there is only one constant of integration. This is illustrated in Worked Example 13.2.

Worked Example 13.2

Integrate the following with respect to x (a) $2x^2 + 3x^4$, (b) $1.8x^{2.2} - 3x^{-0.2} + 3$.

Solution

(a) $$\int (2x^2 + 3x^4)\,dx = \frac{2x^{2+1}}{2+1} + \frac{3x^{4+1}}{4+1} + K$$
$$= \frac{2}{3}x^3 + \frac{3}{5}x^5 + K$$

(b) $$\int (1.8x^{2.2} - 3x^{-0.2} + 3)\,dx = \frac{1.8x^{2.2+1}}{2.2+1} - \frac{3x^{1-0.2}}{1-0.2} + 3x + K$$
$$= 0.5625x^{3.2} - 3.75x^{0.8} + 3x + K$$

13.5 Integration of trigonometrical functions

Using the integrals of trigonometrical functions in Table 13.1, we see that

$$\int 3\sin 2\theta.d\theta = 3\int \sin 2\theta.d\theta = 3(-\frac{1}{2}\cos 2\theta) + K$$
$$= -\frac{3}{2}\cos 2\theta + K$$

The reader will observe that the constant (= 3) can be taken outside the integral sign without affecting the integration (but *variables must not be taken outside the integral sign*).

We can also see that

$$\int 5\sin(\theta + 15^\circ)\,d\theta = 5\int \sin(\theta + 15^\circ)\,d\theta$$
$$= -5\cos(\theta + 15^\circ) + K$$

and

$$\int \cos(4\theta - \frac{\pi}{2})\,d\theta = \frac{1}{4}\sin(4\theta - \frac{\pi}{2}) + K$$

Worked Example 13.3

Integrate the following expressions: (a) $4\sin 3\theta$, (b) $3\sin 2\theta$, (c) $2\cos\frac{1}{2}\theta$, (d) $5\cos 2\theta - 4\sin 3\theta$, (e) $2\cos(4\theta - \pi/8)$, (f) $3\sin\left(\frac{\pi}{2} - \theta\right)$.

Solution

(a) $$\int 4\sin 3\theta\, d\theta = -\frac{4}{3}\cos 3\theta + K$$

(b) $$\int 3\sin 2\theta\, d\theta = -\frac{3}{2}\cos 2\theta + K$$

(c) $$\int 2\cos\frac{1}{2}\theta d\theta = \frac{2}{\frac{1}{2}}\sin\tfrac{1}{2}\theta + K = 4\sin\tfrac{1}{2}\theta + K$$

(d) $$\int(5\cos 2\theta - 4\sin 3\theta)\, d\theta = \frac{5}{2}\sin 2\theta - \left[-\frac{4}{3}\cos 3\theta\right] + K$$
$$= \frac{5}{2}\sin 2\theta + \frac{4}{3}\cos 3\theta + K$$

(e) $$\int 2\cos(4\theta - \pi/8)d\theta = \frac{2}{4}\sin(4\theta - \pi/8) + K$$
$$= \frac{1}{2}\sin(4\theta - \pi/8) + K$$

(f) $$\int 3\sin\left(\frac{\pi}{2} - \theta\right) d\theta = -\frac{3}{-1}\cos\left(\frac{\pi}{2} - \theta\right) + K$$
$$= 3\cos\left(\frac{\pi}{2} - \theta\right) + K$$

13.6 The definite integral – area under a curve

Consider the graph in Figure 13.1, in which y is a function of x, that is

$$y = f(x)$$

The area $ABDEFA$ under the curve lies somewhere between the areas $ABCDGFA$ and $ABEFA$, that is between the area given by $(y + \delta y)\delta x$ and the area $y\delta x$. We will call this area δA. It follows that

$$(y + \delta y)\delta x > \delta A > y\delta x$$

Dividing through the above expression by δx gives

$$(y + \delta y) > \frac{\delta A}{\delta x} > y$$

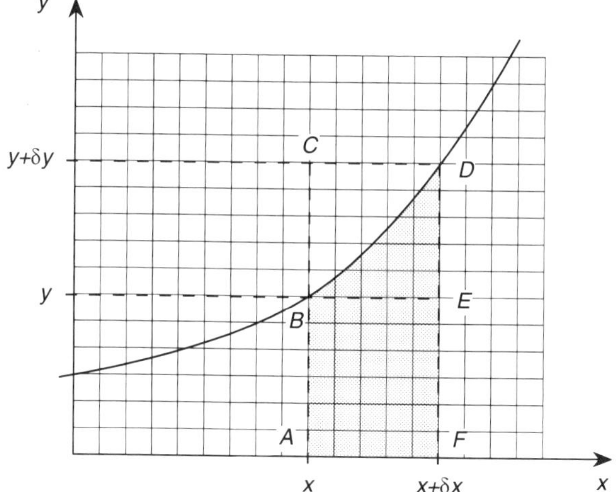

Figure 13.1 The area under a graph

As δx tends to zero, $y + \delta y$ tends to y, and $\delta A/\delta x$ becomes dA/dx. That is

$$\frac{dA}{dx} = y$$

or

$$dA = y\,dx$$

Clearly the total area under the curve is given by

$$A = \int dA = \int y\,dx$$

Such an integration leaves a constant of integration and, to determine the area under the curve, we need to eliminate the constant of integration. To find the area under the curve between, say, $x = x_1$ and $x = x_2$ (where $x_2 > x_1$), we need to subtract the value of the integral when $x = x_1$ from the value of the integral when $x = x_2$. That is

$$\text{Area } A = \begin{bmatrix}\text{value of integral} \\ \text{when } x = x_2\end{bmatrix} - \begin{bmatrix}\text{value of integral} \\ \text{when } x = x_1\end{bmatrix}$$

Since the constant of integration, K, has the same value in both cases, it will vanish from the calculation. The above calculation is written in the form

$$A = \int_{x_1}^{x_2} y\,dx$$

This is known as the **definite integral**, the two limiting values or **limits** being respectively written at the top of the integral sign (the *upper limit*) and the bottom of the integral sign (the *lower limit*).

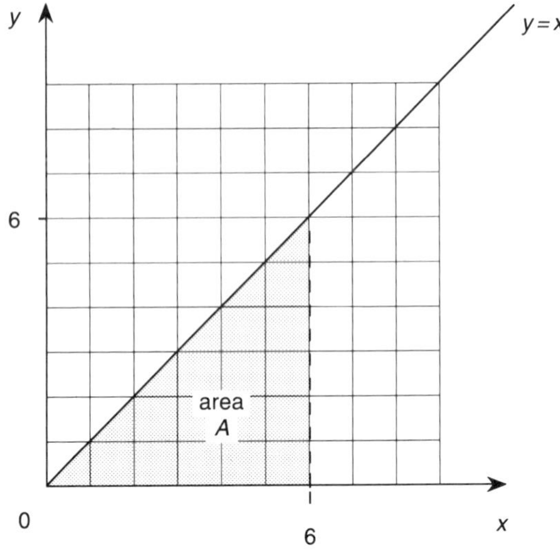

Figure 13.2 Simple application of integration to determine the area under a graph between two limits

Consider now the case of the area enclosed under the straight-line graph in Figure 13.2. The equation of the graph is $y = x$, and the area under the graph between $x = 0$ and $x = 6$ is given by

$$\int_{x=0}^{x=6} x\,dx = \left[\frac{x^2}{2}\right]_0^6$$

We enclose the result of the integration inside square brackets, and place the upper and lower limits as shown. Next, we replace each x value inside the brackets by the values given by the limits as follows

$$\left[\frac{x^2}{2}\right]_0^6 = \left[\frac{6^2}{2} - \frac{0^2}{2}\right] = 18 \text{ square units}$$

This value is easily verified by the fact that

$$\begin{aligned}\text{area of triangle} &= \tfrac{1}{2} \times \text{base} \times \text{height}\\ &= \tfrac{1}{2} \times 6 \times 6 = 18 \text{ square units}\end{aligned}$$

Let us now determine the area under the graph in Figure 13.2 between $x = 2$ and $x = 6$ as follows

$$\begin{aligned}\int_2^6 x\,dx &= \left[\frac{x^2}{2}\right]_2^6 = \left[\frac{6^2}{2} - \frac{2^2}{2}\right] = 18 - 2\\ &= 16 \text{ square units}\end{aligned}$$

The reader will find it an interesting exercise to verify the result.

Worked Example 13.4

Determine the area under the curve $y = x^2 + 3$ between $x = 2$ and $x = 4$.

Solution

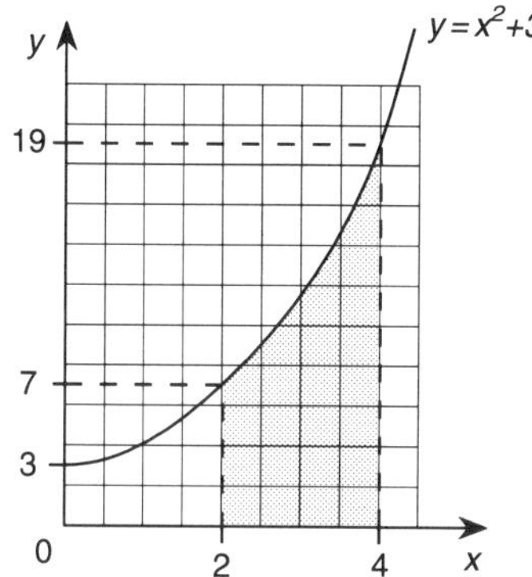

Figure 13.3 Solution to Worked Example 13.4

The graph of the curve is drawn in Figure 13.3, and the required area is

$$\text{area} = \int_2^4 (x^2 + 3)\, dx = \left[\frac{x^3}{3} + 3x\right]_2^4$$

$$= \left[\left[\frac{4^3}{3} + (3 \times 4)\right] - \left[\frac{2^3}{3} + (3 \times 2)\right]\right]$$

$$= [33.333 - 8.667] = 24.666 \text{ square units}$$

Worked Example 13.5

What is the area
(a) in the first half-cycle, and
(b) in the second half-cycle
of a sine wave whose maximum value is 1.0.

Solution

In this case we choose to plot the sine wave to a base of angle, that is

$$y = \sin\theta$$

(a) As with many engineering applications of this kind, we use the angular measure of the radian, so that the first half-cycle is complete in π radians, hence

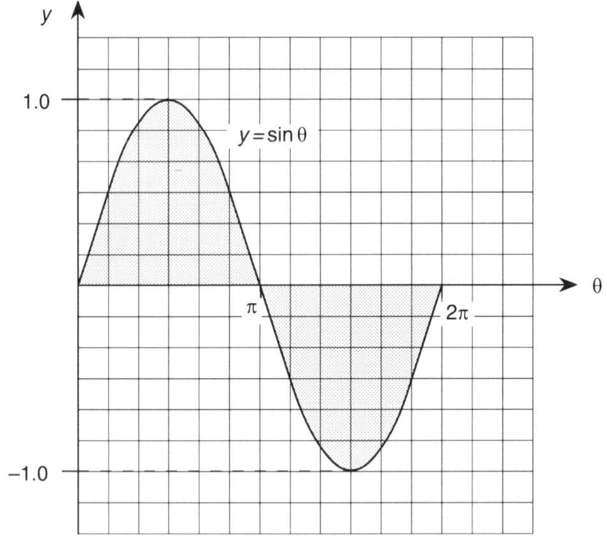

Figure 13.4 Solution to Worked Example 13.5

$$\text{area under curve} = \int_0^\pi \sin\theta d\theta = \Big[-\cos\theta\Big]_0^\pi$$

$$= \Big[(\quad\cos\pi)\quad(\quad\cos 0)\Big]$$

$$= [-(-1) - (-(1))]$$

$$= 1 + 1 = 2 \text{ square units}$$

(b) In the case of the second half-cycle

$$\text{area under curve} = \int_\pi^{2\pi} \sin\theta d\theta = \Big[-\cos\theta\Big]_\pi^{2\pi}$$

$$= \Big[(-\cos 2\pi) - (-\cos\pi)\Big]$$

$$= [-(1) - (-(-1))]$$

$$= -1 - 1 = -2 \text{ square units}$$

It follows from the above that the *total area under the complete alternating wave* is $(2 - 2) = 0$ square units! An inspection of the curve in Figure 13.4 shows that each half-cycle has the same area (but different sign), and the two have the effect of cancelling each other out so far as the total area is concerned!

Worked Example 13.6

Determine the value of (a) $\int_{-4}^{3} (x^3 + x^2 - x)\,dx$, (b) $\int_{p/q}^{q/p} \left(1 + \frac{1}{z^2}\right) dz$

Solution

(a) $$\int_{-4}^{3} (x^3 + x^2 - x)\,dx = \left[\frac{x^4}{4} + \frac{x^3}{3} - x^2\right]_{-4}^{3}$$
$$= (20.25 + 9 - 9) - (64 - 21.33 - 16)$$
$$= -6.42$$

(b) $$\int_{p/q}^{q/p} \left[1 + \frac{1}{z^2}\right] dz = \left[z - \frac{1}{z}\right]_{p/q}^{q/p}$$
$$= \left[\frac{q}{p} - \frac{p}{q}\right] - \left[\frac{p}{q} - \frac{q}{p}\right] = 2\left[\frac{q}{p} - \frac{p}{q}\right]$$

13.7 Volume of revolution

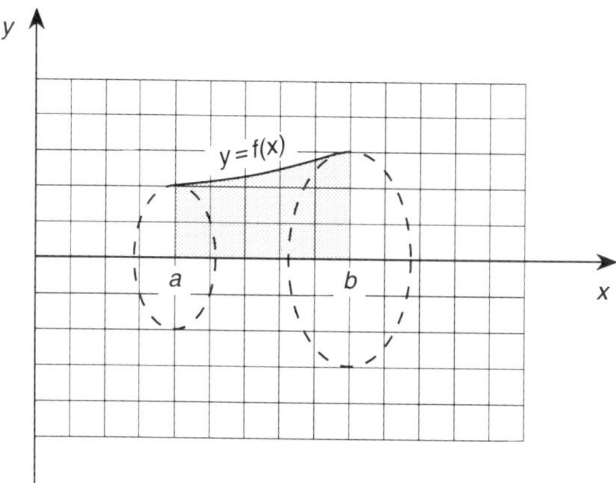

Figure 13.5 Volume of revolution

If the shaded area between a and b in Figure 13.5 is rotated through 360°, it produces a **volume of rotation** or **solid of revolution**, whose volume is

$$\int_a^b \pi y^2\,dx$$

where y is a function of x.

Worked Example 13.7

Determine an equation for the volume of the cylinder in Figure 13.6.

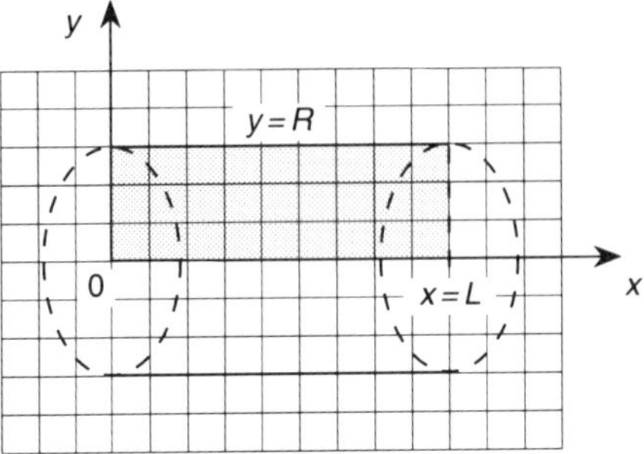

Figure 13.6 Volume of a cylinder

Solution

The equation of the line describing the outer edge of the cylinder is $y = R$, i.e., y is a constant, and the volume of the cylinder is

$$V = \int_{x=0}^{x=L} \pi y^2 \, dx = \pi \int_0^L R^2 \, dx = \pi \left[R^2 x \right]_0^L$$

$$= \pi R^2 \left[x \right]_0^L = \pi R^2 (L - 0) = \pi R^2 L$$

Worked Example 13.8

Determine an expression for the volume of the sphere of radius R in Figure 13.7.

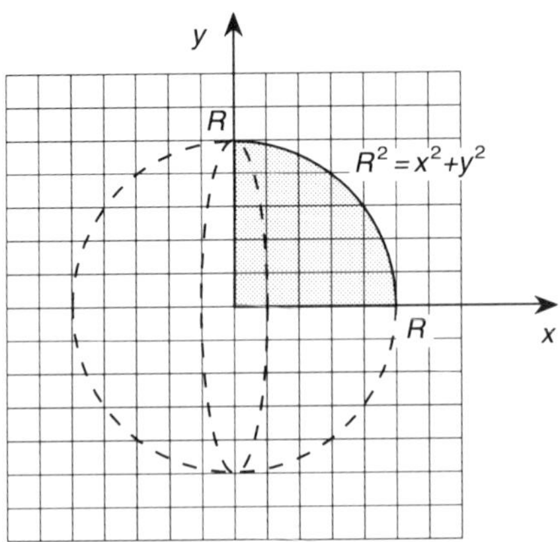

Figure 13.7 Volume of a hemisphere

Solution

The equation of the curve bounding the *hemisphere* in the x-y plane in the figure is

$$R^2 = x^2 + y^2 \text{ or } y^2 = R^2 - x^2$$

hence

$$\text{volume of hemisphere} = \int_{x=0}^{x=R} \pi y^2 \, dx$$

$$= \pi \int_0^R (R^2 - x^2) \, dx = \pi \left[R^2 x - \frac{x^3}{3} \right]_0^R$$

$$= \pi \left[\left(R^3 - \frac{R^3}{3} \right) - (0 - 0) \right] = \frac{2}{3} \pi R^3$$

That is, the *volume of the sphere* is

$$\text{volume} = \frac{4}{3} \pi R^3$$

13.8 Mean value or average value of an alternating waveform

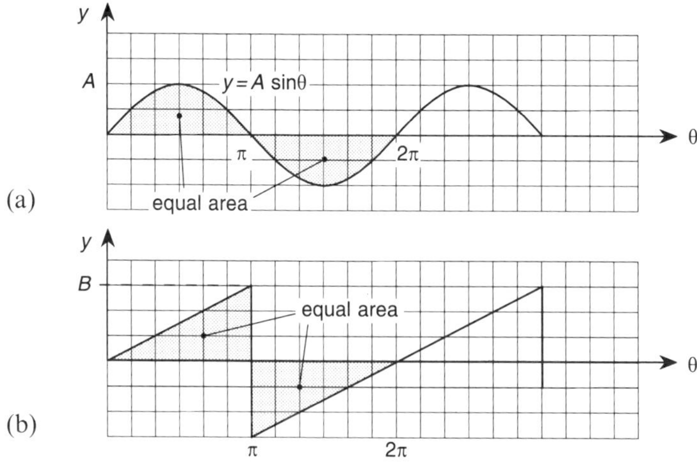

Figure 13.8 Examples of alternating waveforms

An **alternating waveform** is a periodic waveform having equal values both above and below the x-axis (see Figure 13.8). The *mathematical average value* of any waveform is defined as

$$\frac{\text{area under the curve over the complete cycle}}{\text{'length' of the base}}$$

As outlined above (see also Worked Example 13.5), the area under the positive half-cycle is equal to the area under the negative half-cycle, so that *the total area under the complete cycle is zero*. That is, the mathematical average value is zero.

Engineers have defined another type of **average value** or **mean value**, which is the *rectified average value*. For our purposes, we can regard this to be *the average value under the positive half-cycle of the wave*.

If the equation of the curve is a function of θ, then the average value taken over the positive half-cycle is

$$\text{average value} = \frac{\text{area under the curve between } \theta = 0 \text{ and } \theta = \pi}{\pi}$$

$$= \frac{1}{\pi}\int_0^{\pi} f(\theta)\,d\theta$$

Worked Example 13.9

Determine the average value of (a) the sinewave in Figure 13.8(a), (b) the triangular wave in Figure 13.8(b).

Solution

(a) The equation of the sinewave is $y = A\sin\theta$, where A is the maximum value of the wave, hence

$$\text{average value} = \frac{1}{\pi}\int_0^{\pi} A\sin\theta d\theta = \frac{A}{\pi}\int_0^{\pi}\sin\theta d\theta$$

$$= \frac{A}{\pi}\Big[-\cos\theta\Big]_0^{\pi} = \frac{A}{\pi}\Big[(-\cos\pi) - (-\cos 0)\Big]$$

$$= \frac{A}{\pi}(1 - (-1)) = \frac{2A}{\pi} = 0.637A$$

In practice we are dealing either with a voltage wave of maximum value V_M, or a current wave of maximum value I_M, whose average value is V_{av} or I_{av}, respectively, so that

$$V_{av} = 0.637V_M$$

$$I_{av} = 0.637I_M$$

The reader will recall that in Chapter 8 (Worked Example 8.4), the average value of a sinusoidal voltage of peak value 100 V was evaluated by approximate (numerical) methods as

mid-ordinate rule = 63.924 V = $0.639V_M$

Simpson's rule = 63.66 V = $0.6366V_M$

and the reader will observe that Simpson's rule gives the more accurate result.

(b) In the case of the triangular wave in Figure 13.8(b), the gradient of the curve is B/π, and the equation of the wave between $\theta = 0$ and $\theta = \pi$ is $y = B\theta/\pi$, hence

$$\text{average value} = \frac{1}{\pi}\int_{\theta=0}^{\theta=\pi} \frac{B\theta}{\pi}\,d\theta = \frac{B}{\pi^2}\int_0^{\pi} \theta\,d\theta$$

$$= \frac{B}{\pi^2}\left[\frac{\theta^2}{2}\right]_0^{\pi} = \frac{B}{\pi^2}\left[\left[\frac{\pi^2}{2}\right] - \left[\frac{0^2}{2}\right]\right] = \frac{B}{2}$$

That is if $B = 10\,\text{V}$, the average value of the triangular wave is $10/2 = 5\,\text{V}$.

13.9 Effective value or root-mean-square (r.m.s.) value of a wave

The **effective value** or **root-mean-square** (r.m.s.) value of an alternating current or voltage wave is the value which develops the same electrical power in a resistor as an identical value of direct current. For a current wave, the r.m.s. value is determined from the expression

$$\text{r.m.s. current} = \sqrt{\left[\frac{\text{area under } i^2 \text{ curve}}{\text{`length' of base of waveform}}\right]}$$

From the above we see that the effective value of the current wave is given by the **square Root of the Mean value of the sum of the Square values** (r.m.s.) of the wave.

For a sinusoidal current, the equation for the wave is

$$i = I_M \sin\theta$$

hence the effective current, I_{eff}, is calculated from

$$I_{eff} = \sqrt{\left[\frac{1}{2\pi}\int_0^{2\pi} {I_M}^2 \sin^2\theta\,d\theta\right]}$$

The reader should note that we can take current waveform over the *complete cycle* because, in the second half-cycle, the negative values of current are 'squared' so that the answer is still a positive value.

It was shown in Chapter 7 that

$$\sin A \sin B = \frac{1}{2}[cos(A - B) - \cos(A + B)]$$

If we let A and B have the value θ, then

$$\sin^2\theta = \frac{1}{2}[\cos(\theta - \theta) - \cos(\theta + \theta)]$$

$$= \frac{1}{2}[\cos 0 - \cos 2\theta] = \frac{1}{2}[1 - \cos 2\theta]$$

Substituting this value into the equation for I_{eff} gives

$$I_{\text{eff}} = \sqrt{\left[\frac{1}{2\pi}\int_0^{2\pi} \frac{I_M{}^2}{2}(1 - \cos 2\theta)\, d\theta\right]}$$

$$= \sqrt{\left[\frac{I_M{}^2}{4\pi}\left[(2\pi - \frac{1}{2}\sin 4\theta) - (0 - \frac{1}{2}\sin 0)\right]\right]}$$

$$= \sqrt{\left[\frac{I_M{}^2}{4\pi}\left[(2\pi - 0) - (0 - 0)\right]\right]} = \sqrt{\left[\frac{I_M{}^2}{2}\right]} = \frac{I_M}{\sqrt{2}}$$

$$= 0.7071 I_M$$

Similarly, it may be shown that for a voltage sinewave the effective value is

$$V_{\text{eff}} = \frac{V_M}{\sqrt{2}}$$

One method of approximate numerical integration for determining the r.m.s. value of a sinewave is shown in Worked Example 13.10.

Worked Example 13.10

Using a simple numerical method, determine the r.m.s. value of a voltage sinewave of maximum value V_M.

Solution

For simplicity, we will use the mid-ordinate rule. The equation of the wave to be integrated is $v = V_M \sin\theta$, so that $v^2 = V_M{}^2 \sin^2\theta$. A table of v^2 values for mid-ordinates taken at 15° intervals (the first being at 15°/2 = 7.5°) for the first 180° is given in Table 13.2.

TABLE 13.2 Solution to Worked Example 13.10

$\theta°$	$v^2 = V_M{}^2 \sin^2\theta$
7.5	$0.017 V_M{}^2$
22.5	$0.1464 V_M{}^2$
37.5	$0.3706 V_M{}^2$
52.5	$0.6294 V_M{}^2$
67.5	$0.8536 V_M{}^2$
82.5	$0.983 V_M{}^2$
97.5	$0.983 V_M{}^2$
112.5	$0.8536 V_M{}^2$
127.5	$0.6294 V_M{}^2$
142.5	$0.3706 V_M{}^2$
157.5	$0.1464 V_M{}^2$
172.5	$0.017 V_M{}^2$
sum	$5.96 V_M{}^2$

Since the wave is symmetrical, the sum of the mid-ordinates v^2 values in the second half-cycle is $5.96V_M{}^2$, hence the sum of the mid-ordinates over the complete cycle is $11.92V_M{}^2$. The mean value of the mid-ordinates of v^2 taken over the complete cycle is therefore

$$\frac{11.92V_M{}^2}{24 \text{ mid-ordinates}} = 0.4967V_M{}^2$$

The r.m.s. value of the wave is therefore

$$\begin{aligned} V_{\text{eff}} &= \sqrt{(\text{mean value of the } v^2 \text{ graph})} \\ &= \sqrt{(0.4967V_M{}^2)} = 0.705V_M \end{aligned}$$

This should, of course, be compared with the value of $0.7071V_M$ obtained by the calculus method.

Worked Example 13.11

Determine the r.m.s. value of the triangular wave in Figure 13.9.

Solution

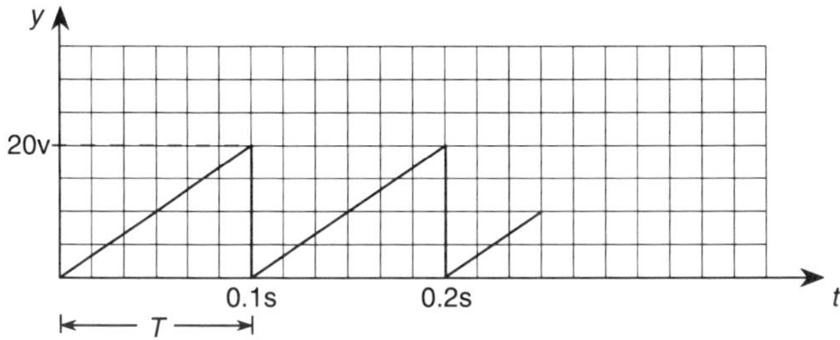

Figure 13.9 Worked Example 13.11

In this case the graph is plotted to a base of time, and the periodic time of the wave is $T = 0.1$ s. The gradient of the curve is

$$\frac{\text{maximum value}}{\text{periodic time}} = \frac{20}{0.1} = 200 \text{ V/s}$$

Hence the equation of the wave between $t = 0$ and $t = 0.1$ s is

$$y = \text{slope} \times t = 200t$$

The r.m.s. value of the wave is

$$V_{\text{eff}} = \sqrt{\left[\frac{1}{T}\int_0^T y^2\, dt\right]}$$

$$= \sqrt{\left[\frac{1}{0.1}\int_0^{0.1} (200t)^2\, dt\right]}$$

$$= \sqrt{\left[10\int_0^{0.1} 40\,000t^2\, dt\right]}$$

$$= \sqrt{\left[40\,000\left[\frac{t^3}{3}\right]_0^{0.1}\right]}$$

$$= \sqrt{\left[\frac{400\,000}{3}[0.1^3 - 0^3]\right]} = \sqrt{133.33}$$

$$= 11.55 \text{ V}$$

Self-test questions

13.1 Integrate the following with respect to x (a) $-6x^2 + 2x - 3$, (b) $(2x + 1)(3x - 2)$, (c) $1/x^4$, (d) $(4 - 5x)^2/x^2$, (e) $\sqrt{(x^5)}$, (f) $(mx + c)^3$, (g) e^{4x}, (h) $e^x(1 - e^x)^2$, (i) $6\cos^2 x$.

13.2 Determine the area bounded by the given equations and the x-axis, between the given values of x (a) $y = x$ between $x = 2$ and $x = 6$, (b) $ay = bx$ between $x = 0$ and $x = a$, (c) $y = 9 - x^2$ between $x = -3$ and $x = +3$, (d) $y = 2\sqrt{x}$ between $x = 4$ and $x = 9$, (e) $y = 1 + \sin x$ between $x = 0$ and $x = \pi$.

13.3 Calculate the volume of revolution when the area under the given curve is rotated about the x-axis, and between the given values of x: (a) $y = x$ between $x = 2$ and $x = 4$, (b) $y = x^2$ between $x = 0$ and $x = 5$, (c) $2y = x + 4$ between $x = 0$ and $x = 8$, (d) $xy = 6$ between $x = 2$ and $x = 9$, (e) $y = \sin x$ between $x = 0$ and $x = \pi$.

13.4 Determine the average and r.m.s. value of the waveform in Figure 13.10.

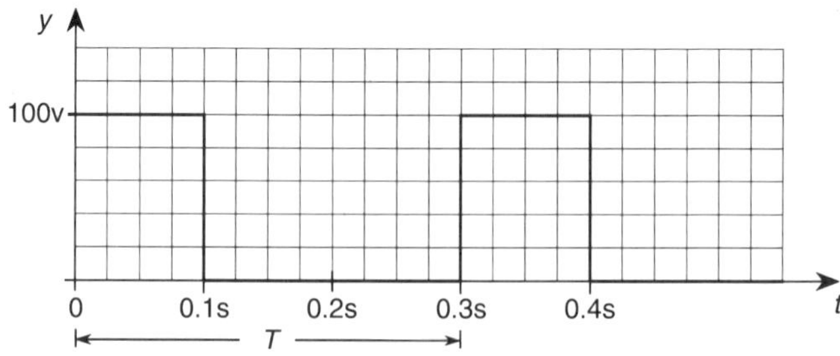

Figure 13.10 Self-test question 13.4

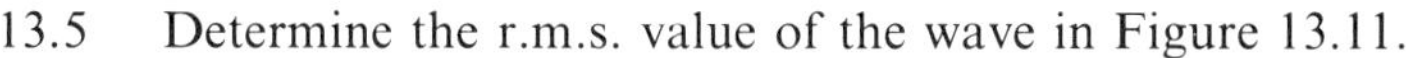

13.5 Determine the r.m.s. value of the wave in Figure 13.11.

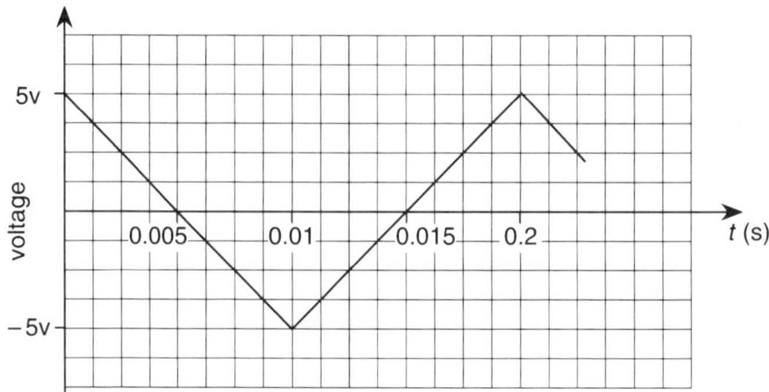

Figure 13.11 Self-test question 13.5

13.6 Evaluate the average and effective value of the waveform in Figure 13.12.

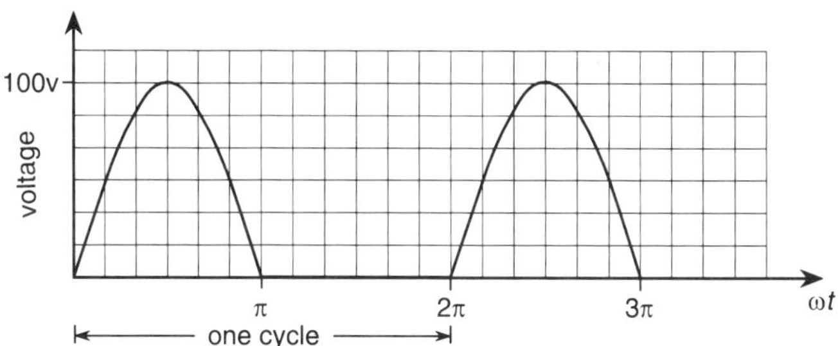

Figure 13.12 Self-test question 13.6

Summary of important facts

Integration is the *inverse process to differentiation*, i.e., the process of determining a function from its derivative.

An integral without specified limits is known as an **indefinite integral**, and its solution **must contain an arbitrary constant of integration**. The value of the constant of integration is obtained by inserting known values (the *boundary conditions*) of x and y into the equation.

The integral of a sum of differentials is **the sum of the separate integrals**.

An integral with specified limiting conditions is known as a **definite integral**, the upper limit of integration being written at the top of the integral sign, and the lower limit being written at the bottom of the integral sign.

The value of a definite integral gives the **area under the curve** between the specified limits of integration. When a curve is rotated about the x-axis, it produces a **volume of revolution** or **solid of revolution**, the volume being given by the expression

$$\int_a^b \pi y^2 \, dx$$

where a and b are the lower and upper limits of integration, respectively, and y is the expression which defines the curve.

The **average value** or **mean value** under a curve is given by

$$\frac{\text{area under the curve}}{\text{length of the base}}$$

An alternating waveform has equal positive and negative areas, so that *its mathematical average value is zero*. Engineers define the average value of an alternating wave as the *rectified average value*, that is it is the mean value of the positive half-cycle of the wave, or

$$\text{average value} = \frac{1}{\pi}\int_0^{\pi} f(\theta)\, d\theta = \frac{1}{T/2}\int_0^{T/2} f(t)\, dt$$

where T is the periodic time of the wave.

The **effective value** of an alternating wave is the **root-mean-square** (r.m.s.) value, and is calculated from

$$\begin{aligned}
\text{r.m.s. value} &= \left[\begin{array}{c}\text{square root of the mean of} \\ \text{the square value of the wave}\end{array}\right] \\
&= \sqrt{\left[\frac{\text{area under } (f(x))^2 \text{ wave}}{\text{base of wave}}\right]} \\
&= \sqrt{\left[\frac{1}{2\pi}\int_0^{2\pi} (f(x))^2 \, dx\right]} \\
&= \sqrt{\left[\frac{1}{T}\int_0^{T} (f(t))^2 \, dt\right]}
\end{aligned}$$

14 Transients in electrical circuits

14.1 Introduction

The dictionary defines a **transient phenomenon** as something which is not durable, and passes away with time. So it is with electrical circuits which contain energy storage elements such as inductors and capacitors. When there is a change in the circuit conditions in these circuits, such as a change in supply voltage or current, the voltage across and the current in the circuit elements changes in a predictable fashion, and it is this we investigate here.

It is the purpose of this chapter to show how we can, mathematically, predict the way in which the current and voltage change in simple resistor-capacitor and resistor-inductor circuits under transient conditions.

Initially we will see how the differential equations of simple *R-C* and *R-L* are formulated, and how they are solved.

Broadly speaking, an electrical circuit containing only one type of energy storage element, such as a capacitor or an inductor, is known as a **single-energy circuit** or a **first-order circuit**, and it is these we will study in this chapter.

A circuit containing both capacitors and inductors is known as a **double-energy circuit** or a **second-order circuit**. These are outside the range of this book, and the reader should study more advanced books on electrical and electronic engineering for details of these. Many industrial systems employ third-, fourth-, fifth-, and higher-order circuits.

The reader who hopes to study electrical and electronic engineering to a higher level, will find that this chapter gives long-term benefit to their knowledge.

By the end of this chapter, the reader will be able to

- understand how a differential equation is formulated,
- solve a first-order differential equation of the variables separable kind,
- write down and solve the differential equation of an *R-C* circuit both for capacitor charging and discharging conditions,
- sketch and plot graphs for the voltage across the circuit elements and the current through them in an *R-C* circuit during the charge and discharge period,
- deal with *R-C* circuits in which the capacitor has an initial charge,
- write down and solve the differential equation for an *R-L* circuit both for the rise and decay of current in the circuit,
- sketch and plot graphs for an *R-L* circuit during transient conditions,

- understand the problems involved in breaking the current in an inductive circuit,
- calculate the time constant, the rise-time, the fall-time and the transient period of *R-C* and *R-L* circuits.

14.2 An introduction to differential equations

A differential equation is an equation containing differential coefficients, such as

$$\frac{dy}{dx} = 4x^2 + 6$$

The **order** of a differential equation is the number of times differentiation has been carried out. The above equation is a *first-order* equation; an equation containing d^2y/dx^2 is a *second-order* differential equation. The **degree** of the equation is the highest power to which the *whole derivative* is raised. The above equation is one of the first order and first degree, and the following is a first-order, second-degree differential equation.

$$\left[\frac{dy}{dx}\right]^2 = 6x^2 + 7$$

When solving a differential equation, we initially obtain a **general solution** which contains an arbitrary constant of integration (see Chapter 13 for details) such as

$$y = 3x^2 - x + K$$

where K is the constant of integration. Providing that we can insert the value of x and y at a particular point (the *boundary conditions*), we can determine the value of the constant K. In most engineering cases, the known boundary conditions usually occur when the circuit is switched on or switched off, and are known as the **initial conditions** in the circuit. Examples of these were given in Chapter 13.

When the value of the constant of integration has been inserted into the equation, the resulting solution is known as the **particular solution** of the equation.

14.3 Solution of a differential equation whose variables can be separated

Perhaps the simplest type of differential equation we meet with in electrical engineering contains two variables, such as voltage and time, which can physically be separated on either side of the equals sign. This type is known as the **variables separable** type, and we will look at its mathematics in this chapter.

Mathematically, this type of differential equation is of the form

$$\frac{dy}{dx} = f(x)f(y)$$

where $f(x)$ is a function of x, and $f(y)$ is a function of y; in electrical applications, x may typically be a voltage and y is time. We can rewrite the equation in the form

$$\frac{dy}{f(y)} = f(x)\,dx$$

Next, we *integrate both sides of the equation* as follows

$$\int \frac{dy}{f(y)} = \int f(x)\,dx$$

When each integral is complete we, theoretically, have two constants of integration (one for each integral). However, in practice, we combine them into one constant as shown in Worked Example 14.1.

Worked Example 14.1

Solve $\frac{dy}{dx} = 4yx^3$, given that $x = 1$ when $y = 1$.

Solution

We will re-write the equation in the form

$$\frac{dy}{dx} = 4x^3\,dx$$

Integrating both sides of the equation gives

$$\int \frac{dy}{y} = 4x^3\,dx$$

that is

$$\ln y = \frac{4x^{3+1}}{3+1} + K = x^4 + K$$

The reader should note that we only have one constant of integration! Inserting the specified boundary conditions, namely $x = 1$ when $y = 1$, gives

$$\ln 1 = 1^4 + K$$

or

$$0 = 1 + K$$

therefore

$$K = -1$$

The *particular solution* of the differential equation is therefore

$$\ln y = x^4 - 1$$

14.4 Capacitor charge

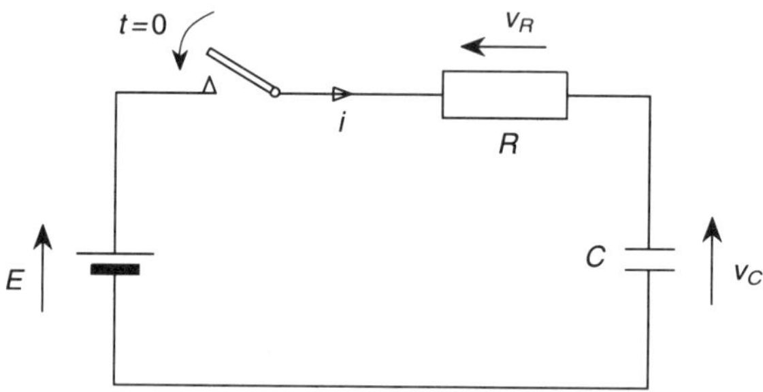

Figure 14.1 Capacitor charge

In the circuit in Figure 14.1, the switch is closed when $t = 0$ and, applying Kirchhoff's voltage law (KVL) to the circuit gives

$$E = v_R + v_C \tag{14.1}$$

where v_R is the voltage across the resistor, and v_C is the voltage across the capacitor.

Now, from electrical circuit theory, we know that the current flowing in the capacitor is given by $i = C\dfrac{dv_C}{dt}$ and, since this current flows through R, then $v_R = iR = RCdv_C/dt$. Inserting these expressions into the circuit equation gives

$$E = v_R + v_C = RC\frac{dv_C}{dt} + v_C$$

Since E and v_C have the same dimensions, i.e. voltage, we can collect them together as follows

$$E - v_C = RC\frac{dv_C}{dt}$$

or

$$\frac{dt}{RC} = \frac{dv_C}{E - v_C} \tag{14.2}$$

What we have done here is to *separate the variables*. On the right-hand side of the equation we have

$$\frac{dv_C}{E - v_C} = \frac{\text{change in voltage}}{\text{voltage difference}}$$

Since this is a ratio of two voltages, it is *dimensionless*. Since the parts to the left and to the right of the equals sign in (14.2) are equal to one another, it follows that both sides of the equations have the same dimensions, i.e., the ratio dt/RC must also be dimensionless. This means that the product RC *must have the dimensions of time*. For this reason we describe the product RC as the **time constant**, τ, of the circuit. Hence we may re-write the equation in the form

$$\frac{dt}{\tau} = \frac{dv_C}{E - v_C}$$

To solve the equation we simply integrate both sides as follows

$$\int \frac{dt}{\tau} = \int \frac{dv_C}{E - v_C} \tag{14.3}$$

If we let $z = E - v_C$, then

$$\frac{dz}{dv_C} = -1 \text{ or } dv_C = -dz$$

Inserting this into (14.3) gives

$$\int \frac{dt}{\tau} = \int \frac{-dz}{z}$$

Integrating both sides of the above equation yields

$$\frac{t}{\tau} = -\ln z + K = -\ln(E - v_C) + K \tag{14.4}$$

where K is the constant of integration. Equation (14.4) is the *general solution* of the differential equation, since it contains the unknown constant of integration, which we will now calculate.

Assuming that the capacitor is initially discharged (see section 14.5 for the case where the capacitor is initially charged) when the switch is closed, that is $v_C = 0$ when $t = 0$, we can use this condition as the *initial condition* in eqn. (14.4) to determine the value of K as follows

$$\frac{0}{\tau} = -\ln(E - 0) + K$$

or

$$K = \ln E$$

Inserting this value into (14.4) tells us that

$$\frac{t}{\tau} = -\ln(E - v_C) + \ln E = \ln\left[\frac{E}{E - v_C}\right]$$

It will be seen from the work in Chapter 3 on logarithms that if

$$x = \ln y, \text{ then } e^x = y$$

hence the above equation or $\frac{t}{\tau}$ tells us that

$$e^{t/\tau} = \frac{E}{E - v_C}$$

or

$$E - v_C = E/e^{t/\tau} = Ee^{-t/\tau}$$

therefore the voltage across the capacitor at time t is

$$v_C = E - Ee^{-t/\tau} = E(1 - e^{-t/\tau}) \qquad (14.5)$$

It was shown in Chapter 9 on graphs that the mathematical form in (14.5) is that of an *exponentially rising curve*, and is plotted in Figure 14.2(a). It was shown in Chapter 9 that transients of the type described by eqn. (14.5) have decayed after a period of 5τ ($= 5RC$). We therefore describe the first period of 5τ as the **transient period**, and the remaining time as the **steady-state period** (since the circuit has achieved steady-state operating conditions after this time).

The initial rate of change of v_C can be determined as follows. From the original circuit equations, it can be seen that the slope of v_C at any time is

$$\frac{dv_C}{dt} = \frac{E - v_C}{RC}$$

The initial slope is determined by putting the initial conditions in the circuit (that is $v_C = 0$ when $t = 0$) into the equation as follows

$$\left[\frac{di}{dt}\right]_{t=0} = \frac{E - 0}{RC} = \frac{E}{\tau}$$

That is, the slope of the v_C curve at $t = 0$ is E/τ V/s. This means that if the initial rate of rise of v_C were maintained, then v_C would have a value of E after the first τ s (see the chain-dotted line in Figure 14.2(a)). This allows us to define the time constant of the circuit as follows.

> **The time constant of an *R-C* circuit is equal to the time which would be taken for the voltage across the capacitor to reach the final voltage if the initial rate of change of v_C were maintained constant.**

We will now determine the actual value of v_C when $t = \tau$; this is done by inserting $t = \tau$ into (14.5) as follows

$$[v_C]_{t=\tau} = E(1 - e^{-t/\tau}) = E(1 - e^{-1})$$
$$= E(1 - 0.368) = 0.632E$$

This expression allows us to give the following alternative definition of the time constant of an *R-C* circuit

> **The time constant of an *R-C* circuit is the time taken for the voltage across *C* to rise from zero to 63.2 per cent of its final value.**

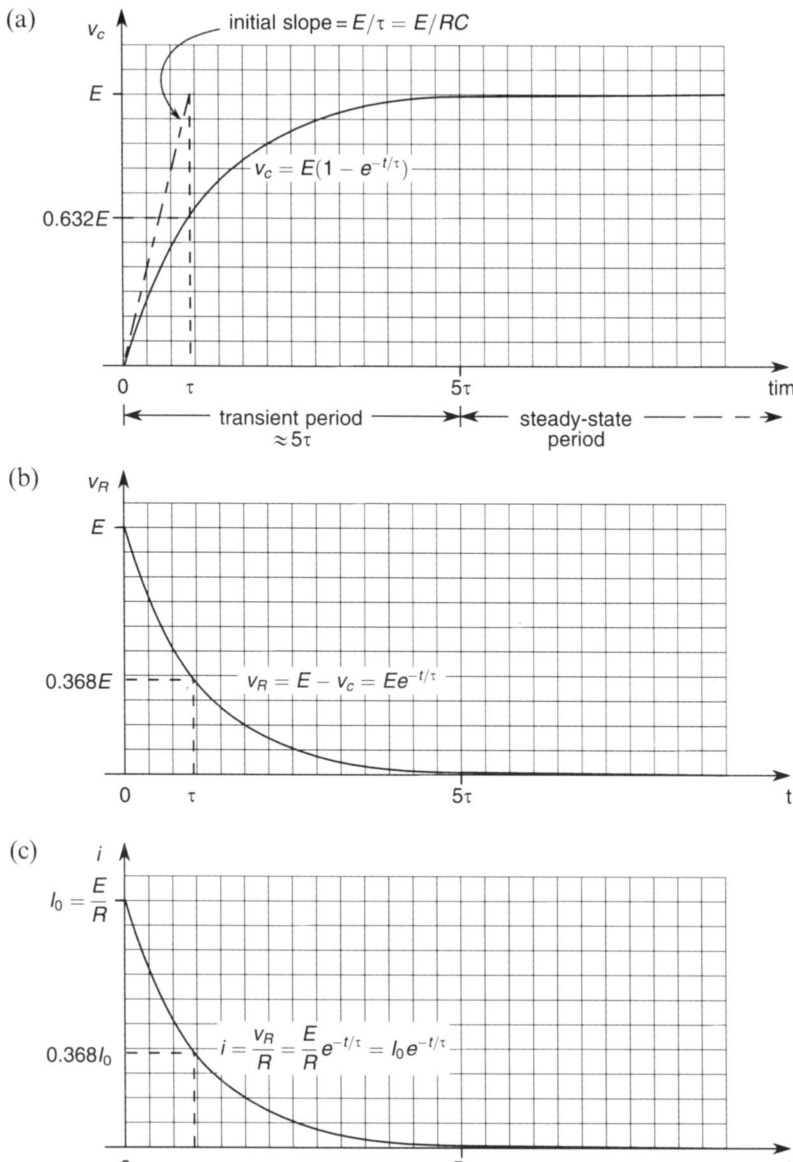

Figure 14.2 Transients in an *R-C* circuit during capacitor charge

(a) The voltage across the resistor during charging

From (14.1) we see that

$$E = v_R + v_C$$

or

$$v_R = E - v_C = E - E(1 - e^{-t/\tau}) = Ee^{-t/\tau}$$

This is the equation which commences at a value of E when $t = 0$, and falls exponentially with a time constant of τ. Once again, in such a curve, the *transient period* is complete when $t = 5\tau$, and thereafter (in the steady-state period) the voltage across R is practically zero.

It is left as an exercise for the student to complete, to show that the voltage across the resistor reduces to 36.8 per cent of its original value when $t = \tau$ (see Figure 14.2(b)).

(b) Capacitor charging current

From Ohm's law the current in the circuit is

$$i = \frac{v_R}{R} = \frac{E}{R}e^{-t/\tau} = I_0e^{-t/\tau}$$

where I_0 is the charging current when $t = 0$. The curve for this expression is shown in Figure 14.2(c), and it falls from an initial value of I_0 with a time constant of τ; the transient period of the curve is complete in a time of 5τ and, thereafter, the current is practically zero.

As an exercise, readers should show that the current in the circuit falls to 36.8 per cent of its original value when $t = \tau$ (see Figure 14.2(c)).

Worked Example 14.2

A 10 μF capacitor is connected via a 10 kΩ resistor and a switch to a 100 V battery. Write down an expression after the switch is closed for (a) the voltage across the capacitor, (b) the voltage across the resistor and (c) the current in the circuit. Calculate the value of (d) v_C when $t = 0.2$ s, (e) v_R when $t = 0.3$ s and (f) i when $t = 0.4$ s.

Solution

The time constant of the circuit is

$$\tau = RC = (10 \times 10^3) \times (10 \times 10^{-6}) = 0.1 \text{ s}$$

This tells us that the transients in the circuit will have decayed when $t = 5\tau = 0.5$ s.

(a) The expression for v_C is

$$v_C = E(1 - e^{-t/\tau}) = 100(1 - e^{-t/0.1})$$
$$= 100(1 - e^{-10t})\,\text{V}$$

(b) The expression for v_R is

$$v_R = Ee^{-t/\tau} = 100e^{-t/0.1} = 100e^{-10t}\,\text{V}$$

(c) The initial value of the charging current is $I_0 = E/R = 100/10 \times 10^3 = 0.01$ A, hence the expression for i is

$$i = I_0 e^{-t/\tau} = 0.01e^{-t/0.1} = 0.01e^{-10t}\,\text{A}$$

(d) When $t = 0.2$ s, we have

$$v_C = 100(1 - e^{-10t}) = 100(1 - e^{-2})$$
$$= 100(1 - 0.135) = 86.47\,\text{V}$$

(e) When $t = 0.3$ s, we have

$$v_R = 100e^{-10t} = 100e^{-3} = 100 \times 0.05 = 5\,\text{V}$$

(f) When $t = 0.4$ s

$$i = I_0 e^{-t/\tau} = 0.01e^{-0.4/0.1} = 0.01e^{-4}$$
$$= 0.01 \times 0.018 = 0.18 \times 10^{-3}\,\text{A or } 0.18\,\text{mA}$$

14.5 Charging a capacitor when it initially stores some charge

In many practical cases, the capacitor in Figure 14.1 may initially be charged to some voltage before the switch is closed. We need to know the way in which the circuit responds to the new charging voltage.

The mathematical procedure for the solution of the circuit is the same up to and including (14.4). The initial charge on the capacitor is accounted for in the way we calculate the value of the arbitrary constant of integration, K, in that equation.

Let us suppose that the capacitor is charged to voltage V_C at $t = 0$, the polarity of V_C opposing E. That is $v_C = +V_C$ when $t = 0$; inserting this value into (14.4) gives

$$\frac{0}{\tau} = -\ln(E - V_C) + K$$

or

$$K = \ln(E - V_C)$$

It is left as an exercise for the reader to re-insert this in the equation and show that the capacitor voltage is given by

$$v_C = E - V_C e^{-t/\tau}$$

We can simplify this expression by letting the ratio V_C/E have the value k. This allows the above expression to be written as

$$v_C = E - kEe^{-t/\tau} = E(1 - ke^{-t/\tau})$$

If, for example, $E = 100\,\text{V}$ and the initial charge on the capacitor is $V_C = 50\,\text{V}$, then $k = 0.5$ and

$$v_C = 100(1 - 0.5e^{-t/\tau})$$

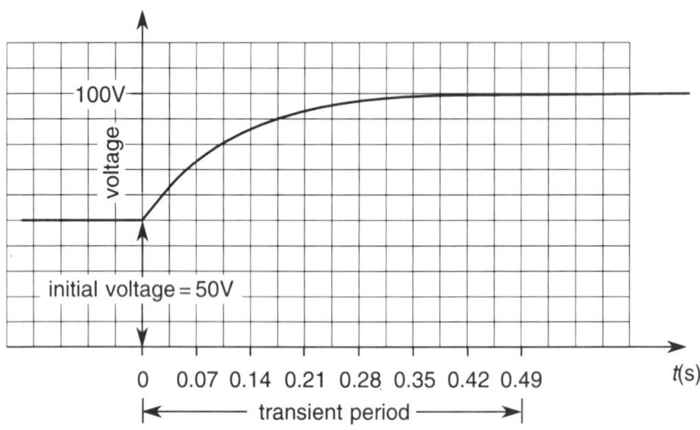

Figure 14.3 Capacitor charge with an initial charge on the capacitor

A graph for v_C for the above equation for $\tau = 0.1\,\text{s}$ is drawn in Figure 14.3, and it is left as an exercise for the reader to plot the graph in detail to verify its shape. The reader will note that the time scale has been subdivided into increments of $0.7\tau = 0.7RC$ simply for the convenience of sketching the graph (see Chapter 9 for details).

Since the supply voltage is 100 V, the capacitor voltage rises exponentially with a time constant of 0.1 s, from the initial capacitor voltage of 50 V to the final voltage of 100 V. Once again, it takes a time equal to five time constants to reach its final voltage.

As with any exponential curve, the graph changes by 50 per cent of the possible change for each 0.7τ time interval ($= 0.07\,\text{s}$). That is, in the first 0.07 s, v_C changes from 50 V to $(50 + [100 - 50]/2) = 75\,\text{V}$.

14.6 Capacitor discharge

Suppose that the switch in the circuit in Figure 14.4 has been in position *A* long enough for the capacitor to become fully charged to *E*.

When $t = 0$, we change the switch blade to position *B*, so that the capacitor begins to discharge. For the purpose of continuity, we assume that the current flows in the same direction both during the charge and discharge of the capacitor. This may seem strange, but it means that there is continuity

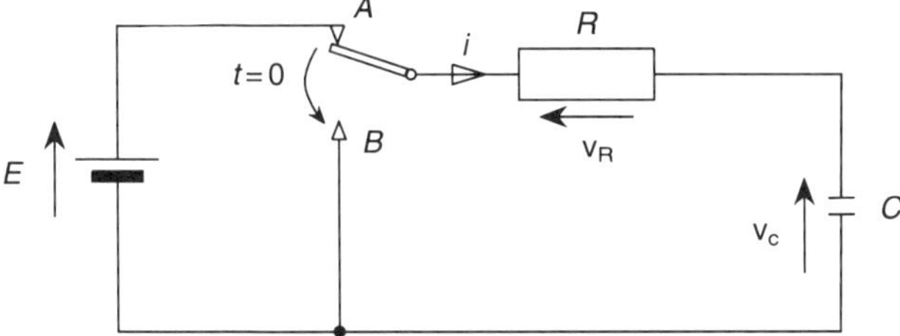

Figure 14.4 Capacitor discharge

between the equations for the charge and discharge periods and, equally importantly, we can easily account for the direction of current later in the procedure.

When the switch blade is in position *B*, the e.m.f. *E* is disconnected from the circuit, and the only voltage acting in the circuit is the voltage across the capacitor. Applying Kirchhoff's voltage law to the loop containing *R* and *C* when the switch blade is in position *B*, we get

$$0 = v_R + v_C$$

or

$$v_R = -v_C$$

Since the capacitor current is $i = Cdv_C/dt$, then

$$v_R = iR = RC\frac{dv_C}{dt} = -v_C$$

and since $RC = \tau$, then

$$\tau\frac{dv_C}{dt} = -v_C$$

Separating the variables in the equation gives

$$\frac{dt}{\tau} = \frac{dv_C}{v_C}$$

Integrating both sides of the equation leaves us with

$$\frac{t}{\tau} = -\ln v_C + K$$

where *K* is the arbitrary constant of integration. As was stated earlier, the initial condition in the circuit is $v_C = E$ when $t = 0$. Inserting this in the above equation gives $K = \ln E$, hence

$$\frac{t}{\tau} = -\ln v_C + \ln E = \ln\frac{E}{v_C}$$

and taking antilogarithms gives

$$e^{t/\tau} = \frac{E}{v_C}$$

or

$$v_C = Ee^{-t/\tau}$$

The reader will note that this form of equation is that of an exponential curve which decays from a maximum value of E (when $t = 0$) with a time constant of τ ($= RC$). That is, the v_C transient will have decayed to one per cent of its original value in a time of about 5τ. The capacitor voltage decay curve is shown in Figure 14.5(a).

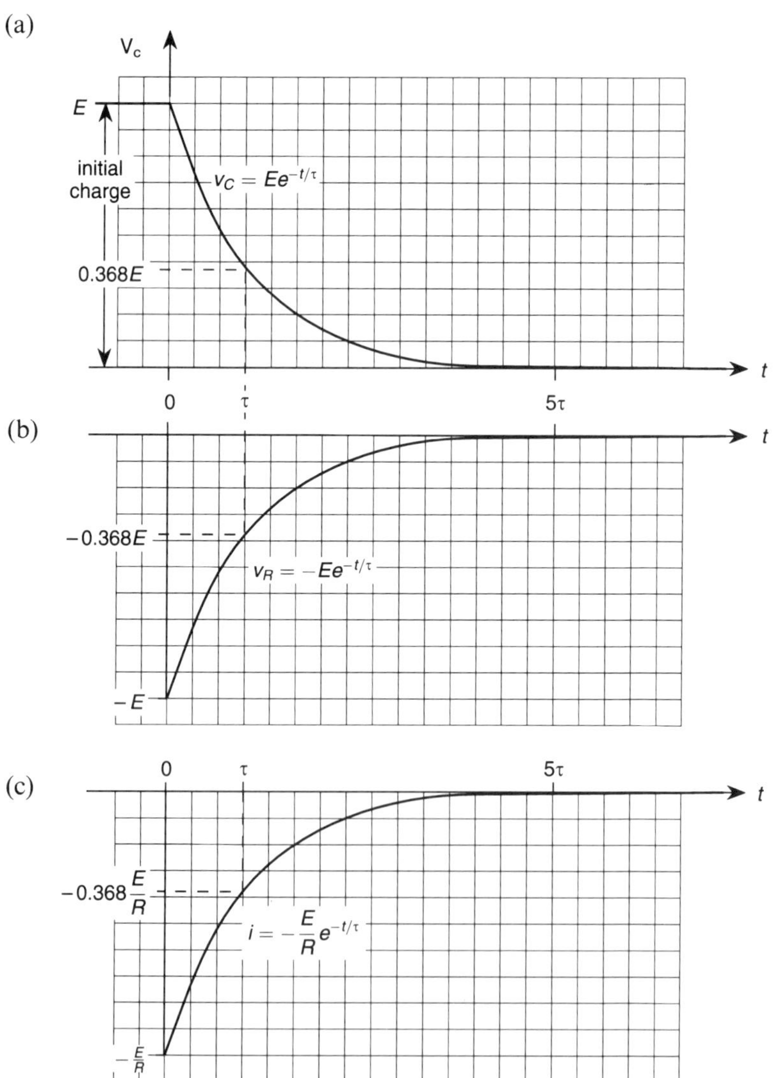

Figure 14.5 Capacitor discharge curves

(a) Voltage across the resistor during discharge

During the discharge period, Kirchhoff's voltage law tells us for the circuit that

$$v_C + v_R = 0$$

or

$$v_R = -v_C = -Ee^{-t/\tau}$$

That is, the graph for v_R is a mirror image of the voltage across the capacitor (see Figure 14.5(b)). Consequently, at the instant the switch blade in Figure 14.4 is changed from A to B, the voltage across the resistor becomes $-E$, and it decays exponentially towards zero with a time constant of τ.

(b) Capacitor discharge current

From Ohm's law

$$i = \frac{v_R}{R} = -\frac{E}{R}e^{-t/\tau} = -I_0 e^{-t/\tau}$$

where I_0 is the initial value of the discharge current. The current decays towards zero with a time constant of τ; the shape of the discharge current curve is given in Figure 14.5(c). The negative sign in front of the equation tells us that the discharge current flows in the opposite direction to that shown in Figure 14.4.

Worked Example 14.3

A 0.1 μF capacitor is charged to 10 V, and is discharged through a 100 kΩ resistor, commencing at $t = 0$. Determine (a) the time constant of the circuit, (b) the time taken for the voltage across the capacitor to fall to 5 V, (c) the voltage across the resistor at the instant the discharge commences, (d) the voltage across the resistor 20 ms after the discharge commences and (e) the time taken for the *magnitude* of the discharge current to fall to 0.04 mA.

Solution

(a) The time constant of the R-C circuit is

$$\tau = RC = (100 \times 10^3) \times (0.1 \times 10^{-6})$$
$$= 0.01 \text{ s or } 10 \text{ ms}$$

(b) Since the capacitor voltage is given by $v_C = Ee^{-t/\tau}$ then, when $v_C = 5\,\text{V}$, we have

$$5 = 10e^{-t/0.01} = 10e^{-100t}$$

or

$$\frac{5}{10} = e^{-100t}$$

transposing gives

$$e^{100t} = \frac{100}{50} = 2$$

Taking Naperian logarithms of both sides of the equation gives

$$100t = \ln 2 = 0.6931$$

hence

$$t = 0.6931/100 = 0.00693\,\text{s or } 6.93\,\text{ms}$$

(c) When $t = 0$, the voltage across the resistor is

$$v_R = -Ee^{-t/\tau} = -10e^0 = -10\,\text{V}$$

(d) When $t = 20\,\text{ms} = 0.02\,\text{s}$, the value of v_R is

$$v_R = -Ee^{-t/\tau} = -10e^{-0.02/0.01} = -10e^{-2}$$
$$= -10 \times 0.135 = -1.35\,\text{V}$$

(e) The discharge current is given by

$$i = -I_0e^{-t/\tau}$$

where I_0 is the initial discharge current and is

$$I_0 = E/R = 10/100 \times 10^3 = 0.0001\,\text{A or } 0.1\,\text{mA}$$

The expression for the *magnitude* of the discharge current is

$$i = I_0e^{-t/\tau}$$

When the discharge current is 0.04 mA, the equation becomes

$$0.04 \times 10^{-3} = 0.1 \times 10^{-3} \times e^{-t/0.01}$$
$$= 10^{-4} \times e^{-100t}$$

hence

$$e^{100t} = 10^{-4}/0.04 \times 10^{-3} = 2.5$$

Taking natural logarithms of both sides of the equation yields

$$100t = \ln 2.5 = 0.916$$

giving

$$t = 0.916/100 = 9.16 \times 10^{-3}\,\text{s or } 9.16\,\text{ms.}$$

14.7 The rise of current in an inductive circuit

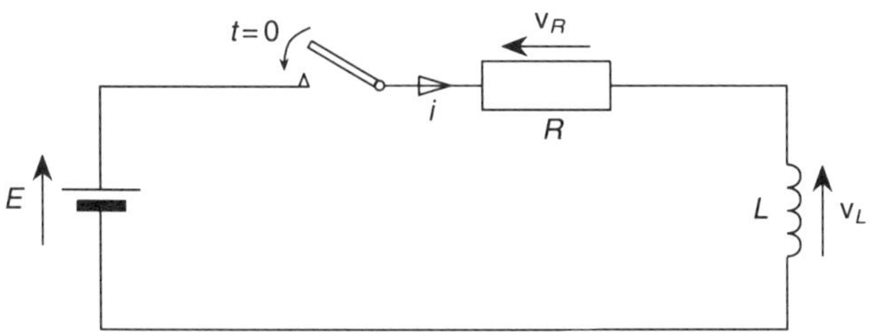

Figure 14.6 Rise of current in an inductive circuit

Figure 14.6 shows a typical *L-R* circuit, in which we close the switch at $t = 0$. When the switch is closed, the loop voltage equation is

$$E = v_R + v_L$$

where v_R is the voltage across the resistor and v_L is the voltage across the inductor. From basic electrical circuit principles, the reader will know that the voltage across the inductor is given by

$$v_L = L\frac{di}{dt}$$

where L is the inductance of the inductor, and di/dt is the rate of change of current through the inductor. By Ohm's law, the voltage across the resistor is

$$v_R = iR$$

where i is the current in the circuit. It therefore follows that

$$E = v_R + v_L = iR + L\frac{di}{dt}$$

Grouping the 'voltage' terms together gives the expression

$$E - iR = L\frac{di}{dt}$$

Since the equation contains di, we will convert the voltage terms into 'current' terms by dividing throughout by R as follows

$$\frac{E}{R} - i = \frac{L}{R}\frac{di}{dt}$$

Next, we rearrange the equation with all the 'current' terms on the right-hand side of the equation as follows

$$\frac{dt}{L/R} = \frac{di}{\frac{E}{R} - i}$$

Since the right-hand side of the equation is dimensionless (i.e., it is the ratio of current/current), then the left-hand side of the equation is also dimensionless. That is, the ratio L/R has the dimensions of time, and is the **time constant**, τ, of the L-R circuit.

In the above equation, we have *separated the variables*, and we can integrate both sides as follows.

$$\int \frac{dt}{\tau} = \int \frac{di}{\frac{E}{R} - i}$$

that is

$$\frac{t}{\tau} = -\ln\left[\frac{E}{R} - i\right] + K \qquad (14.6)$$

where K is the arbitrary constant of integration. The method of integrating the expression on the right-hand side of the equation is carried out in much the same way as for (14.2) in section 14.4.

To determine the value of constant K, we will insert the initial value of i in (14.6), namely $i = 0$ when $t = 0$, as follows

$$0 = -\ln\left[\frac{E}{R} - 0\right] + K$$

or

$$K = \ln(E/R)$$

Reinserting this into (14.6) gives

$$\frac{t}{\tau} = -\ln\left[\frac{E}{R} - i\right] + \ln\frac{E}{R} = \ln\left[\frac{E/R}{(E/r) - i}\right]$$

From the work on logarithms in Chapter 3, it can be shown that (the reader should do this as an exercise)

$$e^{t/\tau} = \frac{E/R}{(E/R) - i}$$

Cross-multiplying gives

$$\frac{E}{R} - i = \frac{E}{R}e^{-t/\tau}$$

or

$$i = \frac{E}{R} - \frac{E}{R}e^{-t/\tau} = \frac{E}{R}\left[1 - e^{-t/\tau}\right]$$

$$= I\left[1 - e^{-t/\tau}\right] \qquad (14.7)$$

where, as will be shown below, I is the **final value** or **steady-state current** in the circuit.

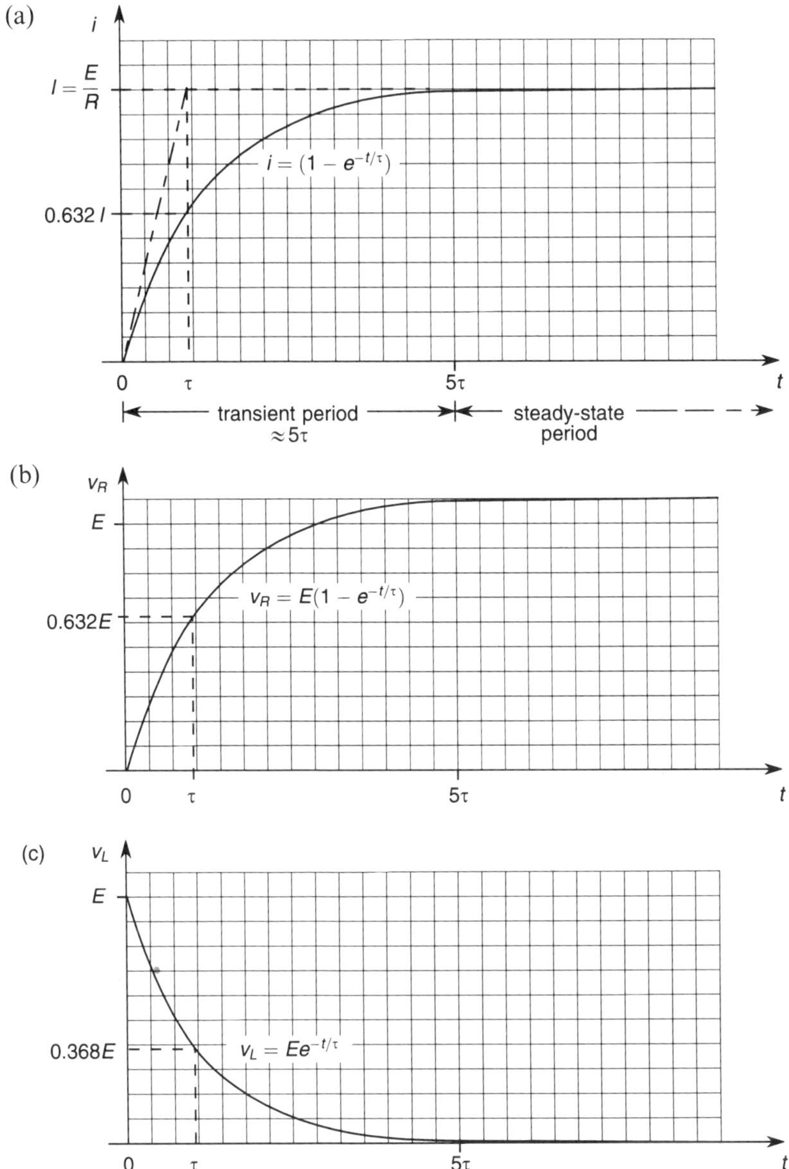

Figure 14.7 Curves during the rise of current in an *L-R* circuit

From Chapter 9 on graphs, the reader will appreciate that (14.7) is that of an exponential curve which rises from zero to a value of I ($= E/R$) with a time constant of τ ($= L/R$); this curve can be quickly and accurately sketched using the method outlined in Chapter 9.

As with other rising exponential curves, the final value is reached in a time of about 5τ, and this period of time is known as the **transient period**.

By the time the circuit transients have settled down, the circuit enters its **steady-state period**, when the current and the circuit voltages have reached a steady value.

The *initial rate of change of i* can be determined as follows. From the original circuit equation, it can be seen that

$$\frac{di}{dt} = \frac{E - iR}{L}$$

Putting the initial conditions in the circuit (that is, $i = 0$ when $t = 0$) into this equation gives

$$\left[\frac{di}{dt}\right]_{t=0} = \frac{E - 0}{L} = \frac{E}{L}$$

If we divide both the numerator and the denominator in the above expression by R we get

$$\left[\frac{di}{dt}\right]_{t=0} = \frac{E/R}{L/R} = \frac{I}{\tau} = \frac{\text{final current}}{\text{time constant}}$$

This allows us to define the time constant of the L-R circuit as follows

> **The time constant of an *L-R* circuit is equal to the time which would be taken for the current in the circuit to reach its final value if the initial rate of rise of current were maintained.**

It is of interest to engineers to determine the value of i when $t = \tau$. Inserting $t = \tau$ into (14.7) gives

$$\begin{aligned}[i]_{t=\tau} &= I(1 - e^{-t/\tau}) = I(1 - e^{-1}) = I(1 - 0.368)\\ &= 0.632I\end{aligned}$$

This value is shown in Figure 14.7(a), and can be used to provide another definition of the time constant as follows

> **The time constant of an *L-R* circuit is the time taken for the current to rise from zero to 63.2 per cent of its final value.**

(a) The voltage across the resistor

From Ohm's law

$$v_R = iR = \frac{E}{R}(1 - e^{-t/\tau}) \times R = E(1 - e^{-t/\tau})$$

Once again, this is an expression for a rising exponential curve, having a final value of E and a time constant of τ. That is, it reaches its final value in a time of about 5τ. The corresponding graph is shown in Figure 14.7(b).

It is left as an exercise for the reader to show that the value of v_R is $0.632E$ when $t = \tau$ (see Figure 14.7(b)).

(b) The voltage across the inductor

The original equation for the circuit tells us that

$$E = v_R + v_L$$

or

$$v_L = E - v_R = E - E(1 - e^{-t/\tau}) = Ee^{-t/\tau}$$

The reader will note that this equation is that of a curve which falls exponentially from an initial value of E, with a time constant of τ. That is, the transient has decayed when $t = 5\tau$. The graph of v_L is shown in Figure 14.7(c).

The reader should test his skills to show that v_L has fallen to $0.368E$ by the time that $t = \tau$ (see Figure 14.7(c)).

14.8 The decay of current in an inductive circuit

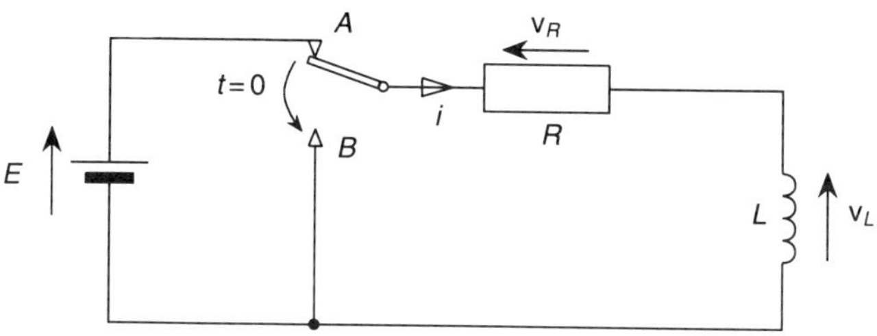

Figure 14.8 Decay of current in an *L-R* circuit

Let us suppose that the contact of the switch in Figure 14.8 has been in position A long enough for all the transients in the circuit to have died away, so that the current in the circuit is

$$I_0 = E/R$$

We wish to study what happens in the circuit when, at $t = 0$, the switch blade is *instantaneously* changed from A to B (the word 'instantaneously' is important, because the contacts of a *practical switch* cannot change over instantaneously. More is said about this in section 14.9).

One of the important laws in electrical science is Lenz's law, which states that an e.m.f. is induced in an inductor whenever the current in the coil changes; moreover, the e.m.f. acts in a direction to oppose the change in current. In effect, the law says that if the current is reduced by, say, altering the supply voltage, then an e.m.f. is induced in the coil which tries to maintain the current at its original direction.

The net result is that (when the switch blade is changed from A to B) the current in the circuit begins to reduce, and an e.m.f. is induced in the coil which tends to maintain the current. That is, changing the position of the switch blade does not instantaneously cut off the current in the circuit.

For $t > 0$, the loop voltage equation for Figure 14.8 is

$$v_L + v_R = 0$$

or

$$L\frac{di}{dt} + Ri = 0$$

That is

$$Ri = -L\frac{di}{dt}$$

hence

$$\frac{R}{L}\,dt = -\frac{di}{i}$$

The left-hand side of the equation can be written in the form

$$\frac{R}{L}\,dt = \frac{dt}{L/R} = \frac{dt}{\tau}$$

Therefore

$$\frac{dt}{\tau} = -\frac{di}{i}$$

Integrating both sides of the equation gives

$$\int \frac{dt}{\tau} = -\int \frac{di}{i}$$

The result of the integration is

$$\frac{t}{\tau} = -\ln i + K \tag{14.8}$$

where K is the arbitrary constant of integration. When the initial condition of $i = E/R$ at $t = 0$ is inserted into (14.8), we get

$$0 = -\ln(E/R) + K$$

or

$$K = \ln(E/R) = \ln I_0$$

Reinserting the above value of K into (14.8) gives (the reader should verify this)

$$i = I_0 e^{-t/\tau} \tag{14.9}$$

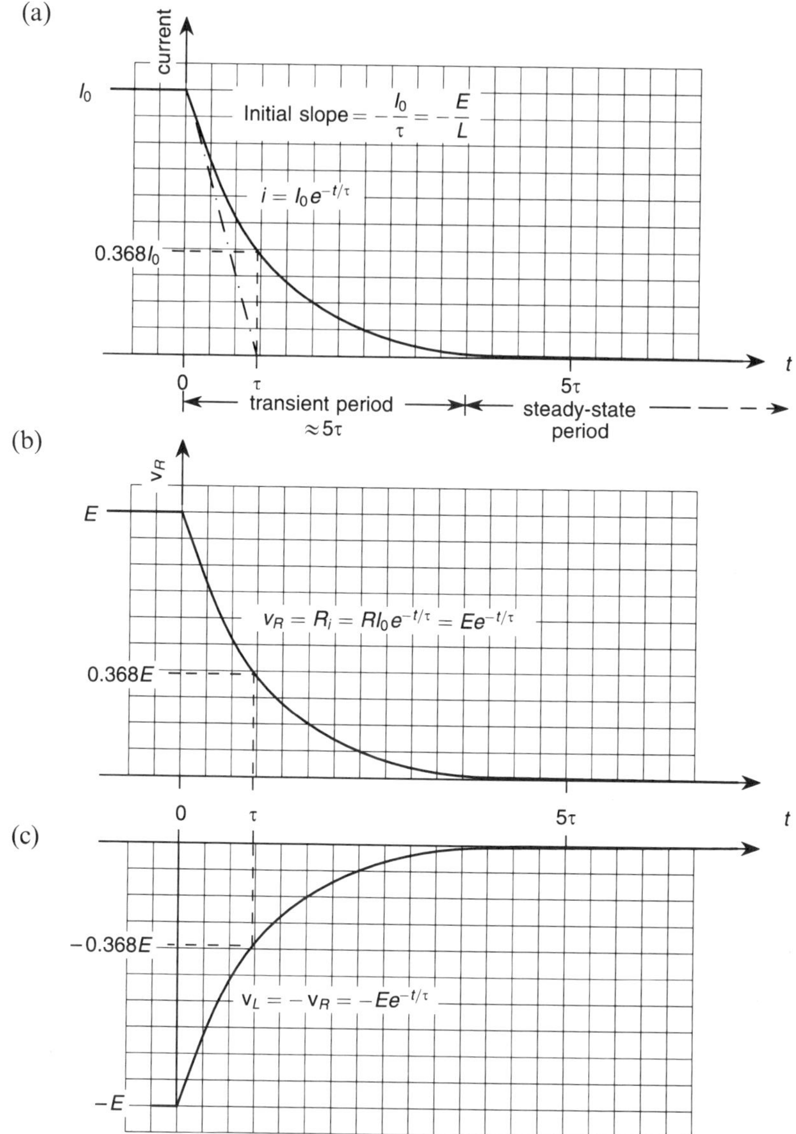

Figure 14.9 Curves during the decay of current in an inductive circuit

Equation (14.9) describes an exponentially decaying curve commencing from I_0, and decaying with a time constant of τ. That is, the transient period is complete in $5\tau = 5L/R$.

The initial rate of decay of i can be determined by inserting the initial condition in the basic equation of the circuit, that is in the equation

$$\frac{di}{dt} = \frac{Ri}{L}$$

Putting the initial condition into this equation gives

$$\left[\frac{di}{dt}\right]_{t=0} = -\frac{R}{L}\left[i\right]_{t=0} = -\frac{R}{L}\left[\frac{E}{R}\right] = -\frac{E}{L}$$

$$= \frac{E/R}{L/R} = \frac{I_0}{\tau}$$

The chain-dotted line in Figure 14.9(a) shows this initial rate of decay, and the reader will see that if this rate of fall were maintained, the current would become zero when $t = \tau$.

The value of i when $t = \tau$ can be determined by inserting $t = \tau$ into (14.9) as follows

$$[i]_{t=\tau} = I_0 e^{-t/\tau} = I_0 e^{-1} = 0.368 I_0$$

(a) The voltage across R during the decay of current

From Ohm's law we see that

$$v_R = iR = I_0 e^{-t/\tau} \times R = I_0 R e^{-t/\tau} = E e^{-t/\tau}$$

Once again, this is the equation of a decaying exponential curve (see Figure 14.9(b)), which will have completely decayed in a time of about $t = 5\tau$. The voltage across the resistor when $t = \tau$ is $0.368E$ (the reader should verify this).

(b) The voltage across L during the decay of current

From the basic equation of the circuit we see that

$$v_L + v_R = 0$$

or

$$v_L = -v_R = -E e^{-t/\tau}$$

That is, the curve for v_L commences at $-E$ when $t = 0$, and decays to zero exponentially in a time of about 5τ (see Figure 14.9(c)). The reader should show that the voltage across the inductor when $t = \tau$ is $-0.368E$.

Worked Example 14.4

A voltage pulse of amplitude 5 V and duration 5 ms is applied to a relay coil of inductance 0.1 H and resistance 100 Ω. The relay contacts close when the current in the coil has risen to 40 mA, and open when the current has fallen to 15 mA. Determine (a) the time delay before the contacts close and (b) the length of time the contacts remain closed. Assume that the current in the coil is initially zero, and that the internal resistance of the pulse source is zero.

Solution

This question involves both the rise and decay of current in an inductive circuit. The maximum (steady-state) value that the current can reach is

$$I = E/R = 5/100 = 0.05\,\text{A or } 50\,\text{mA}$$

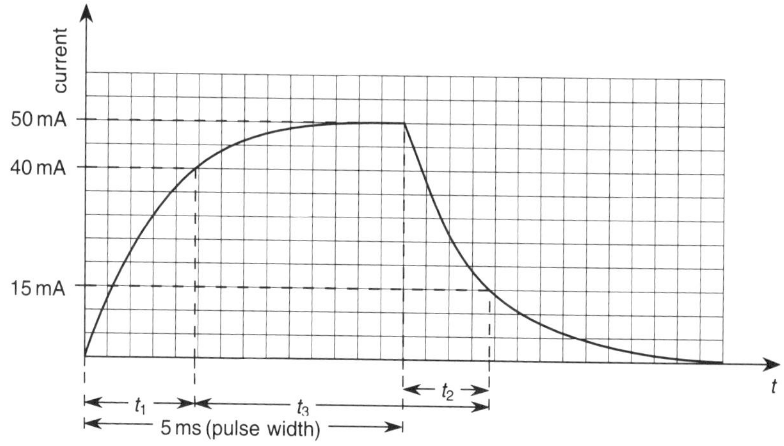

Figure 14.10 Solution to Worked Example 14.4

The waveform of the current in the coil is shown in Figure 14.10 in which

t_1 = time delay before the contacts close,
t_2 = time delay for the contacts to open after the applied voltage has been reduced to zero,
t_3 = length of time the contacts remain open
$= 5\,\text{ms} - t_1 + t_2$.

The time constant of the circuit is

$$\tau = L/R = 0.1/100 = 0.001 \text{ or } 1\,\text{ms}$$

Since it takes $5\tau = 5\,\text{ms}$ for the current to reach its final value, and the voltage pulse has a duration of 5 ms, a current of 50 mA flows in the coil at the end of the voltage pulse.

(a) Determination of t_1.

Initially, the current rises exponentially, and the current at t_1 is 40 mA. From (14.7) we see that

$$i = I(1 - e^{-t_1/\tau})$$

or

$$40 \times 10^{-3} = 50 \times 10^{-3}(1 - e^{-t_1/0.001})$$

It is left as an exercise for the reader to transpose the equation for t_1, giving

$$\begin{aligned} t_1 &= \tau \ln 5 = 0.001 \times 1.609 \\ &= 1.609 \times 10^{-3}\,\text{s or } 1.609\,\text{ms} \end{aligned}$$

(b) Determination of t_2.

Equation (14.9) mathematically describes the decay of the current in the circuit, in which $I_0 = 50\,\text{mA}$, hence

$$i = I_0 e^{-t_2/\tau}$$

or

$$15 \times 10^{-3} = 50 \times 10^{-3} e^{-t_2/0.001}$$

Solving for t_2 (the reader should do this) gives

$$\begin{aligned} t_2 &= \tau \ln(50/15) = 0.001 \times 1.204 \\ &= 0.001204\,\text{s or } 1.204\,\text{ms} \end{aligned}$$

(c) Determination of t_3.

From the expression given earlier for t_3, the length of time the contacts remain closed is

$$t_3 = 5 - t_1 + t_2 = 5 - 1.609 + 1.204 \approx 4.6\,\text{ms}$$

14.9 Breaking the current in an inductive circuit

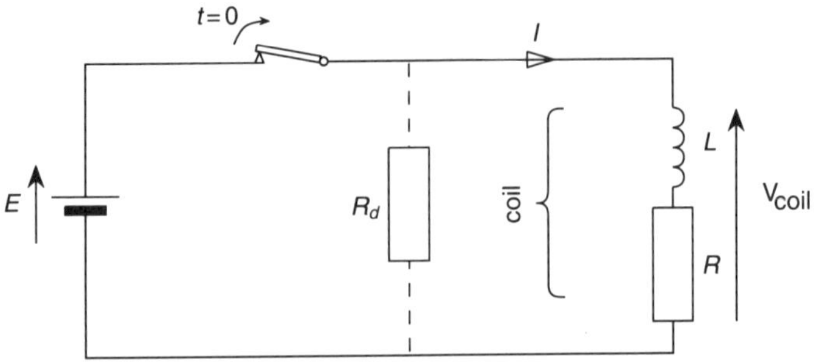

Figure 14.11 Breaking an inductive circuit

The equation for the voltage across the coil, V_{coil}, in the circuit drawn in full line in Figure 14.11 is

$$V_{coil} = Ri + L\frac{di}{dt}$$

where di/dt is the rate of change of current in the coil, and $L\,di/dt$ is the self-induced e.m.f. in the coil.

If the switch in the circuit is ideal, it can theoretically cut off the current in the inductor in zero time! If this is the case then, at the instant the switch is opened, $i = 0$ and $di/dt = -\infty$! Inserting this value into the above equation gives

$$V_{coil} = (R \times 0) + (L \times (-\infty)) = -\infty \text{ V}$$

That is, the magnitude of the voltage across the coil at the instant the switch is opened is infinite. In practice, we cannot reduce the current to zero in zero time, but the rate of current can be very high and, with it, the voltage induced in the coil is also very high.

The net result is that we often see arcing at the contact of a switch in an inductive circuit when it is opened (even in a low-voltage bell circuit; it is for this reason that gas service engineers *never ring a door bell* because of the potential risk of a gas explosion!).

We will now look at one method of reducing the voltage across the coil (and, therefore, across the switch contacts) to a reasonable level. The method discussed here (and there are alternative methods) involves connecting resistor R_d (shown in broken line in Figure 14.11) across the coil; this resistor is sometimes called a *spark quench resistor*.

The steady-state current in the coil is

$$I = E/R$$

and when the switch is opened at $t = 0$, the induced e.m.f. in the coil (at the instant the switch is opened) acts to maintain this value of current flowing in the coil. When the switch contacts are opened, the path for the current in the coil is through R and R_d, so that I flows in R_d, and the voltage across the coil at this time is $V_{coil} = IR_d$.

If, for example, $E = 10$ V and $R = 2\,\Omega$, then $I = 10/2 = 5$ A. Hence if $R_d = 100\,\Omega$ them, at the instant the switch is opened

$$V_{coil} = IR_d = 5 \times 100 = 500 \text{ V}$$

which is 50 times greater than E! If $R_d = 10\,\Omega$, then

$$V_{coil} = IR_d = 5 \times 10 = 50 \text{ V}$$

That is, the value of R_d controls the voltage across the coil at the instant of opening the switch.

The voltage across the switch contacts when the switch is opened is $(V_{coil} + E)$, which can be considerably greater than E (the reader should use basic circuit theory to verify this equation).

Self-test questions

14.1 A 10 μF capacitor is connected to a d.c. source via a 1 MΩ resistor. Determine the time taken for the capacitor to receive 90 per cent of its final charge.

14.2 A 5 μF capacitor is connected to a d.c. supply through a 2 MΩ resistor. If the d.c. source is short-circuited, determine the time taken for the capacitor to lose (a) 50 per cent, (b) 63.2 per cent and (c) 95 per cent of its charge.

14.3 How long does it take for the current i in Figure 14.12 to reach 25 mA?

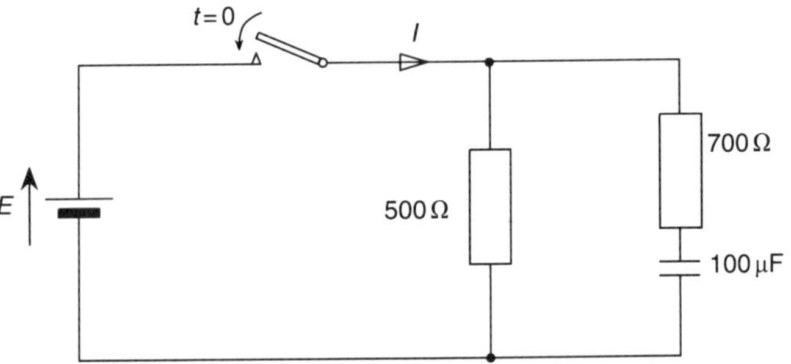

Figure 14.12 Self-test question 14.3

14.4 A 75 μF capacitor is connected in series with a 10 kΩ resistor to a 100 V d.c. supply. Determine (a) the time constant of the circuit, (b) the initial rate of change of the voltage across the capacitor, (c) the voltage across the capacitor after a time equal to two time constants, (d) the initial value of the charging current and (e) the time taken for the charging current to fall to 25 per cent of its initial value.

14.5 A 50 μF capacitor is initially charged to 100 V. If it is suddenly connected through a 20 kΩ resistor to a 150 V supply at $t = 0$, determine the voltage across the capacitor when $t = 0.75$ s.

14.6 A circuit containing a coil of resistance R and inductance L is connected to a d.c. source, and the current reaches 0.632 of its final value in 1 s. When the current has reached its final value, the coil is short-circuited. What is the current in the coil in terms of the maximum current 2 s after it is short-circuited?

14.7 Plot a graph showing the rise in current in a coil of inductance 10 H and resistance 2 Ω when it is connected to a 100 V d.c. source (use a time base of 30 s). What is the current in the coil 7.5 s after it is connected to the d.c. supply?

14.8 A coil of inductance 0.5 H and resistance 20 Ω is connected to a 200 V d.c. supply. Determine the rate of change of current in the coil (a) at the instant it is connected to the supply and (b) after a time equal to the time constant of the coil. Calculate also (c) the steady-state value of the current in the coil.

14.9 A coil of resistance 40 Ω and inductance 10 H is connected in the circuit in Figure 14.13. The switch blade has been in position *A* long enough for all transients to have settled down, when the switch blade is changed to position *B*.

(a) If $R = 500\,\Omega$, determine the voltage across the coil at the instant the switch is changed over and (b) what should be the value of *R* if the voltage across the coil is allowed to rise to 200 V at the instant of switching.

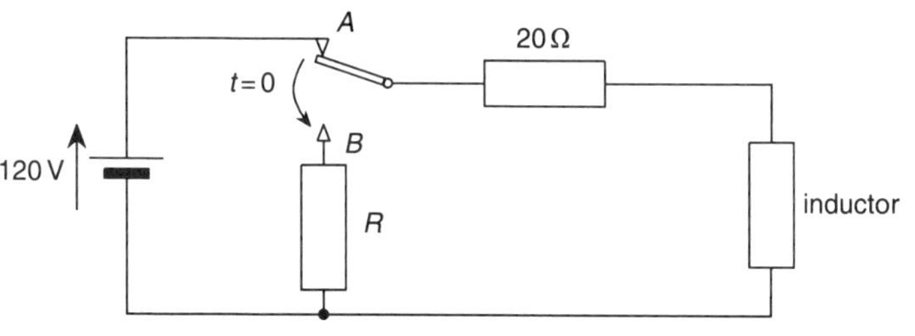

Figure 14.13 Self-test question 14.9

Summary of important facts

A **transient** is a phenomenon which passes away with time. A **single-energy circuit** or **first-order circuit** is one containing a single energy-storage element (such as a capacitor or an inductor).

A **differential equation** is an equation containing differential coefficients, and the **order** of the equation is the number of times differentiation has been carried out. The **degree** of the equation is the highest power to which the highest derivative is raised. For example

$$LC\frac{d^2i}{dt^2} + RC\frac{di}{dt} + i = 0$$

is of the second order and first degree.

There are many types of differential equation, the most common in electrical circuits being the **variables separable** type, which is of the form

$$\frac{dy}{f(y)} = f(x)\,dx$$

which is solved by integrating both sides of the equation. This leaves us with the **general solution** which includes an **arbitrary constant of integration**. The value of this constant is determined by inserting a set of **boundary conditions** (which are usually **initial conditions** in electrical circuits).

The equation for the charge of a capacitor from a d.c. source is (see Figure 14.1)

$$E = iR + RC\frac{dv_C}{dt}$$

in which all the terms have been defined earlier. If the capacitor is initially discharged (i.e. $v_C = 0$ at $t = 0$), then

$$v_C = E(1 - e^{-t/\tau})$$

$$v_R = Ee^{-t/\tau}$$

$$i = I_0e^{-t/\tau}$$

where $\tau = CR$ and is the **time constant** of the circuit, and $I_0 = E/R$ and is the **initial value of the charging current**. Also v_C has risen to $0.632E$ when $t = \tau$, v_R has fallen to $0.368E$ when $t = \tau$, and i has fallen to $0.368I_0$ when $t = \tau$.

The equations for the **discharge of a capacitor** (see Figure 14.4) are

$$v_C = Ee^{-t/\tau}$$

$$v_R = -Ee^{-t/\tau}$$

$$i = -I_0e^{-t/\tau}$$

where $I_0 = E/R$ and is the initial value of the discharge current.

The circuit equation for **the rise of current in an inductive circuit** when it is connected to a d.c. source (see Figure 14.6) is

$$E = iR + L\frac{di}{dt}$$

the terms having been defined earlier. If there is no initial current in the inductor (i.e. $i = 0$ when $t = 0$), then

$$i = I(1 - e^{-t/\tau})$$

$$v_R = E(1 - e^{-t/\tau})$$

$$v_L = Ee^{-t/\tau}$$

where $\tau = L/R$, and is the **time constant** of the L-R circuit, and I is the **final value** or **steady-state value** of the current. Also, when $t = \tau$, i has a value of $0.632I$, $v_R = 0.632E$, and $v_L = 0.368E$.

The equations for the **decay of current** in an inductor (see Figure 14.8) are

$$i = I_0e^{-t/\tau}$$

$$v_R = Ee^{-t/\tau})$$

$$v_L = -Ee^{-t/\tau}$$

where $I_0 = E/R$, and is the initial current in the inductor at the time that the decay of current commences.

15 Boolean algebra and logic circuits

15.1 Introduction

It is ironic to think that the foundations of modern **electronic logic theory** was laid down by the Rev. George Boole in 1847 before electronics were even thought of! He wrote a paper entitled *Mathematical Analysis of Logic*, where he showed that algebraic formulae can be used to express logical relationships. Mathematicians refer to logic theory as **set theory**, or the theory of 'sets'.

In this chapter we look at the basis of logic theory, and see how it is implemented in electronic **logic gates**, which can be 'opened' or 'closed' by appropriate combinations of input signals to the gate. This type of theory is used in the design of control systems for modern industry and commerce.

By the end of this chapter, the reader will be able to

- understand the meaning of positive logic and negative logic,
- appreciate the operation of AND, OR and NOT gates, and design basic logic systems,
- manipulate logical (Boolean) equations, and understand the laws of logic,
- design logic circuits using Karnaugh maps, understand the concept of *redundancy* in logic circuits, and simplify logic circuits,
- understand and apply De Morgan's theorem,
- understand what is meant by 'fuzzy' logic.

15.2 Logic signal levels

In the world of logical algebra, every question has a definite answer, so that every problem provides either a 'yes' or **true** solution or a 'no' or **false** solution.* That is, we are dealing with a **binary** or two-level system.

Digital electronic circuits operate within specific bands of voltage levels and, typically, a voltage in the range +3 V to +5 V may be a 'true' or **logic '1'** signal, and a voltage in the range zero to about +0.5 V may be a 'false' or **logic '0'** signal. The voltage level used depends, of course, on the type of electronic circuit in use. If the 'true' voltage level is higher (more positive) than the 'false' voltage level, then we say we are using **positive logic**. If the reverse is the case, then we are using **negative logic**.

* There is a version of logic known as **fuzzy logic**, in which the answer can be any one of three types, namely *yes*, *no* or *maybe*. This, of course, is much closer to real life, and is introduced in section 15.12.

15.3 The AND gate

A **logic gate** is one which a given combination of 'input' signals will open it to the flow of information, and which another combination will 'close'.

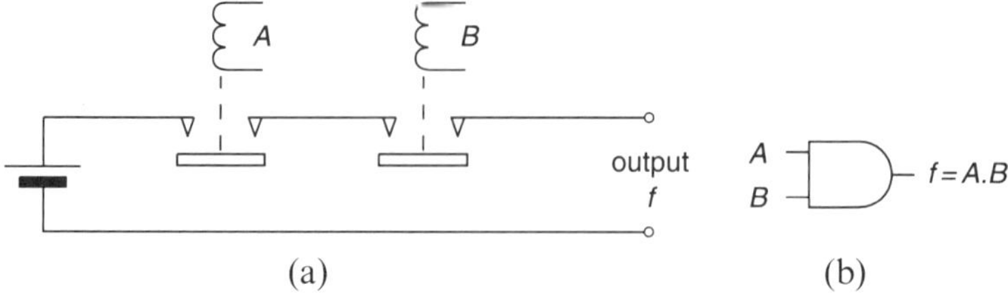

Figure 15.1 A simple relay two-input AND gate

One of the simplest forms of electronic gate is the **AND gate**, a simple 2-input relay AND gate being illustrated in Figure 15.1(a). The gate comprises two relays, having normally-open contacts which are connected in series. When either relay coil is energised, we say that a logic '1' signal is applied to it (this is an 'input' signal), and when it is de-energised we say that a logic '0' signal is applied to it.

That is, signal A may either be '1' or '0', and signal B may either be '1' or '0'. Similarly the output, f, from the gate may either be '1' or '0'. Using the concept of '1' and '0', we avoid the necessity of referring to specific voltage levels.

If there are n input signals which may be applied to a gate, there are 2^n possible combinations of these inputs; in the case of a 2-input gate ($n = 2$), there are $2^2 = 4$ possible combinations of the inputs, which are as follows

$$A = 0,\ B = 0$$

$$A = 0,\ B = 1$$

$$A = 1,\ B = 0$$

$$A = 1,\ B = 1$$

For each input combination which can be applied to a gate, there is a specific output, f, from the gate. A table showing all the possible combinations of input and output signals is known as the **truth table** of the gate. For a 2-input AND gate, this is shown in Table 15.1.

TABLE 15.1 Truth table for a two-input AND gate

Inputs		*Output*
A	B	$f = A.B$
0	0	0
0	1	0
1	0	0
1	1	1

In Table 15.1 we list the four combinations of input signals in the 'input' columns of the table (which, it should be noted, are the first four pure binary values). Next we look at the circuit to decide what signal should appear in the 'output' column.

We can see that if any input is energised by a logic '0' signal, the appropriate relay is de-energised and the relay contact is open. That is, *the output from the gate is '0' if any input signal is '0'*; this occurs in the first three rows of the truth table. Only when $A = 1$ and $B = 1$ are both relays energised, and both contacts closed, when the output is '1'.

The truth table of an AND gate (*any type of AND gate*) may be summarised as follows

> **The output from an AND gate is logic '1' when ALL inputs are logic '1', otherwise the output is '0'.**

We can represent the output from the gate in the form

$$f = A \text{ AND } B = A.B$$

The 'dot' (.) symbol is used by engineers to represent the logic AND operation; mathematicians use the 'set' theory symbol ∩ (the 'cap' symbol), so that we can say

$$f = A \cap B$$

The AND function is sometimes known as the *logical product function*, since it appears from the truth table that f is the 'product' of the values in the A and B input columns. However, the reader should be very cautious about thinking that there is a simple relationship between logical algebra and conventional mathematical algebra.

Many and varied circuit symbols have been used to represent the AND gate, the most popular being the 'D' symbol in Figure 15.1(b), with the input signals entering the 'flat' side of the gate.

15.4 The OR gate

A typical 2-input relay **OR gate** is shown in Figure 15.2(a), together with its international symbol in diagram (b). The relay gate comprises two sets of relay contacts connected in parallel with one another, and the output from the gate is given by

$$f = A \text{ OR } B = A + B$$

where the 'plus' (+) symbol is used by engineers as the OR connective. Mathematicians use the 'cup' (∪) symbol for the same purpose, so that $f = A \cup B$.

It is seen that when either relay has a logic '1' applied to its input, the associated relay contacts are closed, and the output from the gate is logic '1'.

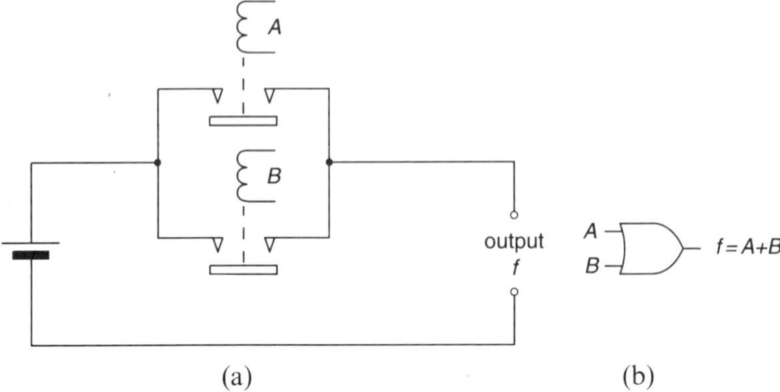

Figure 15.2 A two-input OR gate, (a) a relay logic circuit and (b) its international symbol

Also, when both relays are energised simultaneously (i.e., both sets of contacts are closed), the output is logic '1'. Only when both relays are de-energised ($A = 0$ and $B = 0$) is the output logic '0'. The corresponding truth table for the OR gate is given in Table 15.2. The truth table can be summarised as follows

> **The output from an OR gate is logic '1' when ANY input is logic '1', otherwise the output is logic '0'.**

TABLE 15.2 Truth table for a two-input OR gate

Inputs		*Output*
A	B	$f = A + B$
0	0	0
0	1	1
1	0	1
1	1	1

Since there are only two inputs to the gate in Figure 15.2 there are, once again, $2^2 = 4$ possible input signal combinations to the gate (see Table 15.2). The final combination of inputs are of interest, because we are saying, logically, that

$$A + B = 1 + 1 = 1$$

which should be read as follows.

'1' OR '1' is equal to '1'

The logical OR function is sometimes described as the *logical sum function*, which should not be confused with the arithmetic sum.

15.5 Truth table for a gate with more than two input signals

If a gate has n input signals, there are **2^n possible combinations of the input signals**; for example, if $n = 3$, there are $2^3 = 8$ possible combinations, if $n = 4$ there are $2^4 = 16$ possible combinations, etc.

TABLE 15.3 Truth table for three-input AND and OR gates

Inputs			*Output*	
A	*B*	*C*	AND	OR
0	0	0	0	0
0	0	1	0	1
0	1	0	0	1
0	1	1	0	1
1	0	0	0	1
1	0	1	0	1
1	1	0	0	1
1	1	1	1	1

Consider the case of an AND and an OR gate with three inputs. The truth table for both gates is drawn up in Table 15.3. Initially we write down all the combinations of the input signals in the INPUT columns; these are the first $2^3 = 8$ combinations in the pure binary numbering system. Next we write down the output for each gate in the appropriate OUTPUT column.

Since we are dealing with basic gates, we use the rules already laid down earlier for each gate. Namely, the only '1' in the AND gate output column occurs when A AND B AND C are all 1s, and the only '0' in the OR gate output column occurs when all three inputs are logic '0'.

The logical equation of an n-input AND gate may therefore be written

$$f = A.B.C. \ldots .L.M.N$$

and for an n-input OR gate is

$$f = A + B + C \ldots L + M + N$$

15.6 The NOT gate

The circuit of a simple relay **NOT gate** is shown in Figure 15.3(a), the output from the gate being taken across the relay contacts. It is important to note that *the NOT gate has only one input signal.* The corresponding international logic symbol is shown in diagram (b); the triangular symbol represents a non-inverting 'buffer', and the circle represents the NOT function itself.

When $A = 0$, the relay is de-energised and the contacts are open, so that a voltage appears between the output terminals, that is $f = 1$.

When $A = 1$, the relay is energised, and the output terminals are short-circuited, and $f = 0$. The corresponding truth table for the gate is given in

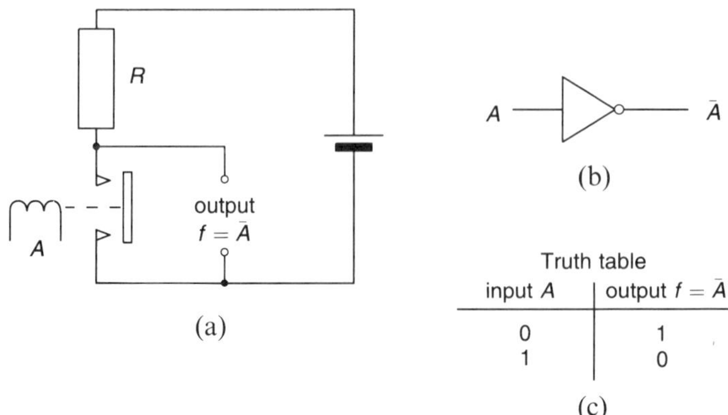

Figure 15.3 The NOT gate, (a) relay logic circuit, (b) international symbol and (c) its truth table

Figure 15.3(c). We see that, for both input signals, the output has the opposite logic level, that is

$$f = \text{NOT } A = \bar{A}$$

The NOT function is symbolised by writing a 'bar' above the variable.

In the circuit in Figure 15.3(a), resistor R simply acts as a current limiting resistor when the output terminals are short-circuited, which occurs when $A = 1$.

The NOT function is known as *logical inversion* or *logical negation*, which has no real counterpart in arithmetic.

Worked Example 15.1

Design a logic system for a drink vending machine in which the cost of a drink is 50 p. The machine accepts either a 50 p coin or a £1 coin, and must dispense 50 p change from a 'change' coin stack if a £1 coin is inserted. If the 'change' coin stack is empty, the machine must display a 'USE CORRECT CHANGE ONLY' sign.

Solution

We will design the electronics of the vending machine in a step-by-step manner and will, initially, consider how a signal is sent to the vending mechanism when either a 50 p or a £1 coin is inserted.

This part of the circuit is shown in Figure 15.4(a), and uses a simple 2-input OR gate. Input F represents a 50 p piece being inserted, and P represents a £1 piece being inserted. Putting either coin into the machine produces a logic '1' at output V, which is used to actuate the vending mechanism, that is

$$V = F \text{ OR } P = F + P$$

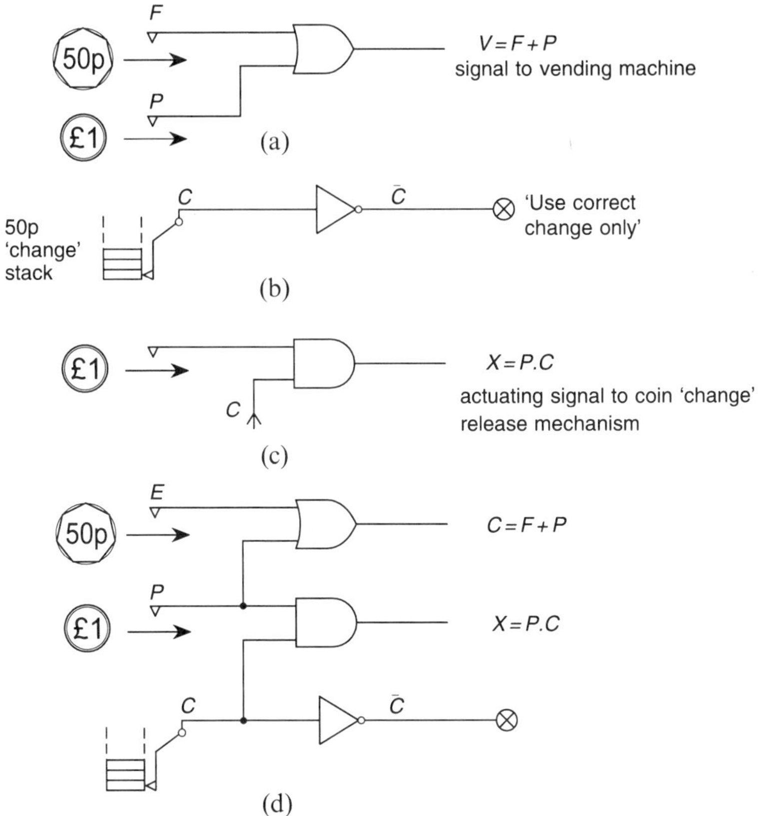

Figure 15.4 Block diagram for a simple vending machine

Next we look at the way in which the machine monitors the number of coins in the 'change' stack inside the machine. Figure 15.4(b) shows how a NOT gate monitors the bottom coin in the stack. If a coin is present ($C = 1$), the output from the gate is '0' ($\bar{C} = 0$) which prevents the 'USE CORRECT CHANGE ONLY' lamp from being illuminated. However, if there are no coins in the 'change' stack, then $C = 0$ and $\bar{C} = 1$, causing the sign to be illuminated.

In Figure 15.4(c) we see one method of actuating the coin 'change' release mechanism via a 2-input AND gate. Provided that we put a £1 coin into the machine AND there is a 50 p coin in the coin stack, then output X ($= P.C$) from the AND gate causes the coin release mechanism to be activated.

Finally, in Figure 15.4(d) we combine the sections of the circuit. This diagram is known as a **logic block diagram**, which shows each gate as a simple logical block, together with the wires which make up the interconnections between the gates (but not the power supplies).

Worked Example 15.2

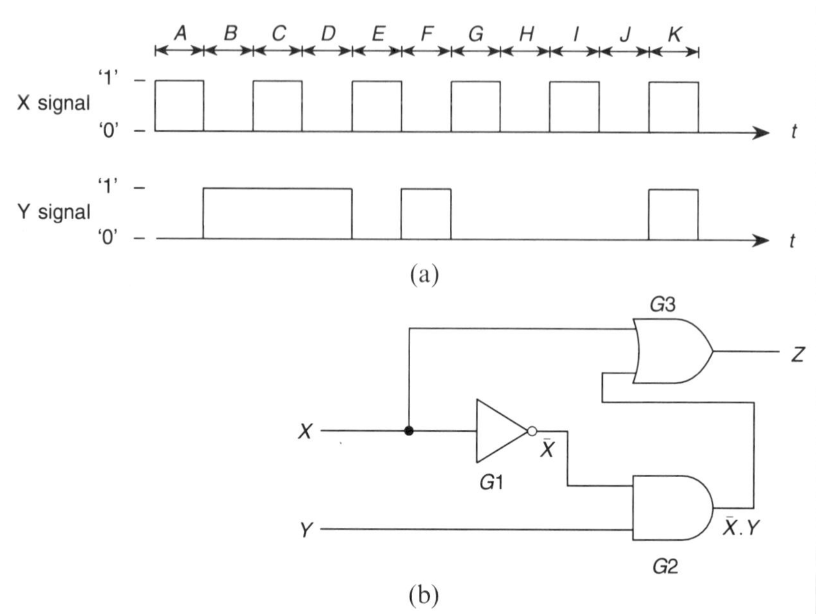

Figure 15.5 Worked Example 15.2

The waveforms at X and Y in Figure 15.5(a) are applied to the logic circuit in Figure 15.5(b). Deduce the truth table for output Z, and draw the waveform at output Z. Also write down a logical expression for output Z, and state what type of gate may be used to replace the complete circuit.

Solution

Since there are only two inputs (X and Y) to the combination of gates in the figure, we can check the output corresponding to the $2^2 = 4$ possible input states from the waveforms for X and Y.

TABLE 15.4 Input conditions: Solution to Worked Example 15.2

Input conditions		*Period when it occurs*
X	Y	
0	0	H, J
0	1	B, D, F
1	0	A, E, G, I
1	1	C, K

For example, during period A we have $X = 1$ and $Y = 0$ and, during period B, $X = 0$ and $Y = 1$, etc. Table 15.4 lists when each input combination occurs, and from this we see that it is only necessary to look in detail at the combination in the periods A, B, C and H, since all the events in other periods are duplicated.

We see from the circuit in Figure 15.5(b) that, since signals $\bar{X}$ and Y are applied to AND gate $G2$, its output is $\bar{X}$ AND $Y = \bar{X}.Y$; this signal together with signal X are simultaneously applied to OR gate $G3$. The final output from $G3$ is therefore

$$Z = \bar{X}.Y \text{ OR } X = \bar{X}.Y + X$$

TABLE 15.5 Logical combination for Figure 15.5(b): Solution to Worked Example 15.2

Input combinations		*Intermediate combinations*		*Output*
X	Y	$\bar{X}$	$\bar{X}.Y$	$Z = X + \bar{X}.Y$
0	0	1	0	0
0	1	1	1	1
1	0	0	0	1
1	1	0	0	1

Let us use the input combinations in Table 15.4 to decide what the truth table for the complete circuit looks like, which is given in Table 15.5. To determine what the truth table looks like we must, initially, invert the state of the X column to give us an $\bar{X}$ column (column 3 in Table 15.5), after which we AND this with the Y column (column 2) to give a $\bar{X}.Y$ column (column 4). Bearing in mind that a logic '1' can only appear in the latter column when both $\bar{X} = 1$ AND $Y = 1$, we see that there is a '1' in the second row of the $\bar{X}.Y$ column.

Finally, the output from the logic circuit is given by $Z = X + \bar{X}.Y$, corresponding to column 1 being ORed with column 4 of Table 15.5. In this case a '1' appears in the Z output column when a '1' appears either in the X column OR in the $\bar{X}.Y$ column. If we compare the input and output columns of Table 15.5 with that of the 2-input OR gate in Table 15.2, we see that the somewhat complicated circuit in Figure 15.5(b) can be replaced by a single 2-input OR gate!

This brings us to the concept of **redundancy** in logic circuits. Using special techniques (see later in the chapter for some methods), we can predict whether we can simplify the block diagram to make it more effective. In this case, the circuit is highly redundant, since two of the three gates can be eliminated without affecting the operation of the circuit.

The input signals at X and Y are combined in Figure 15.6 to show the output waveform at Z.

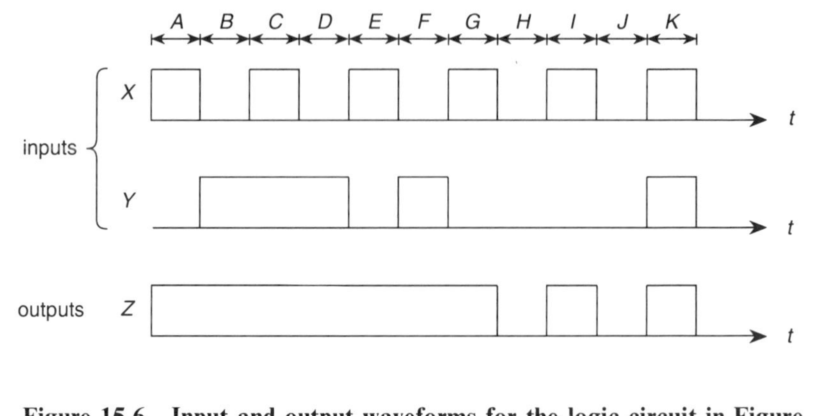

Figure 15.6 Input and output waveforms for the logic circuit in Figure 15.5(b)

15.7 Boolean algebra or the algebra of logic

The Reverend George Boole, an English mathematician, showed how algebraic formulae can be used to express logical relations and, even now, we use this method to write down logical equations. In fact, we have already introduced the basic Boolean concepts of AND, OR and NOT.

There are many laws of logical algebra which are in common with conventional algebra, and there are others which are significantly different. We have already highlighted one of these differences in connection with the OR gate, namely '1' OR '1' = '1'. The basic laws of logic are as follows.

Commutative law

$$A + B = B + A$$

$$A.B = B.A$$

This law states that the result of an operation does not depend on the order of the elements.

Associative law

$$(A + B) + C = A + (B + C)$$

$$(A.B).C = A.(B.C)$$

This states that the result of a given combination does not depend on how pairs of elements are grouped. The reader should note that great care must be taken when bracketing terms together, otherwise mistakes can easily be made.

Distributive law

$$A.(B + C) = A.B + A.C$$
$$A + (B.C) = (A + B).(A + C)$$

The first expression gives the *sum of products* form, and the second the *product of sums*.

The second statement of the distributive law does not apply to conventional algebra, and both statements are best understood from the use of the Karnaugh map (see section 15.9).

Sum rules

$$A + 0 = A$$
$$A + 1 = 1 \quad \text{(a null law)}$$
$$A + A = A$$
$$A + \bar{A} = 1$$

These rules are explained in section 15.7(a).

Product rules

$$A.0 = 0 \quad \text{(a null law)}$$
$$A.1 = A$$
$$A.A = A$$
$$A.\bar{A} = 0$$

These rules are explained in section 15.7(a).

Absorbtion laws

$$A + A.B = A.(1 + B) = A.1 = A$$
$$A.(A + B) = A$$
$$A + \bar{A}.B = A + B$$

These rules are best understood using the Karnaugh map (see section 15.9).

Double Inversion rule

$$\bar{\bar{A}} = A$$

This is explained in section 15.7(a).

(a) Explanation of some of the rules of Boolean algebra

The *sum rules* can be explained by thinking of applying the signals involved to a two-input OR gate. We must bear in mind that the variable A can either have the value '1' or '0', so that if we look at the rule $A + 0 = A$ we get, when $A = 1$

$$1 + 0 = 1$$

and when $A = 0$, we get

$$0 + 0 = 0$$

That is $A + 0 = A$. Using this concept, all the sum rules can be understood.

The *product rules* can be explained by thinking in terms of applying the appropriate inputs to a two-input AND gate. Consider for the moment the rule $A.0 = 0$; if $A = 1$, we get

$$1 \text{ AND } 0 = 1.0 = 0$$

and when $A = 0$ we get

$$0 \text{ AND } 0 = 0.0 = 0$$

That is $A.0 = 0$. All the product rules can be understood on this basis.

TABLE 15.6 Double inversion rule

A	$\bar{A}$	$\bar{\bar{A}} = A$
0	1	0
1	0	1

The *double-inversion rule* can be understood from Table 15.6. When the value of A is '0' then $\bar{A} = 1$; if $\bar{A}$ is applied to the input of a second NOT gate, then its output is NOT(NOT A) = NOT 1 = 0. That is $\bar{\bar{A}} = A$.

Worked Example 15.3

Logic signals from sensors A, B and C in a security system give an indication of the presence of an intruder when the following logical conditions are satisfied

$$f = A.B.C + A.\bar{B}.C + A.B.\bar{C}$$

The output, f, from the system is logic '1' when an intruder is detected. Simplify the expression for f.

Solution

We see that the term A.B appears in the first and third groups of the expression, and we group these together as follows

$$f = A.B.C + A.B.\bar{C} + A.\bar{B}.C \quad \text{(commutative law)}$$
$$= A.B.(C + \bar{C}) + A.\bar{B}.C \quad \text{(distributive law)}$$
$$= A.B.1 + A.\bar{B}.C \quad \text{(sum rules)}$$
$$= A.B + A.\bar{B}.C \quad \text{(product rules)}$$
$$= A.(B + \bar{B}.C) \quad \text{(distributive law)}$$

This is only one possible form of the solution. Other possibilities include the following

$$f = A.(C + B.\bar{C})$$

and

$$f = A.(B + C)$$

The reader will find it an interesting exercise to verify *both* of the alternative solutions.

15.8 De Morgan's theorem

Augustus De Morgan, an English mathematician, proposed the following useful laws in 1847. He stated that the complement of a logic function is obtained if we

1. logically invert each term in the expression, and
2. interchange the 'dots' (AND) with the 'plusses' (OR) and vice versa.

For example

$$\overline{A.B.C} = \bar{A} + \bar{B} + \bar{C}$$

and

$$\overline{A + B + C} = \bar{A}.\bar{B}.\bar{C}$$

Worked Example 15.4

Using De Morgan's theorem, show that (a) $\overline{A.B.\bar{C}} = A + \bar{B} + C$, (b) $C.(\overline{A + \bar{B}}) = C + A.B$

Solution

(a) In this case we apply De Morgan's rules directly as follows

$$\overline{A.B.\bar{C}} = \bar{A} + \bar{B} + \bar{\bar{C}} = \bar{A} + \bar{B} + C$$

(b) If we let $(A + \bar{B}) = Z$, the expression can be written in the form

$$\overline{C.Z} = \bar{C} + \bar{Z} = \bar{C} + \overline{A + \bar{B}}$$

Next we apply De Morgan's laws to the second of these expressions as follows

$$\overline{A+\bar{B}} = \bar{A}.\bar{\bar{B}} = \bar{A}.B$$

Therefore

$$\overline{C(A+\bar{B})} = \bar{C} + \bar{A}.B$$

15.9 Karnaugh maps

John Venn introduced the **Venn diagram** in 1881 to diagramatically represent the relationship between logical variables, and comprised a series of overlapping circles. It was not until 1953 that M. Karnaugh introduced the more systematic **Karnaugh map**, which proved to be very useful in the analysis and design of logic circuits.

Karnaugh maps have the advantage over the conventional logic laws and theorems described earlier, in that they provide a pictorial method of representing a Boolean equation. By this method we can quickly and easily simplify a logical equation, and eliminate redundant terms in the expression.

(a) Karnaugh map for two variables

As mentioned earlier, a 2-variable logic problem has $2^2 = 4$ possible combinations of the input variables and range from $\bar{A}.\bar{B}$, through $\bar{A}.B$, $A.\bar{B}$ to $A.B$. These can be arranged in a Karnaugh map in planar or flat form as shown in Figure 15.7(a). The map is divided into four **cells**, each cell representing the **union** or **intersection** of the two variables.

Initially, the map is divided into two columns representing the two conditions associated with the variable A, namely that A does not exist, i.e., $A = 0$ or $\bar{A}$, and that A does exist, i.e., $A = 1$. Similarly, the map is divided into two rows representing B and $\bar{B}$, respectively. Consequently, the top left-hand cell in Figure 15.7(a) represents the intersection of $\bar{A}$ AND $\bar{B}$, the cell to its right represents the intersection of A AND $\bar{B}$, etc. The corresponding intersections are listed in the cells in the Karnaugh map in Figure 15.7(a).

TABLE 15.7 Truth table for $f = \bar{A}.B$

Inputs		*Output*
A	B	f
0	0	0
0	1	$1 = \bar{A}.B$
1	0	0
1	1	0

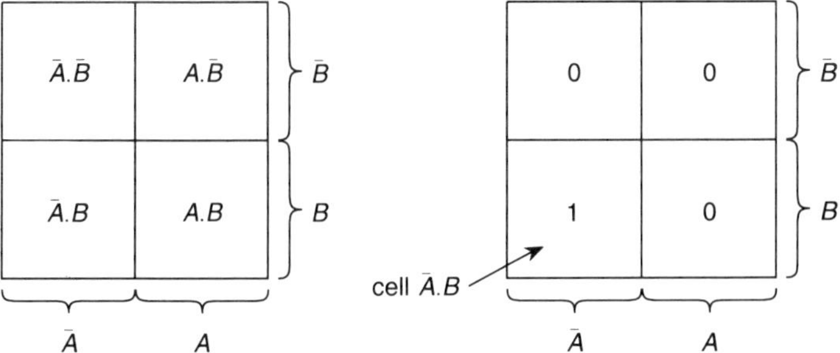

Figure 15.7 Karnaugh map for two variables

If we wish to represent the truth table in Table 15.7 on a Karnaugh map, we simply write the value in the output column in Table 15.7 in the appropriate cell in Figure 15.7(b). That is we write a '1' in the lower left-hand cell in the Karnaugh map (corresponding to the intersection of $\bar{A}.B$, and 0s in the other cells.

If we have a have a more complex statement such as

$$f = \bar{A}.\bar{B} + \bar{A}.B + A.\bar{B}$$

we simply write a '1' in each cell included in the function, and a '0' in the remaining cell, as shown in Figure 15.8.

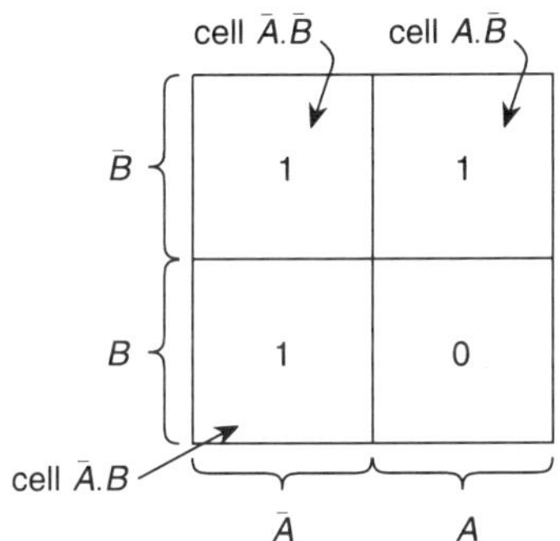

Figure 15.8 Karnaugh map for $f = \bar{A}.\bar{B} + \bar{A}.B + A.\bar{B}$

(b) Karnaugh map for three variables

If a logical problem contains three variables *A*, *B* and *C*, there are $2^3 = 8$ possible combinations of the signals. We can show these on the Karnaugh map in Figure 15.9(a), in which the map is divided vertically between the variables *A* and *B*, each taking up one-half of the map. The reader will note that area *B* overlaps with both *A* and NOT *A*, and area *A* overlaps with both *B* and NOT *B*.

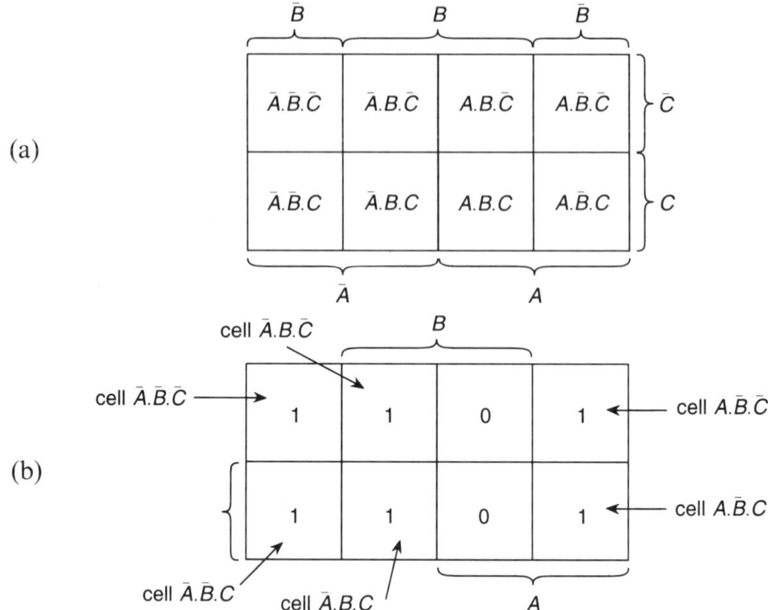

Figure 15.9 Karnaugh map for three variables

It therefore follows that the part which is NOT A also takes up one-half of the map, and the part which is NOT B also takes up one-half of the map. Once again, the reader can see that the part which is NOT A overlaps with B and with NOT B, and the part which is NOT B overlaps with the part that is A and the part that is NOT A.

The map is also divided up horizontally to give areas which define C and NOT C. This gives us a map which defines all eight intersections of A, B and C, ranging from $\bar{A}.\bar{B}.\bar{C}$ through to $A.B.C$ (see Figure 15.9(a)).

Using this type of map we can represent the logical equation

$$f = \bar{A}.\bar{B}.\bar{C} + \bar{A}.B.\bar{C} + A.\bar{B}.\bar{C} + \bar{A}.\bar{B}.C + \bar{A}.B.C + A.\bar{B}.C$$

as shown in Figure 15.9(b), in which each of the cells on the right-hand side of the expression contain a '1', and the remaining cells contain a '0'.

In fact, it can be shown that the Karnaugh maps in Figures 15.8 and 15.9 are identical because *variable C is completely redundant*! This is one aspect of Karnaugh maps which is of particular interest to engineers, because we can quickly decide if any term in an expression is redundant. We look at this aspect in section 15.10.

15.10 Simplification of Karnaugh maps

Cells which are adjacent on the Karnaugh map and which contain a logic '1' can be grouped together to form a *logical block*. Additionally, *the cells must*

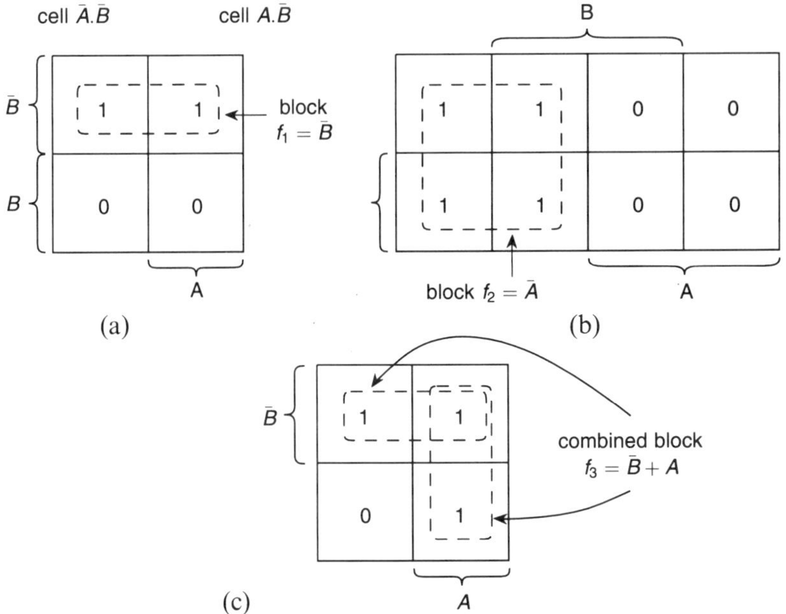

Figure 15.10 Adjacent cells in the Karnaugh map

form a binary grouping, i.e., the cells are in groups of 2 cells, 4 cells, 8 cells, etc.

Where two cells are adjacent, as shown grouped in broken line in Figure 15.10(a), we can say that the grouped cells represent the logical expression $\bar{A}.\bar{B}$ OR $A.\bar{B}$. We can manipulate this using Boolean algebra as follows

$$f_1 = \bar{A}.\bar{B} + A.\bar{B} = \bar{B}.(\bar{A} + A) = \bar{B}.1 = \bar{B}$$

Boolean algebra shows, after some manipulation, that the two adjacent cells on the Karnaugh map represent the NOT B, i.e., f_1 = NOT B. However, the Karnaugh map tells us much more quickly that this is the case because, if we look at the area on the map which is grouped together (the top half), we can 'see' that the two adjacent cells represent NOT B. This enables us to **simplify the logical expression** without the use of Boolean algebra.

In Figure 15.10(b), four adjacent cells are grouped together

$$\begin{aligned} f_2 &= \bar{A}.\bar{B}.\bar{C} + \bar{A}.\bar{B}.C + \bar{A}.B.\bar{C} + \bar{A}.B.C \\ &= \bar{A}.\bar{B}.(\bar{C} + C) + \bar{A}.B.(\bar{C} + C) = \bar{A}.B.1 + \bar{A}.B.1 \\ &= \bar{A}.\bar{B} + \bar{A}.B = \bar{A}.(\bar{B} + B) = \bar{A}.1 = \bar{A} \end{aligned}$$

The above procedure requires us to make the correct selections from our logical algebraic knowledge in order to get the correct solution. However, when we look at the Karnaugh map, we can 'see' that the four adjacent cells cover the area of the map represented by $f_2 = \bar{A}$.

The Karnaugh maps we have looked at so far contain cells which are grouped in binary combinations. The three cells in Figure 15.10(c) do not represent a binary grouping, so that we cannot write down a simple logical expression which represents the map. However, we can group the cells into two pairs, having one cell in common to the two groups. Using Boolean algebra, we can represent the three cells as follows.

$$f_3 = \bar{A}.\bar{B} + A.\bar{B} + A.B = \bar{A}.\bar{B} + (A.\bar{B} + A.\bar{B}) + A.B$$

The centre bracketed term $A.\bar{B} = (A.\bar{B} + A.\bar{B})$ can be seen to be correct from the 'Sum rules' in section 15.7. It follows that

$$\begin{aligned} f_3 &= (\bar{A}.\bar{B} + A.\bar{B}) + (A.\bar{B} + A.B) \\ &= \bar{B}.(\bar{A} + A) + A.(\bar{B} + B) = \bar{B}.1 + A.1 = \bar{B} + A \end{aligned}$$

Clearly, simplifying the expression by Boolean algebra is not straightforward, and we will see how to do it from the Karnaugh map below.

When we look at the Karnaugh map in Figure 15.10(c), we see that the two cells grouped horizontally represent $\bar{B}$, and the two cells grouped vertically represent A. That is, the three adjacent cells in Figure 15.10(c) represent the function

$$f_3 = \bar{B} + A$$

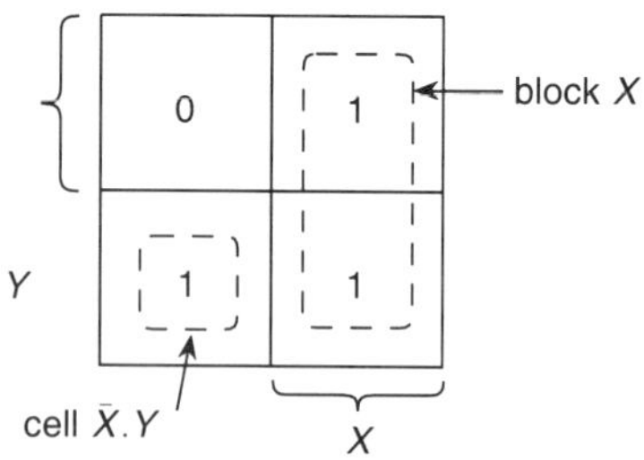

Figure 15.11 Karnaugh map, Worked Example 15.2

If we draw the Karnaugh map for the expression $Z = \bar{X}.Y + X$ (see Worked Example 15.2), we get the map in Figure 15.11. We can say, by observation, that

$$Z = X + Y$$

which agrees with the solution in the example, thereby reducing the amount of labour involved in its solution.

When the Karnaugh map for three variables was defined, we quite arbitrarily decided to position variable A in the right-hand half of the map, and B in the centre (see Figure 15.9). There is, in fact, no reason to do this, and we could reverse their positions.

Figure 15.12(a) shows the positions of A and B interchanged when compared with Figure 15.9, and in Figure 15.12(a) we show the group of

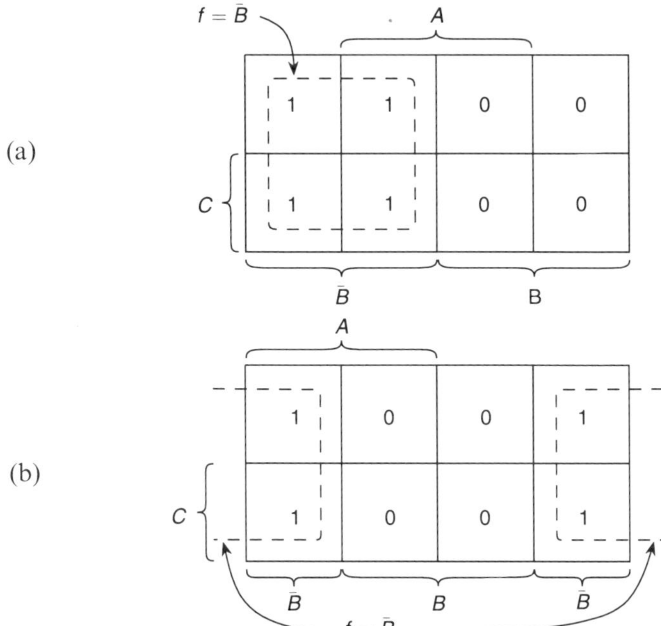

Figure 15.12 End-to-end adjacency on a three-variable Karnaugh map

four cells representing the expression $f = \bar{B}$. Suppose, in Figure 15.12(b) we change the relative positions of A and B again, but we still show all the $\bar{B}$ cells marked with a '1'. Since *both maps* represent the function $f = \bar{B}$, it follows that *the cells at the ends of the rows are also adjacent to one another.*

That is, we can think of a three-variable Karnaugh map as being a continuous loop which, arbitrarily, has been cut along a 'seam' and opened flat for our convenience. Therefore *cells containing 1s at the end of rows are adjacent to one another.*

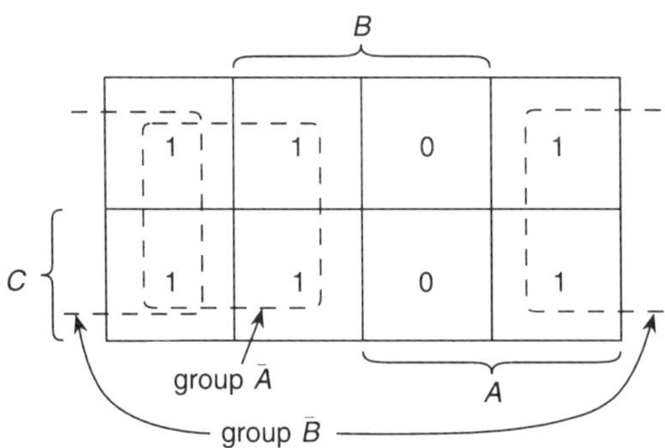

Figure 15.13 Cells on the Karnaugh map in Figure 15.9(b) redrawn and grouped together

Let us repeat the Karnaugh map in Figure 15.9(b) again in Figure 15.13. Here we see that two pairs of cells at the end of the Karnaugh map are adjacent to one another and the total area marked with 1s is defined by the expression

$$f = \bar{A} + \bar{B}$$

That is, variable C is completely redundant! This agrees with the comment in the section 15.9(b).

Worked Example 15.5

Design a minimal logic network which satisfies truth table 15.8. Draw the corresponding logic block diagram.

TABLE 15.8 Truth table for Worked Example 15.5

Inputs			*Output*	*Comment*
A	*B*	*C*	*f*	
0	0	0	0	
0	0	1	1	$\bar{A}.\bar{B}.C$
0	1	0	0	
0	1	1	0	
1	0	0	1	$A.\bar{B}.\bar{C}$
1	0	1	1	$A.\bar{B}.C$
1	1	0	0	
1	1	1	0	

Solution

The truth table for the system shows that it must provide an output of logic '1' for three conditions, namely

$$f = \bar{A}.\bar{B}.C + A.\bar{B}.\bar{C} + A.\bar{B}.C$$

Although it is possible to minimise this by Boolean algebra, it is rather tricky, and the reader may try many solutions before a minimal solution is obtained. In fact, the reader should use this example as a means of getting experience in the solution of a logic network using Boolean algebra. We will use the Karnaugh map method here.

The Karnaugh map corresponding to Table 15.8 is drawn in Figure 15.14, and we see that there are three 1s on the map, which can be grouped into two adjacent pairs of 1s, which are enclosed in broken lines.

One pair, representing the grouping $A.\bar{B}$, is at the right-hand end of the map and the other group, representing $\bar{B}.C$, is grouped by the end-to-end adjacent cells in the bottom row. That is, the truth table is represented by the equation

$$f = A.\bar{B} + \bar{B}.C = \bar{B}.(A + C)$$

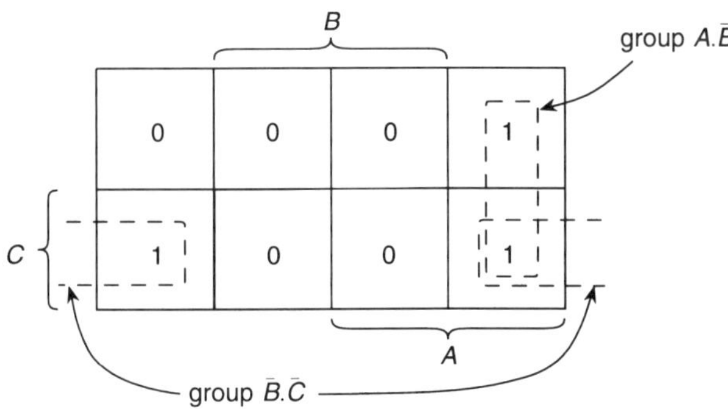

Figure 15.14 Karnaugh map, Solution to Worked Example 15.5

The corresponding logic block diagram is shown in Figure 15.15.

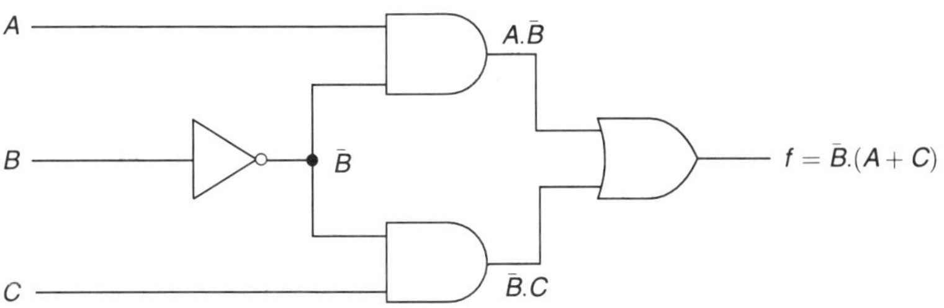

Figure 15.15 Logic block diagram, Solution to Worked Example 15.5

15.11 Design of an electronic adding circuit

One of the basic building blocks of electronic circuits is the electronic adder. The basic circuit described here is the **half-adder**, first mentioned in section 2.10(a), where we discussed binary addition. If two binary variables, A and B, are to be added together (without a 'carry' from a previous addition), the truth table showing the two variables together with the sum and carry produced by the addition is given in Table 15.9.

TABLE 15.9 Truth table for a half-adder circuit

Inputs		*Outputs*	
A	B	SUM	CARRY
0	0	0	0
0	1	1	0
1	0	1	0
1	1	0	1

The truth table shows that there are two input variables (A and B), and two outputs (SUM and CARRY). Each output can be separately related to the inputs (it is left as an exercise for the reader to verify the relationships), and are as follows

$$\text{SUM} = \bar{A}.B + A.\bar{B}$$
$$\text{CARRY} = A.B$$

Fortunately we can combine the circuits for the SUM and CARRY into one complete logic circuit, as shown in Figure 15.16.

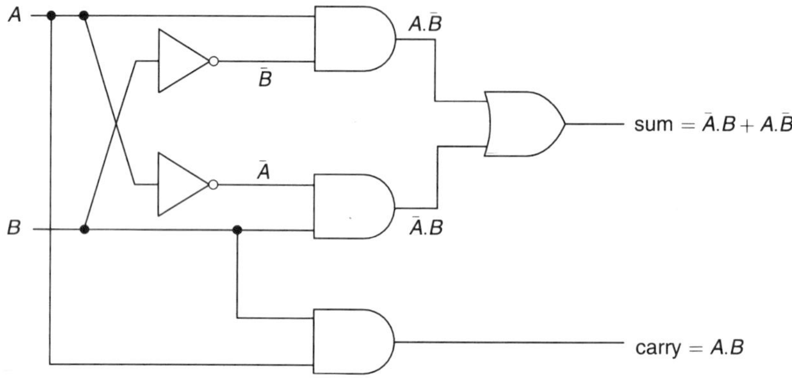

Figure 15.16 Half-adder circuit

The SUM section of the half-adder is also known as a **NOT-EQUIVALENT circuit**, because SUM = 1 when

$$(A = 0 \text{ AND } B = 1) \text{ OR } (A = 1 \text{ AND } B = 0)$$

that is SUM = 1 when A IS NOT EQUIVALENT TO B.

The NOT-EQUIVALENT circuit is important in circuits used to compare two values, such as comparing the length of a manufactured item with that of a test piece. If the length of the item is equal to the length of the test piece, the NOT-EQUIVALENT circuit gives an output of logic '0'; if the two lengths are not equivalent to one another, the circuit gives an output of logic '1'. This circuit can be used as a simple ACCEPT OR REJECT process on a production line.

A **full-adder** circuit is one having three input signals, namely an addend signal, and augend signal and a CARRY-IN signal from the previous stage of addition (see also Chapter 2). It has two outputs, namely a SUM and a CARRY-OUT. The design of such a circuit is outside the scope of the book, but will prove to be a worthy project for the reader to solve.

15.12 An introduction to fuzzy logic

As we have already seen, logic circuits require precise information in order to produce a precise result.

Fuzzy logic or **continuous logic** is a process by which results can be obtained from imprecise data. Some of the logic statements involved differ from the standard Boolean expressions we are used to. Fuzzy logic uses the standard Boolean expression such as AND and OR, but it also uses such expressions as IF and THEN (see below).

Since the inputs from practical systems are imprecise, we assign values such as VERY LOW, LOW, OKAY, HIGH and VERY HIGH. The system responses are mathematical proportions of the 'normal' output (for example, it may be a 'per cent' value).

Consider the production of, say, cement in a kiln. To operate the plant we need measurements of such things as the kiln temperature and oxygen (O_2) level (these are the input signals). To control the quality of the cement, we can control the feed rate of the material into the kiln and the amount of fuel we use. Typical fuzzy logic statements which control the plant may be:

IF temperature OK AND O_2 OK THEN 0% feed and 0% fuel
IF temperature OK AND O_2 LOW THEN −3% feed and 0% fuel
IF temperature OK AND O_2 HIGH THEN +3% feed and +3% fuel
IF temperature LOW AND O_2 HIGH THEN 0% feed and +6% fuel

Clearly, fuzzy logic provides excellent quality control, but the circuit designer needs to know a great deal about the precise requirements of the control system.

Self-test questions

15.1 The voltages measured at the inputs and output of a gate are shown below

Inputs		*Output*
A	*B*	*f*
−2 V	−2 V	−2 V
6 V	6 V	6 V
6 V	−2 V	−2 V
−2 V	6 V	−2 V

Give the name of the logic function generated if (a) positive logic is used, (b) negative logic is used.

15.2 Draw up the truth table for a 4-input logic system whose output is given by $f = A.(B + \overline{C.D} + D)$. Can the expression be minimised?

15.3 What Boolean expression represents the data given below?

Inputs		*Output*
A	B	f
0	0	0
0	1	1
1	0	1
1	1	0

Draw the corresponding logic block diagram.

15.4 Use truth tables to verify that

(a) $A + B.C = (A + B).(A + C)$
(b) $A.(B + C + D) = A.B + A.C + A.D$

15.5 Use truth tables to verify the following De Morgan's statements

(a) $\overline{A.B} = \overline{A} + \overline{B}$
(b) $\overline{A + B} = \bar{A}.\bar{B}$

15.6 Show that

$$A.\bar{B}.\bar{C} + B.C + B.\bar{C} = B + A.\bar{C}$$

15.7 Prove by means of Boolean algebra

$$A.\bar{C} + B + C.\bar{B} = A + B + C$$

15.8 Show that

$$A.B.(\overline{\overline{C.(A + \bar{B}) + A.B.\bar{C}}}) = A.B.C$$

15.9 Prove that

$$(\overline{\overline{\bar{B}.C + D}}).(\bar{A} + \bar{B}).(\bar{A}.D) = \bar{A}.D$$

15.10 Which term is redundant in the following expression?

$$f = A.\bar{C} + A.B + B.C + \bar{A}.C$$

15.11 Which of the following is equal to logic '0'?
(a) $A + 1$, (b) $A.\bar{A}$, (c) $A + A.\bar{A}$, (d) $\bar{A} + 1$,
(e) $(\bar{A} + B).B.(A + \bar{A}.\bar{B})$.

15.12 Show that

$$A.\bar{B}.C.\bar{D} + A.B.C + \bar{A}.C.D + A.C.D + C.D = C.(D + A)$$

Summary of important facts

A **logic gate** is a circuit which may either be **opened** or **closed** to the flow of data by suitable logic input signals. A **truth table** is a table showing all combinations of input signals, together with the output signal(s) of a gate or system. A gate which has n inputs has 2^n combinations of the input signals.

Boolean algebra is the algebra of logic, and obeys the laws given in section 15.7.

An **AND gate** gives an output of logic '1' only when all inputs to the gate are logic '1'. The AND function is represented by a 'dot' (.) or the cap ($\cap$) symbol. That is

$$f = A.B.C \ldots M.N = A \cap B \cap C \ldots M \cap N$$

An **OR gate** gives an output of logic '1' when any input to the gate is logic '1'. The OR function is represented by a 'plus' (+) or a cup ($\cup$) symbol. That is

$$f = A + B + C \ldots M + N = A \cup B \cup C \ldots M \cup N$$

The **NOT gate** logically inverts the input signal, so that if the input is A, then the output is NOT A. The NOT function is represented by writing a 'bar' over the function, i.e.,

$$f = \bar{A}$$

Boolean algebraic functions can be represented graphically either on a **Venn diagram** or on a **Karnaugh map** the latter being, from an engineering viewpoint, more systematic.

Logical expressions can be simplified either by Boolean algebra or by a Karnaugh map.

16 Computer solution of electric circuits

16.1 Introduction

The teaching of the mathematics of electronic and electrical engineering has been revolutionised by the use of computer software.

A wide range of software packages exist for the analysis of electrical and electronic circuits, and the attention of the reader is directed to one of the most popular, namely **SPICE** or the Simulation Program with Integrated Circuit Emphasis, developed at the University of California, Berkeley. There are many versions of SPICE including PSpice, ALLSPICE, IS_SPICE, Z/SPICE, etc.; a low-cost version of PSpice available from the address given in section 16.11 and through many Shareware Magazines and suppliers. All the problems in the chapter have been checked using this package.

Although the SPICE package was originally designed to solve integrated circuit design problems, it is so versatile that it can be used to solve almost any type of problem ranging from a simple d.c. circuit up to the most complex research problem.

A range of introductory circuits examples are discussed in this chapter ranging from d.c. series and parallel circuits, through electronic amplifiers, transients and a.c. circuits, up to the use of subcircuits (or subroutines).

By the end of this chapter the reader will be able to

- appreciate the use of a popular programming language such as SPICE,
- write programs for the solution of electronic and electrical circuits using the SPICE language,
- use some of the specialist aspects of the SPICE language,
- deal with a.c. circuits, basic semiconductor circuits, transient analysis of circuits, and use subcircuits.

16.2 A simple series circuit

In this first example we will discuss the basic principles of SPICE software so that, in later examples, we can build on the knowledge gained.

The circuit to be analysed is described using a **text editor**, which allows the user to create an **input file**, using one program line per circuit element. For example, the following line can be used to describe the circuit position and the value of a resistor

$R1$ 2 3 10

which tells us that $R1$ is connected between nodes 2 and 3, and has a value of $10\,\Omega$. The letter 'R' at the beginning of the line tells SPICE that it is dealing with a resistor (see also Table 16.3), and it assumes that the value given (= 10) is in ohms (see Table 16.2 for SPICE multiples). A more detailed description is given later.

In most cases, the way in which we tell SPICE the resistor is connected does not matter, because it can usually be connected either way. That is we could write

$R1$ 3 2 10

However, there are some situations where we need to be specific about the way in which the resistor is connected into the circuit, but this does not affect us here.

In the following we will look at a simple series circuit and its input file. When preparing a circuit for SPICE analysis we must follow certain rules, which are

1. Draw the circuit diagram, and give it a *title name* which can be used in the title line of the input file.
2. Label *every element* in the circuit. You will use this label every time you refer to the element.
3. Number *every node* in the circuit, the *reference node* or *zero-voltage node* MUST be node zero (0); take great care to use the number zero and *not capital O*. You do not have to number the nodes sequentially (although it is usual to do so), and the nodes can be numbered in any order.
4. Decide what type of analysis is to be performed on the circuit. In some cases (as in the case of the series circuit) we do not need to specify any form of analysis. In this case SPICE performs a *small signal bias analysis*, which causes it to calculate the d.c. voltage at every node in the circuit, together with the *current flowing into the positive terminal of each voltage source*. The latter may seem a little unusual, bearing in mind that current usually flows out of the positive terminal of a voltage source, but there are good reasons for the use of this method.

Next, we write the SPICE file for the circuit as follows

A. Write the title name in the first line (the *title line*). The purpose of this line is to give a simple explanation of the purpose of the file; it DOES NOT CONTAIN ANY PROGRAM DATA, and if you do not want to enter a title line, then *the line must be left blank*.
B. Write down a series of *element lines*, *comment lines*, *blank* (empty) *lines* and *control lines* in any order, with the exception that the final line of the file (see item *C* below), which is a control line. The purpose of each type of line is explained in the examples.
C. Terminate the input file with a '.END' line (pronounced 'dot' END); the '.' before the 'END' is important, and must be included.

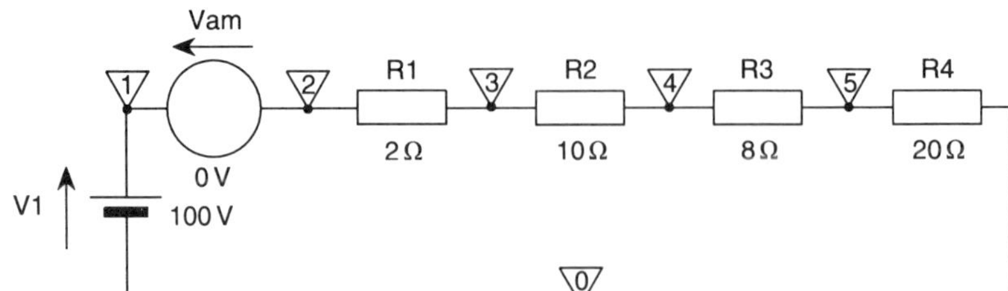

Figure 16.1 Analysis of a simple series circuit: Worked Example 16.1

TABLE 16.1 SPICE input file for Worked Example 16.1

```
   Worked Example 16.1 – Simple series circuit

*name of source   NOTE: THE '*' INDICATES A 'COMMENT' LINE
*| (+) node
*|     |  (-) node
*|     |      |optional data
*|     |      |       |   value
*|     |      |       |     | optional data
*|     |      |       |     |  |
V1     1      0      DC   100V

*Circuit elements
*resistor name
*| (+) node
*|     |  (-) node
*|     |      |    value
*|     |      |       |  optional data
*|     |      |       |  |
R1     2      3      2ohms
R2     3      4      10
*                   SPICE suffix
*                      |                'in-line' comment
*                      |                  |
R3     4      5    0.008K               ; 8 ohms
R4     5      0    20000M               ; 20 ohms

*Vam is used as an ammeter
*source name
*| (+) node
*|     |  (-) node
*|     |      |    value
*|     |      |       |
Vam    1      2       0  ; current flows from (+) node to (-) node

.OPTIONS NOPAGE  ; This option limits the amount of paper printed

.END             ; END of program
```

The circuit to be analysed is shown in Figure 16.1, and the associated input file is in Table 16.1. Each element in the circuit diagram has been labelled with a 'name', e.g., *V*1, *R*1, *R*2, etc., its value written down, and the circuit nodes are numbered. Also, a potential arrow points towards the most positive node of each voltage source.

The circuit is excited by voltage *V*1, which is a 100 V d.c. source connected between node 1 (the positive pole) and node 0 (the negative pole). Also shown is a voltage source *V*am, whose voltage is zero; the reason for this source is described below. As mentioned above, node 0 is the reference node, and the voltage of each node is evaluated with respect to it. From Ohm's law, we would expect the current in the circuit to be

$$\begin{aligned} I &= V1/(R1 + R2 + R3 + R4) \\ &= 100/(2 + 10 + 8 + 20) = 2.5\,\text{A} \end{aligned}$$

and the power consumed to be

$$P = V1 \times I = 100 \times 2.5 = 250\,\text{W}$$

The first line of the input file – the title line – is simply

Worked Example 16.1 – Simple series circuit

As explained above, this simply states the purpose of the file and *is not part of the circuit description*. In effect, it is a special form of comment line.

The next line is left blank simply for the purpose of improving the presentation of the input file. This is followed by seven **comment lines**, which give information about the first **element line**, which describes the connections and value of *V*1. Each comment line commences with a '*', and contains information which makes the file more readable; in this case, each comment line refers to the reason for a section of the element line describing *V*1. An independent voltage source commences with a '*V*' and contains the following data:

V<name> <(+) node> <(–) node> <*DC*> <value>

The 'name' is usually a number, i.e., 1, 2, 3, etc., so that we could have *V*1, *V*2, *V*3, etc., in our circuit. The '(+) node' and the '(–) node' are the nodes to which the positive and negative terminals, respectively, of *V*1 are connected. The '*DC*' term is optional information which can either be provided or omitted (see *V*am in Table 16.1 and also below); if it is omitted, SPICE assumes that it is dealing with a d.c. source. The final item of data in the line is the value or magnitude of the voltage. In our case we have shown the dimensions as *V*. If a unit size is not given, SPICE assumes that it is dealing with a voltage in volts. That is, V1 could be specified as

*V*1 1 0 100

When we need to use a multiplier or scale suffix for any unit, it must be selected from Table 16.2. If a suffix which is not in Table 16.2 is used,

TABLE 16.2 SPICE scale suffixes

Scale	*SPICE suffix*	*metric prefix*
10^{12}	T	tera-
10^{9}	G	giga-
10^{6}	MEG	mega-
10^{3}	K	kilo-
10^{-3}	M	milli-
10^{-6}	U	micro-
10^{-9}	N	nano-
10^{-12}	P	pico-
10^{-15}	F	femto-

SPICE will ignore it. Thus, when we enter 100V as the value and dimension of $V1$, SPICE ignores the 'V' suffix in the 100V. We can, if we wish, describe $V1$ as follows

$V1$ 1 0 0.1KV

or

$V1$ 1 0 0.1K

SPICE accepts the 'K' as representing 10^3, so that 0.1KV is equal to 100V. At this point, the reader should *carefully note* that, in SPICE files, M means *milli-* (10^{-3}) and MEG means *mega-* (10^6).

TABLE 16.3 Some important circuit elements

First letter in element line	*Element*
C	capacitor
D	diode
E	voltage-controlled voltage source
F	current-controlled current source
G	voltage-controlled current source
H	current-controlled voltage source
I	independent current source
J	junction-gate FET
L	inductor
M	MOSFET
Q	bipolar junction transistor (BJT)
R	resistor
V	independent voltage source
X	subcircuit call

Next we leave a blank line, after which the resistive elements in the circuit are entered. At this point the reader should refer to the list of *element letters* in Table 16.3, which shows some of the more important circuit elements. The list is not comprehensive, and other letters can be used to describe various types of magnetically coupled circuits (transformers), transmission lines, switches and digital devices such as logic gates. Each line used to define a resistor in the input file for Worked Example 16.1 is written as follows:

R <(+) node> <(−) node>

Optionally, we can put the dimension of 'ohms' or 'ohm' after the value of the resistor because, since the letter 'o' does not appear as a SPICE suffix in Table 16.2, SPICE will ignore it. The input file therefore tells us that $R1$ is connected between nodes 2 and 3, and has a value of $2\,\Omega$; $R2$ is connected between nodes 3 and 4, and has a value of 10 (SPICE assumes a default dimension of ohms). The value of $R3$ is $0.008\text{K} = 8$ (ohm), and $R4$ has a value of $20000\text{M} = 20000 \times 10^{-3} = 20$ (ohm).

The reader will note that we have included a comment at the end of the $R3$ and $R4$ lines, and this is described as an 'in-line' comment; the comment is separated from the data in the line by a ';' *separator*.

SPICE does not have an **ammeter** as a circuit element (see also Table 16.3), and a simple technique used to overcome this is to insert a zero-voltage V-source, or a *null voltage source*, which we call Vam (see Figure 16.1 and Table 16.1). SPICE evaluates *the current flowing into the positive node of this source* and will report it; since this is the case, we merely connect Vam so that the current enters its '+' node; that is the current enters the first node in the program line listing. Since the current in the circuit flows from node 1 to node 2, we define Vam as

Vam 1 2 0

SPICE also allows us to use a number of programming options, and one of them is the 'NOPAGE' option. This is an option which suppresses 'paging', and prevents the printer from ejecting a sheet of paper until it is full of data. This prevents waste of paper, and is used in all input files in this chapter. A wide range of options is available and, when used, each is included in the '.OPTIONS' control line.

Finally, the program is terminated with a '.END' line. As mentioned earlier, the '.' *must be included* at the beginning of every control line.

When the input file is complete, it is sent to a **software analyser** (which is an integral part of the SPICE package), which checks the file for errors; if none exist, it performs the required **analysis** and supplies the results. There are many forms of analysis which can be performed and several are listed below.

.AC – 'small-signal' a.c. analysis of the circuit (see sections 16.7 and 16.8).
.DC – determination of the 'd.c.' operating point of the circuit (see section 16.6).
.OP – SPICE solves for the d.c. operating point of the circuit.
.TRAN – transient analysis of the circuit (see section 16.9).
.TF – 'small-signal' d.c. Transfer Function analysis of the circuit (see section 16.8).
.TEMP – strictly speaking this is not a form of analysis, and is merely used to tell SPICE what temperature(s) to simulate (see section 16.5)

In Table 16.1 we have not asked for any of the above analyses to be performed and, by default, SPICE will perform the *small signal bias solution* of the circuit, which calculates the d.c. potential of each node together with the current flowing into the positive node of each V-source. Any reader having access to a copy of SPICE should try inserting a '.OP' line into the file, and see if it makes any difference to the results.

TABLE 16.4 Small signal bias solution: output file for Worked Example 16.1

```
* * *  SMALL SIGNAL BIAS SOLUTION    TEMPERATURE = 27.000 DEG C

NODE VOLTAGE  NODE VOLTAGE  NODE VOLTAGE  NODE VOLTAGE

(    1)  100.0000  (    2)  100.0000  (    3)  95.0000   (    4)  70.0000
(    5)  50.0000

VOLTAGE SOURCE CURRENTS
NAME          CURRENT

V1            -2.500E+00
Vam            2.500E+00

TOTAL POWER DISSIPATION     2.50E+02   WATTS
JOB CONCLUDED
TOTAL JOB TIME                 7.96
```

The relevant part of the output file from the computer is given in Table 16.4. The first line tells us that it has performed the SMALL SIGNAL BIAS SOLUTION, i.e., the d.c. operating point solution at 27°C. This is the default temperature at which all calculations are performed, but which can be altered in the manner outlined in section 16.5. The solution includes the voltage at each node (relative to node 0), and the current *entering the positive node of each voltage source*.

The reader will note that a 'negative' current enters the supply source voltage $V1$; this is in agreement with common sense because we know that a 'positive' current leaves the terminal of $V1$. We also see that a 'positive' current is indicated by the 'ammeter' Vam. This analysis also determines the d.c. power dissipated by the circuit.

16.3 Analysis of a series-parallel circuit

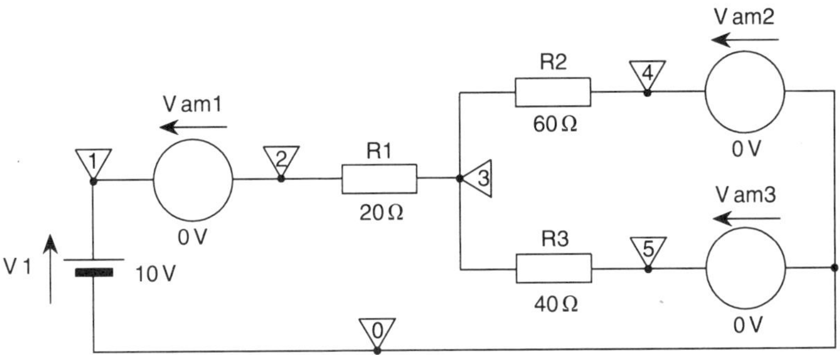

Figure 16.2 A simple series-parallel circuit: Worked Example 16.2

TABLE 16.5 Input file for the analysis of a series–parallel circuit

```
Worked Example 16.2 – Simple series-parallel circuit

* Supply source
V1    1     0     10V

* Ammeter 1
Vam1  1     2     0V

.OPTIONS NOPAGE   ; The command lines (except .END)
                  ; can be placed at any point.

* Circuit elements
R1    2     3     20  ; The dimensions are in ohms.
R3    3     5     40  ; The resistors are in any order.
R2    3     4     60

* Other ammeters (in any order)
Vam3  5     0     0   ; The dimensions are in volts.
Vam2  4     0     0

.END
```

Next, in Worked Example 16.2, we look at the series-parallel circuit in Figure 16.2, for which the input file is in Table 16.5. The presentation of the file generally follows that for the series circuit in Table 16.1, but with a few variations.

Firstly, we have introduced the '.OPTIONS' line at an early point to illustrate that the position of a control line (except '.END') can be inserted at any point in the file. We have also inserted SPICE 'ammeters' *V*am1, *V*am2 and *V*am3 at different points in the file, and resistors *R*1, *R*2 and *R*3 have been introduced in a random fashion. Since no specific analysis has been requested, SPICE performs the SMALL SIGNAL BIAS SOLUTION, shown in Table 16.6; the reader can check the results using a calculator. Since the 'ammeters' are ideal, they have no resistance and have no voltage drop across them.

TABLE 16.6 Small signal bias solution for Worked Example 16.2

```
* * * SMALL SIGNAL BIAS SOLUTION     TEMPERATURE = 27.000 DEG C

NODE VOLTAGE  NODE VOLTAGE  NODE VOLTAGE  NODE VOLTAGE

(    1)  10.0000  (    2)  10.0000  (    3)  5.4545  (    4)  0.0000
(    5)  0.0000

VOLTAGE SOURCE CURRENTS
NAME         CURRENT

V1           -2.273E-01
Vam1          2.273E-01
Vam3          1.364E-01
Vam2          9.091E-02

TOTAL POWER DISSIPATION    2.27E+00   WATTS
```

16.4 An electrical network

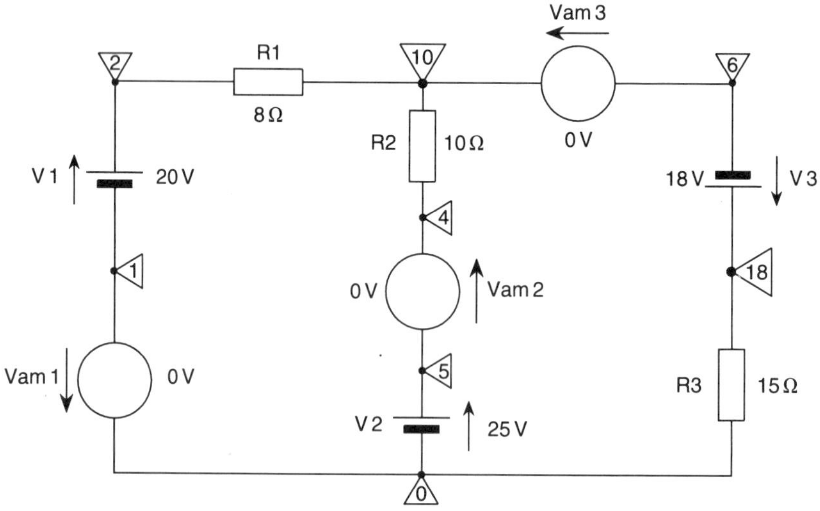

Figure 16.3 Analysis of an electrical network: Worked Example 16.3

The two-mesh electrical network in Figure 16.3 will be solved by SPICE (as Worked Example 16.3), and the reader should verify the solution using one of the methods outlined in Chapter 5.

Each branch contains an e.m.f., a resistor and a SPICE 'ammeter'. At this stage we do not know the direction of the current in the branches, and it has been assumed that the current in *V*am1 flows from node 0 to node 1, that it flows from node 4 to node 5 in *V*am2, and from node 10 to node 6 in *V*am3. Another point to note is that we have used random numbers for the nodes; SPICE accepts this quite happily.

TABLE 16.7 Electrical network for Worked Example 16.3: input file

```
Worked Example 16.3 – An electrical network

*Sources
V1    2    1    20V
V2    5    0    25V
V3    18   6    18V ; some nodes can be omitted

*Ammeters
Vam1  0    1    0V ; current is assumed to enter from node 0
Vam2  4    5    0V ; current is assumed to enter from node 4
Vam3  10   6    0V ; current is assumed to enter from node 10

*Resistors
R1    2    10   8ohm
R2    10   4    10ohm
R3    18   0    15ohm

.OPTIONS NOPAGE
.END
```

TABLE 16.8 Electrical network for Worked Example 16.3: output file

```
*** SMALL SIGNAL BIAS SOLUTION    TEMPERATURE = 27.000 DEG C

NODE VOLTAGE  NODE VOLTAGE  NODE VOLTAGE  NODE VOLTAGE
(  1)  0.0000  (  2) 20.0000  (  4) 25.0000  (  5) 25.0000
(  6) 13.0290  ( 10) 13.0290  ( 18) 31.0290

VOLTAGE SOURCE CURRENTS
NAME        CURRENT

V1          -8.714E-01
V2          -1.197E+00
V3          -2.069E+00
Vam1         8.714E-01
Vam2        -1.197E+00
Vam3         2.069E+00

TOTAL POWER DISSIPATION    8.46E+01   WATTS
```

The input file is given in Table 16.7, and the appropriate section of the output file in Table 16.8. From Table 16.8 we see that the current flow in each branch is as follows

0.8714 A flows in *V*am1
−1.197 flows in *V*am2
2.069 flows in *V*am3

That is, we have correctly chosen the direction of current in *V*am1 and *V*am3, but the direction of flow of current was incorrect in *V*am2. Clearly, the current in *V*am1 and *V*am2 flows towards node 10, and the current in *V*am3 is the sum of the magnitude of *V*am1 and *V*am2 as follows

$$V\text{am}1 + V\text{am}2 = 0.8714 + 1.197 = 2.0684$$

which generally agrees with the value of current predicted for *V*am3 by SPICE. The reader should use these values to verify that the voltage at node 10 ($V(10)$) with respect to node 0 is 13.029 V (see also Table 16.8).

16.5 The use of '.TNOM' and '.TEMP'

So far, all analyses have assumed that the circuit operates at 27°C; in practice this does not happen, and the circuit elements can operate at almost any temperature. Here (as Worked Example 16.4) we consider a resistor having a resistance of 1000 Ω at a temperature of 0°C, and having a linear resistance-temperature coefficient of $\alpha = 0.004$ per °C. Using this data, SPICE will determine its resistance at 20°C; clearly, it will then become possible to solve any circuit, no matter how complex, at any operating temperature with any resistance-temperature coefficient (or with a mixture of coefficients).

The circuit is shown in Figure 16.4, and the corresponding input file is in Table 16.9. The *nominal operating temperature* is established by the '.TNOM' option in the '.OPTIONS' line as 0*C* (the '*C*' being optional,

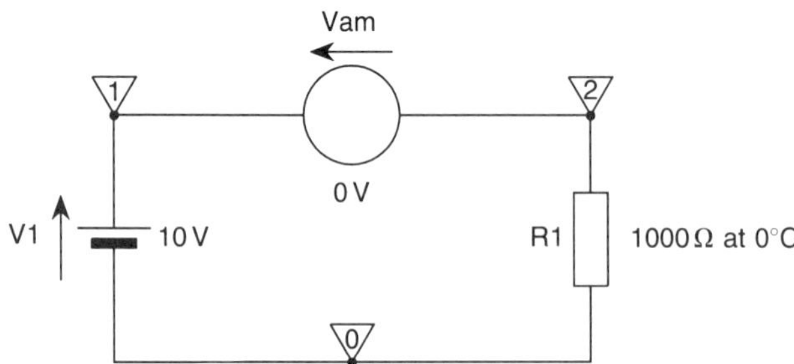

Figure 16.4 The effect of temperature on resistance: Worked Example 16.4

TABLE 16.9 Worked Example 16.4: input file

```
Worked Example 16.4 – Effect of temperature coefficient of resistance

*Supply
V1    1      0      10V

*Ammeter
Vam    1      2      0V

*            Nominal temperature = 0 deg. C
                                 |
.OPTIONS NOPAGE TNOM = 0C   ; 'C' optional

*TEMPerature analysis
*| Analysis at two specified temperatures
*|               |      |
.TEMP      0C     20C   ; 'C' is optional

*Resistor specification
*        Resistance at TNOM (0 C)
*                       |  Linear coefficient of resistance
*                       |              |
R1    2      0  1000ohms        TC = 0.004

.END
```

and can be omitted). In the input file we have asked for a '.TEMP' analysis to be performed, which sets up the temperatures (in °C) at which the circuit is to be analysed. Since '.TNOM' is 0°C, it assumes that the value of $R1$ is given at this temperature. If '.TNOM' is not included in the '.OPTIONS' line, SPICE assumes that the nominal temperature is the default value of 27°C.

Next, the connecting nodes, the value, and the linear temperature coefficient of resistance are specified in the $R1$ element line. The statement $TC = 0.004$ in that line tells SPICE that $\alpha = 0.004$ per °C. The corresponding section of the output file is given in Table 16.10.

Initially, the table shows the SMALL SIGNAL BIAS SOLUTION at 0°C (when $R1 = 1000\,\Omega$), after which it 'adjusts' the temperature to 20°C and calculates the resistance and current. The reader should verify the accuracy of these results.

In fact, SPICE can easily deal with a resistance given by the expression

$$R = R_0(1 + \alpha\theta + \beta\theta^2)$$

where R_0 is the resistance at 0°C, α is the linear resistance-temperature coefficient referred to 0°C, and β is the quadratic resistance-temperature coefficient.

TABLE 16.10 Worked Example 16.4: output file

```
*** SMALL SIGNAL BIAS SOLUTION    TEMPERATURE = 0.000 DEG C

NODE VOLTAGE  NODE VOLTAGE  NODE VOLTAGE  NODE VOLTAGE

(    1)  10.0000  (    2)  10.0000

VOLTAGE SOURCE CURRENTS
NAME          CURRENT

V1            -1.000E-02
Vam            1.000E-02

TOTAL POWER DISSIPATION    1.00E-01   WATTS

** TEMPERATURE-ADJUSTED VALUES    TEMPERATURE = 20.000 DEG C

*** RESISTORS
NAME           VALUE
R1            1.080E+03

*** SMALL SIGNAL BIAS SOLUTION    TEMPERATURE = 20.000 DEG C

NODE VOLTAGE  NODE VOLTAGE  NODE VOLTAGE  NODE VOLTAGE

(    1)  10.0000  (    2)  10.0000

VOLTAGE SOURCE CURRENTS
NAME          CURRENT

V1            -9.259E-03
Vam            9.259E-03

TOTAL POWER DISSIPATION    9.26E-02   WATTS
```

16.6 The use of '.DC' and '.PRINT'

So far we have not specified either the type of analysis that SPICE should perform, or the way in which the results should be formatted. We can specify the way in which the output can be formatted in a '.PRINT' control line, allowing any of the following to be printed:

1. a node voltage, e.g., $V(4)$ or
2. the voltage between a pair of nodes, e.g., $V(4, 8)$ or
3. the voltage across a two-terminal device, e.g., $V(\mathrm{R1})$

The second of the above lines asks for the voltage of node 4 with respect to node 8 to be given. Some versions of SPICE, e.g., PSpice, allow us to print the current flowing through a two-terminal device, e.g., the current in *R*2 is given by I(R2).

An essential feature of a SPICE '.PRINT' line is that *the type of analysis must be specified.* For example, we may have

```
.PRINT   DC   V(2)   V(5,7)
```

or

```
.PRINT   AC   V(6)   V(8,12)
```

We will return to '.PRINT' when we discuss a.c. circuits (see sections 16.7 and 16.8).

At this stage, we are dealing with d.c. circuits, and we look here at a typical '.DC' analysis (Worked Example 16.5). This type of analysis evaluates the d.c. voltage at the nodes in the circuit for various values of source voltage. The values of source voltage are specified in the '.DC' line. This voltage is altered between a *starting value* and an *end value* in specified *increments of voltage.* Consider the circuit in Figure 16.5, in which we need to analyse the circuit when V1 has values of 10 V, 15 V and 20 V. The corresponding input file for the circuit is shown in Table 16.11.

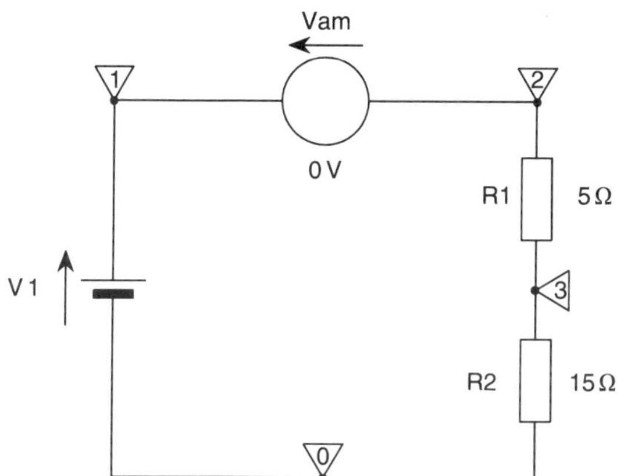

Figure 16.5 The use of '.DC' and '.PRINT': Worked Example 16.5

An interesting point about Table 16.11 is that, although we have specified *V*1 as having a value of zero volts, *this value is overridden* by a value in the '.DC' line. The latter specifies *V*1 as having an initial value of 10 V, which is altered in 5 V steps up to 20 V.

In the '.PRINT' line we must specify not only the type of analysis being performed (which means that we must have a '.DC' or a '.AC' line at some other point in the file), but also the variables to be printed. In our case we have specified

```
.PRINT   DC   I(Vam)   V(2,3)   V(3)
```

TABLE 16.11 Worked Example 16.5: input file

```
Worked Example 16.5 – Use of '.DC' analysis and '.PRINT' command

*Source
*   Value overridden by the '.DC' analysis (see below)
*                          |
V1    1      0      0V

*'.DC' analysis
* | Swept variable name
* |     | Start value
* |     |        | End value
* |     |        |        | Increment
* |     |        |        |        |
.DC  V1     10V    20V     5V

*Series circuit description
R1    2      3    5ohm
R2    3      0    15ohm

*Ammeter
Vam    1      2      0V

*'.PRINT' command
* |    Analysis type
* |           | Value of variables to be printed
.PRINT   DC    I(Vam)  V(2,3)    V(3)
.OPTIONS NOPAGE
.END
```

that is, we have asked for the current through Vam, i.e., I(Vam), the voltage of node 2 with respect to node 3, i.e., V(2,3), and the voltage at node 3, i.e., V(3). These will be *printed in that order* for each value of $V1$, i.e., 10 V, 15 V and 20 V. The corresponding section of the output file is given in Table 16.12; the reader should verify these results using a calculator.

TABLE 16.12 Worked Example 16.5: output file

```
* * * DC TRANSFER CURVES      TEMPERATURE = 27.000 DEG C

    V1          I(Vam)        V(2,3)        V(3)

1.000E+01    5.000E-01    2.500E+00    7.500E+00
1.500E+01    7.500E-01    3.750E+00    1.125E+01
2.000E+01    1.000E+00    5.000E+00    1.500E+01
```

16.7 A '.AC' analysis

In this case (Worked Example 16.6) we investigate the *R-L* a.c. circuit in Figure 16.6. The '.AC' analysis not only performs the d.c. SMALL SIGNAL BIAS SOLUTION of the circuit, but also analyses the circuit at several specified frequencies (in Hz).

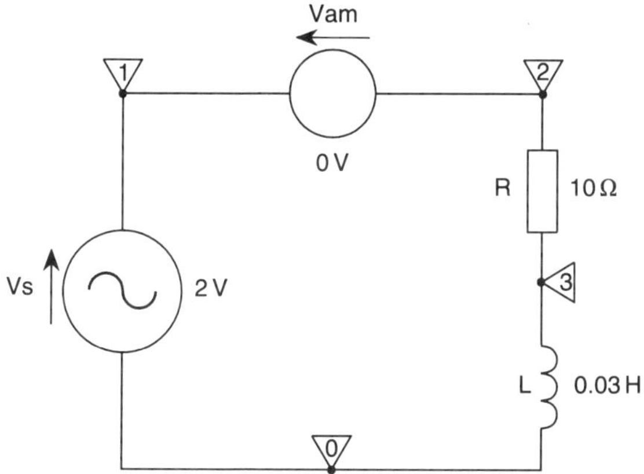

Figure 16.6 Analysis of an a.c. circuit: Worked Example 16.6

An input file for the circuit is given in Table 16.13, and the reader will note that we **must state** in the *Vs* line that we are dealing with an AC source; once SPICE knows this fact, it will look for a '.AC' control line.

The inductance of *L* is given as 30 MH or 30 millihenry; the 'H' is optional, so that the line may, alternatively, be given as

```
L    3    0    30M
```

or as

```
L    3    0    0.03
```

In the '.AC' control line, we state that we are taking three LINear frequency steps from 25 Hz to 75 Hz (the Hz is optional, and can be omitted). That is, we will solve the circuit at frequencies at 25 Hz, 50 Hz and 75 Hz. It is possible to take other frequency steps than LINear steps, but these are beyond the scope of this book.

Next, we look at the '.PRINT' control line. Once again, we must specify the type of analysis being performed, namely an AC analysis, and we must specify the variables to be PRINTed on the computer screen (and, if needed, on a printer). For a.c. analysis, PRINTing V or I can be modified with a suffix as follows

TABLE 16.13 Worked Example 16.6: input file

```
Worked Example 16.6 – Use of '.AC' analysis

*Supply source
*                    'AC' must be stated at this point
*                     |
Vs      1      0     AC    2V

Vam     1      2     0V    ; Vam is a 'SPICE' ammeter

*Circuit elements
R       2      3     10ohms
L       3      0    30MH   ; 30 millihenry inductor

*'.AC' analysis
* |  LINear frequency sweep
* |       |          Number of points in the sweep
* |       |          |  Start frequency
* |       |          |         |  End frequency
* |       |          |         |         |
.AC      LIN         3        25Hz      75Hz

*'.PRINT' command
* | Analysis type
* |       | Current Magnitude
* |       |          | Current Phase (deg.)
* |       |          |         | Real part of V(2,3)
* |       |          |         |         | Imaginary part of V(2,3)
* |       |          |         |         |          |
.PRINT AC    IM(Vam) IP(Vam)  VR(2,3)   VI(2,3)
.OPTIONS NOPAGE
.END
```

VM or IM prints the magnitude of the quantity
VP or IP prints the phase angle (in degrees) of the quantity
VR or IR prints the 'real part' of the quantity
VI or II prints the 'imaginary part' of the quantity

The reader should refer to Chapter 11 for details of complex numbers as applied to electrical and electronic circuit theory. The following '.PRINT' line is in the input file

.PRINT AC IM(Vam) IP(Vam) VR(2,3) VI(2,3)

which prints the following results:

IM(Vam) = magnitude of the current in Vam
IP(Vam) = phase angle of the current in Vam

VR(2,3) = 'real part' of the voltage of node 2 with respect to node 3
VI(2,3) = 'imaginary part' of the voltage of node 2 with respect to node 3.

That is, we have asked for the *polar form* of I(Vam), and the *rectangular form* of V(2,3) (see Chapter 11 for a full explanation of these terms).

TABLE 16.14 Worked Example 16.6: output file

```
*** SMALL SIGNAL BIAS SOLUTION   TEMPERATURE = 27.000 DEG C

NODE VOLTAGE  NODE VOLTAGE  NODE VOLTAGE  NODE VOLTAGE

(    1)  0.0000   (    2)  0.0000   (    3)  0.0000

VOLTAGE SOURCE CURRENTS
NAME         CURRENT

Vs           0.000E+00
Vam          0.000E+00

TOTAL POWER DISSIPATION    0.00E+00  WATTS


*** AC ANALYSIS TEMPERATURE = 27.000 DEG C

  FREQ        IM(Vam)      IP(Vam)       VR(2,3)      VI(2,3)

2.500E+01    1.809E-01   -2.523E+01    1.637E+00    -7.712E-01
5.000E+01    1.455E-01   -4.330E+01    1.059E+00    -9.982E-01
7.500E+01    1.155E-01   -5.473E+01    6.670E-01    -9.429E-01
```

The output file is presented in Table 16.14, and the reader will note that, since Vs is a true alternating wave, the SMALL SIGNAL BIAS SOLUTION (corresponding to the d.c. conditions in the circuit) gives a set of zero results. The AC ANALYSIS provides the value of the first four variables in the '.PRINT' line at frequencies of 25, 50 and 75 Hz, respectively. Let us look at the 50 Hz results, which are as follows. The current in V_{am}, expressed in polar complex form, is

$$I = 0.1455\angle -43.3^\circ \text{ A}$$

and the voltage of node 2 relative to node 3, expressed in rectangular complex form is

$$V_R = 1.059 - j0.9982 \text{ V}$$

The reader will find it an interesting exercise to convert V_R into its polar form (which is $1.455\angle -43.3^\circ$) and, using Ohm's law ($I = V/R$) show that the current, I, has the same value as that determined by SPICE.

16.8 Small signal analysis of a common-emitter amplifier

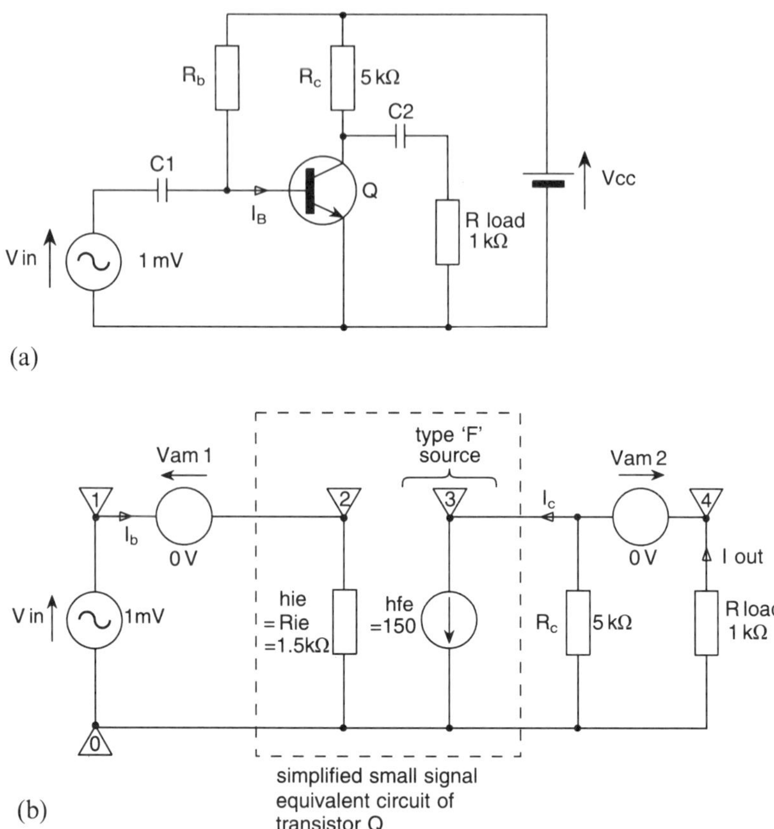

Figure 16.7 (a) Simple common-emitter amplifier, (b) its simplified equivalent circuit: Worked Example 16.7

As Worked Example 16.7, a simple common-emitter transistor amplifier circuit is shown in Figure 16.7(a). In a practical circuit, the reactance of capacitors *C*1 and *C*2 are sufficiently low that they can be thought of as representing no impedance to current flow and, for the purpose of analysis, can be replaced by a short-circuit. Resistor R_b is a 'bias' resistor whose purpose is to 'bias' the transistor *Q* to its working point; the value of R_b is generally very high and, once more, has little effect on simple calculations of the kind we are doing here.

The transistor itself can be replaced by the simplified 'hybrid parameter' equivalent circuit enclosed in broken line in Figure 16.7(b). This comprises the '*h*-parameter' input resistance h_{ie} ($= 1.5\,\text{k}\Omega$) and the *h*-parameter forward current gain parameter h_{fe} ($= 150$). The current gain parameter is the ratio of the collector current (I_c) to the base current (I_b), or I_c/I_b. For the purpose of simple analysis, we may replace the amplifier circuit in Figure 16.7(a) by the simplified equivalent circuit in Figure 16.7(b). The corresponding input file for the circuit is shown in Table 16.15.

TABLE 16.15 Worked Example 16.7: input file

```
Worked Example 16.7 - Analysis of a common-emitter amplifier

* Input a.c. signal
Vin    1    0    AC    1MV  ; 1mV a.c. input signal

* Input current measurement
Vam1   1    2    0V         ; current flows from node 1 to node 2

* Transistor specification
Rie    2    0  1.5Kohm  ; transistor parameter hie

* Current-controlled current source
* | (+) output node
* |       | (-) output node
* |       |       | Controlling current source
* |       |       |       | Current gain
* |       |       |       |       |
Fhfe      3       0       Vam1    150

* Output current measurement
Vam2   4    3    0V         ; load current flows from node 4 to node 3

Rc     3    0   5Kohm
Rload  4    0   1Kohm   ; load resistance

.AC   LIN    1    1KHz  1Khz  ; calculate at one frequency only

.PRINT    AC    IM(Vam1)    IM(Vam2)    V(1)     V(4)
.PRINT    AC    IP(Vam1)    IP(Vam2)    VP(1)    VP(4)

*Transfer Function analysis
* | Output variable
* |       | Input source
* |       |       |
.TF      V(4)     Vin

.OPTIONS NOPAGE
.END
```

Points to note about this file include the fact that *V*am1 and *V*am2 are used, respectively, to measure the base current and the current in the 1 kΩ load. The transistor input resistance parameter h_{ie} has been replaced by R_{ie} because SPICE needs an 'R' line in order to accept a resistance value. Additionally, the transistor current gain parameter h_{fe} has been replaced by a SPICE **controlled source** or **dependent source**, described below.

A controlled source is one in which the output from the source (which may be a voltage or a current) is controlled by another signal (which may be a voltage or a current) in some other part of the circuit. SPICE can handle four types of controlled sources, which are

type 'E' – a voltage-controlled voltage source
type 'F' – a current-controlled current source
type 'G' – a voltage-controlled current source
type 'H' – a current-controlled voltage source

Typical applications of these are

type 'E' – an operational amplifier
type 'F' – a bipolar junction transistor
type 'G' – a field-effect transistor
type 'H' – a separately-excited generator

Since we are dealing with a bipolar junction transistor amplifier, we use a type 'F' dependent source. When defining this type of source we simply need to specify the direction in which the current flows through the controlled source (i.e., the collector current which flows from the collector (node 3) to the emitter (node 0)), the direction of the controlling current (which is the base current, and flows into node 2), and the current gain (= 150) between the controlling current and the controlled current.

A requirement of SPICE is that the controlling current *must flow through an independent voltage source*, or a V-source. Since we measure the transistor base current using *V*am1, we can use the current in *V*am1 as the controlling current source. We will define the current-controlled current source in the input file as *Fhfe* (see Table 16.15), because the parameter h_{fe} is the one we are replacing by the dependent current source.

The '.AC' line is interesting because it says that we are calculating values at only one frequency between a minimum frequency of 1 kHz and a maximum frequency of 1 kHz; that is, we solve the circuit at 1 kHz.

We use two '.PRINT' lines in the file; the first of these gives the magnitude of the base current (IM(Vam1)) and of the load current (IM(Vam2)) together with the magnitude of the input voltage (V(1)) and of the output voltage (V(4)). From these values we can determine the current gain and voltage gain of the amplifier. The reader will note that V(1) is equivalent to VM(1), and V(4) is equivalent to VM(4).

The second of the two '.PRINT' lines gives the phase angle not only of the base current, but also of the load (output) current, the base voltage and the output voltage. This information will enable us to determine the phase shift through the amplifier.

Finally, using a '.TF' line, we ask for a Transfer Function analysis. This type of analysis evaluates the relationship between a specified output and a specified input. In this case we have specified the output voltage (V(4)) and the input voltage (Vin), so that the voltage gain (V(4)/Vin) will be evaluated. In addition, the '.TF' line also determines the input resistance as 'seen' by Vin, and the output resistance as 'seen' at the output terminals.

TABLE 16.16 Worked Example 16.7: output file

```
*** SMALL-SIGNAL CHARACTERISTICS

    V(4)/Vin = -8.333E+01
    INPUT RESISTANCE AT Vin = 1.500E+03
    OUTPUT RESISTANCE AT V(4) = 8.333E+02

*** AC ANALYSIS                    TEMPERATURE = 27.000 DEG C

  FREQ       IM(Vam1)    IM(Vam2)     V(1)        V(4)

1.000E+03    6.667E-07   8.333E-05   1.000E-03   8.333E-02


*** AC ANALYSIS                    TEMPERATURE = 27.000 DEG C

FREQ         IP(Vam1)    IP(Vam2)     VP(1)       VP(4)

1.000E+03   0.000E+00   0.000E+00   0.000E+00   1.800E+02
```

The relevant results are given in Table 16.16, and it is left as an exercise for the reader to verify them using conventional circuit theory. From the '.TF' analysis (see SMALL SIGNAL CHARACTERISTICS), the voltage gain is given as −83.33, that is it has a magnitude of 83.33, and the output voltage is phase inverted when compared with Vin. We can see that this agrees with the '.AC' analysis because

$$V(1) = Vin = 0.001\,V \text{ and } V(4) = 0.0833\,V$$

so that the *magnitude* of the voltage gain is

$$\text{voltage gain} = 0.08333/0.001 = 83.33$$

Also the phase shift involved is

$$VP(1) = 0^\circ \text{ and } VP(4) = 180^\circ$$

so that the *phase shift* through the amplifier is 180°, hence the overall voltage gain is

$$83.33\angle 180^\circ = -83.33$$

Moreover, we see that the base current is

$$I_b = I(Vam1) = 0.6667\,\mu A \text{ at an angle } (IP(Vam1)) \text{ of } 0^\circ$$

and the output current is

$$I_{load} = I(Vam2) = 83.33\,\mu A \text{ at an angle } (IP(Vam2)) \text{ of } 0^\circ$$

That is, the base current and the collector current are in phase with one another, and the current gain between the base current and the load current is

$$\frac{I_{load}}{I_b} = \frac{IM(Vam2)}{IM(Vam1)} = \frac{83.33 \times 10^{-6}}{6.667 \times 10^{-7}} \approx 125$$

16.9 Transients and '.PLOT'

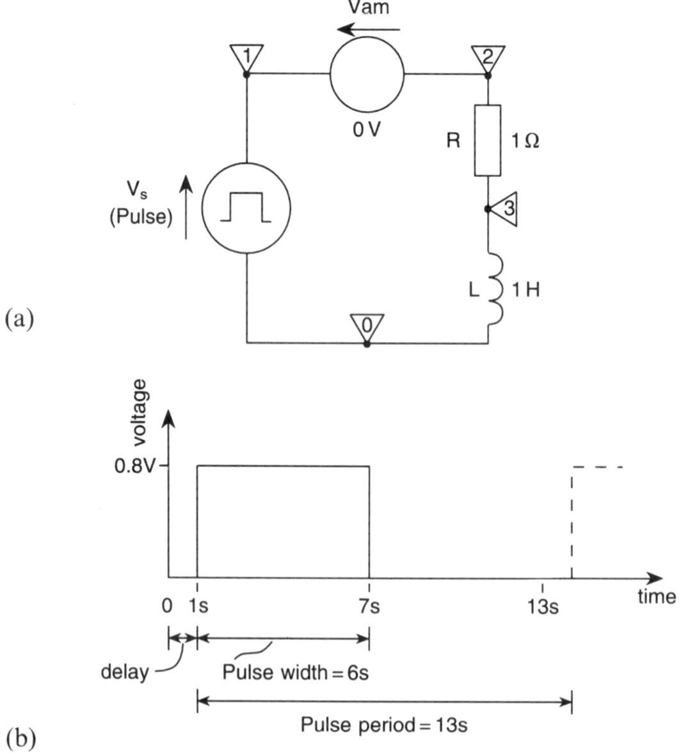

Figure 16.8 (a) An *R-L* series circuit, (b) the pulse applied to the circuit: Worked Example 16.8

Using SPICE we can determine the transient analysis of circuits using special types of excitation signal (Worked Example 16.8). We consider here the use of a PULSE signal, which applies a repetitive pulse to a circuit. The circuit we shall be analysing is shown in Figure 16.8 (a), and the signal applied to it is shown in Figure 16.8(b).

We are using an *R-L* circuit with $R = 1\,\Omega$ and $L = 1$ H, so that the time constant of the circuit is $\tau = L/R = 1/1 = 1$ s; we must therefore expect the transients to have died away in $5\tau = 5$ s. The input file for the circuit is shown in Table 16.17.

TABLE 16.17 Worked Example 16.8: input file

```
Worked Example 16.8 – Transient analysis of an R-L circuit

* The R-L circuit has a time constant of L/R = 1 H/1 ohm = 1 s,
* i.e., the transients will have decayed in about 5 s.

*Name of source
*|          Type of signal
*|          |      Initial value
*|          |      |      Pulsed value
*|          |      |      |       Time delay
*|          |      |      |       |      Rise time
*|          |      |      |       |      |     Fall time
*|          |      |      |       |      |     |     Pulse width
*|          |      |      |       |      |     |     |     Period
*|          |      |      |       |      |     |     |     |
Vs  1   0   PULSE(0V   0.8V  0.999s  1Us   1Us   6s    13s)

*Circuit description
Vam   1   2   0V; ammeter
R     2   3   1ohm
L     3   0   1H

*TRANsient analysis
* |   Step time
* |       |   End of TRANsient analysis
* |       |       |
.TRAN  0.5s      13s

* Type of result to be printed
*          |          Results to be PRINTed
*          |          |          |          |
.PRINT    TRAN       V(3)       I(Vam)     V(2,3)

*'.PLOT' command
*
.PLOT     TRAN       V(3)       I(Vam)

.OPTIONS NOPAGE
.END
```

In this case SPICE produces a table of values not only for the voltage across the inductor (V(3)), but also the current in the circuit (I(Vam)), and the voltage across the resistor (V(2,3)), together with a 'text-type' PLOT or graph of the voltage across the inductor and the current in the circuit (we will explain the meaning of 'text-type' a little later).

Since we are dealing with transients in the circuit, we need to specify the applied voltage as a time-varying voltage which, in our case, is a PULSE voltage. The PULSE used here has the waveform in Figure 16.8(b), and is described as Vs in Table 16.17. The first two values in the Vs line are the nodes between which Vs is connected (positive first), then we tell SPICE that we are applying a PULSE wave between the terminals. The definition of the PULSE is given within the brackets as follows.

The *'Initial value'* is the value of the pulse at $t = 0$; this is zero volts. The *'Pulsed value'* is the maximum value the pulse reaches, which is 0.8 V. The *'Time delay'* at which the pulsed value is applied is 0.999 s (say 1 s) – see Figure 16.8(b). The wave must be a 'practical' rather than a 'theoretical' wave, and it takes a finite time for the applied voltage to change from zero to 0.8 V (and back again some time later); the *'Rise time'* is the time taken for the wave to reach 0.8 V, and is 1 μs. The *'Fall time'* of 1 μs is the time taken for the wave to fall from 0.8 V to zero. The *'Pulse width'* is the time during which the pulsed value remains at 0.8 V, and the *'Period'* of the pulse is the repetition period between the start of one pulse and the start of the next pulse.

The time delay of about 1 s has been introduced so that we can 'see' the effect of applying the pulse to the circuit. Clearly, it takes another 5τ for transients associated with the rise in voltage to have decayed, i.e., in a time of $1\text{ s} + 5\text{ s} = 6\text{ s}$, and another 5τ for the transients to have decayed when the voltage is reduced to zero, i.e., by a time of $6\text{ s} + 5\tau = 6\text{ s} + 5\text{ s} = 11\text{ s}$.

To perform a TRANSient analysis on the circuit, we must include a '.TRAN' line in the input file, and in this line we must give the *'Step time'* or increments at which the transient results are PRINTed or PLOTted, and the *'End of TRANsient analysis'* or the total time needed to look at the transient results. We have specified a step time of 0.5 s and an overall calculation time of 13 s. Since we have given a PULSE delay time of 1 s, the transient calculations at $t = 0$ and $t = 0.5\text{ s}$ will give zero results.

In the '.PRINT' line we must first tell SPICE that the results are from a TRANsient analysis and, after this, we say that the results for V(3), I(Vam) and V(2, 3) are required. The results of the computation are given in Table 16.18 and, as an exercise, the reader should check a selection of these using his calculator.

Next we look at the '.PLOT' line in the input file. This is generally similar to a '.PRINT' line in that we must specify the type of analysis used to derive the results, followed by a list of results to be PLOTted. The 'graph' is PLOTted on a printer in the form of a series of '*' or '+' characters. The advantage of this form of output is that any printer can be used to PLOT the results, but has the disadvantage that the graph is relatively crude, and the

TABLE 16.18 Worked Example 16.8: ouput file

*** TRANSIENT ANALYSIS TEMPERATURE = 27.000 DEG C

TIME	V(3)	I(Vam)	V(2,3)
0.000E+00	0.000E+00	0.000E+00	0.000E+00
5.000E−01	0.000E+00	0.000E+00	0.000E+00
1.000E+00	7.992E−01	8.142E−04	8.142E−04
1.500E+00	4.879E−01	3.121E−01	3.121E−01
2.000E+00	2.949E−01	5.051E−01	5.051E−01
2.500E+00	1.781E−01	6.219E−01	6.219E−01
3.000E+00	1.076E−01	6.924E−01	6.924E−01
3.500E+00	6.494E−02	7.351E−01	7.351E−01
4.000E+00	3.919E−02	7.608E−01	7.608E−01
4.500E+00	2.364E−02	7.764E−01	7.764E−01
5.000E+00	1.425E−02	7.857E−01	7.857E−01
5.500E+00	8.593E−03	7.914E−01	7.914E−01
6.000E+00	5.198E−03	7.948E−01	7.948E−01
6.500E+00	3.147E−03	7.969E−01	7.969E−01
7.000E+00	−7.973E−01	7.973E−01	7.973E−01
7.500E+00	−4.867E−01	4.867E−01	4.867E−01
8.000E+00	−2.942E−01	2.942E−01	2.942E−01
8.500E+00	−1.777E−01	1.777E−01	1.777E−01
9.000E+00	−1.073E−01	1.073E−01	1.073E−01
9.500E+00	−6.479E−02	6.479E−02	6.479E−02
1.000E+01	−3.910E−02	3.910E−02	3.910E−02
1.050E+01	−2.358E−02	2.358E−02	2.358E−02
1.100E+01	−1.422E−02	1.422E−02	1.422E−02
1.150E+01	−8.573E−03	8.573E−03	8.573E−03
1.200E+01	−5.186E−03	5.186E−03	5.186E−03
1.250E+01	−3.140E−03	3.140E−03	3.140E−03
1.300E+01	−1.890E−03	1.890E−03	1.890E−03

points may not lie on a smooth curve. The results of the '.PLOT' line are displayed in Table 16.19. The voltage across the inductor (V(3)) is plotted by a series of '*' characters, and the current in the circuit (I(Vam)) is plotted using a series of '+' characters; the scaling of the graphs is selected automatically by SPICE.

The two columns of results to the left of Table 16.19 are, firstly, a series of time intervals of 0.5 s and, secondly, the value of the first named variable in the '.PLOT' line (V(3)) at that time (see also Table 16.18).

An alternative and better method of plotting the results is to use a plotter or printer which can be used in a graphics mode. PSpice has an optional graphics post-processor called PROBE, which enables the system to be used as a **software oscilloscope**. The 'graphs' in Table 16.19 are plotted using PROBE on a 24-pin dot matrix printer in Figure 16.9, and the improvement in quality is quite marked.

TABLE 16.19 Worked Example 16.8: results of the '.PLOT' line

```
* * * TRANSIENT ANALYSIS                  TEMPERATURE = 27.000 DEG C

LEGEND:

*: V(3)
+: I(Vam)

  TIME       V(3)
(*) ----------    -1.0000E+00 -5.0000E-01  0.0000E+00  5.0000E-01  1.0000E+00
(+) ----------     0.0000E+00  2.0000E-01  4.0000E-01  6.0000E-01  8.0000E-01
                     -----------------------------------------
0.000E+00   0.000E+00  +         .         *         .         .
5.000E-01   0.000E+00  +         .         *         .         .
1.000E+00   7.992E-01  +         .         .         .     *   .
1.500E+00   4.879E-01  .         .    +    .         *         .
2.000E+00   2.949E-01  .         .         .    +*   .         .
2.500E+00   1.781E-01  .         .         .   *     .+        .
3.000E+00   1.076E-01  .         .         .  *      .    +    .
3.500E+00   6.494E-02  .         .         . *       .     +   .
4.000E+00   3.919E-02  .         .         .*        .      +  .
4.500E+00   2.364E-02  .         .         .*        .       + .
5.000E+00   1.425E-02  .         .         *         .        +.
5.500E+00   8.593E-03  .         .         *         .        +.
6.000E+00   5.198E-03  .         .         *         .         +
6.500E+00   3.147E-03  .         .         *         .         +
7.000E+00  -7.973E-01  .   *     .         .         .         .
7.500E+00  -4.867E-01  .         *         .   +     .         .
8.000E+00  -2.942E-01  .         .   *+    .         .         .
8.500E+00  -1.777E-01  .        +.     *   .         .         .
9.000E+00  -1.073E-01  .     +   .      *  .         .         .
9.500E+00  -6.479E-02  .   +     .       * .         .         .
1.000E+01  -3.910E-02  .  +      .        *.         .         .
1.050E+01  -2.358E-02  . +       .        *.         .         .
1.100E+01  -1.422E-02  .+        .         *         .         .
1.150E+01  -8.573E-03  .+        .         *         .         .
1.200E+01  -5.186E-03  +         .         *         .         .
1.250E+01  -3.140E-03  +         .         *         .         .
1.300E+01  -1.890E-03  +         .         *         .         .
                     -----------------------------------------
```

16.10 The use of subcircuits

Many circuits are made from 'building blocks', such as operational amplifiers, logic gates, etc., which can be connected together without us having to know too much about the way in which the elements are built. In fact, SPICE packages have a comprehensive library of subcircuits which we can draw on. In this section we look a the construction of a simple subcircuit, and how it can be used in a SPICE file.

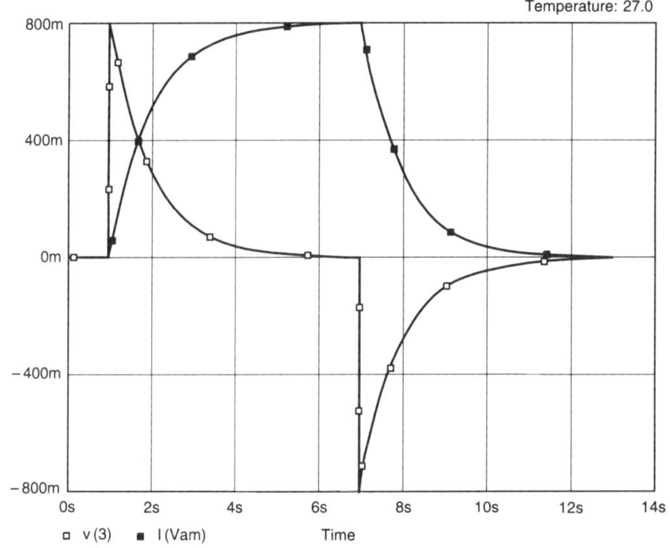

Figure 16.9 'PROBE' graph of the results in Table 16.19: Worked Example 16.8

Suppose (as Worked Example 16.9) that a circuit comprises three series-connected subcircuits of the kind in Figure 16.10(a), the complete circuit being shown in Figure 16.10(b); the final subcircuit has a 100 Ω load connected to it.

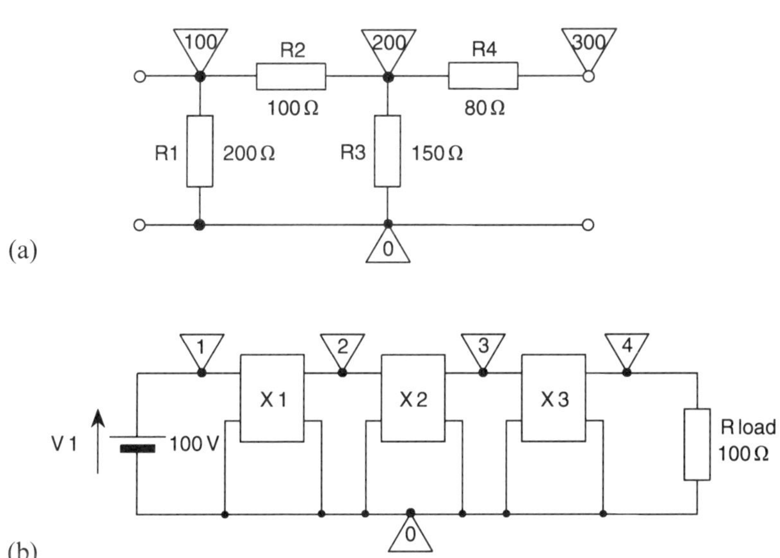

Figure 16.10 The use of subcircuits: Worked Example 16.9

TABLE 16.20 Worked Example 16.9: input file

```
Worked Example 16.9 – Use of subcircuits

*Subcircuit definition
*  |          SUBCKT name
*  |             |
*  |             |  Nodes to be transferred to main circuit
*  |             |        |       |
.SUBCKT    Network    100     300  ; start of SUBCirKiT
* Nodes within the subcircuit
*              |             |
R1            100            0              100ohm  ; subcircuit element
R2            100          200              100ohm  ; subcircuit element
R3            200            0              150ohm  ; subcircuit element
R4            200          300               80ohm  ; subcircuit element
* END of Subcircuit
* |              Name of subcircuit (optional)
* |              |
.ENDS    Network    ; END of Subcircuit definition

* Illustration of use of cascaded subcircuits
* Nodes used in the actual circuit
*       |       |
X1      1       2       Network ; Subcircuit calling routine
X2      2       3       Network ; Subcircuit calling routine
X3      3       4       Network ; Subcircuit calling routine

* Input signal
V1      1       0       DC      100V

* Load resistance
Rload    4   0          100ohm
.OPTION NOPAGE
.END
```

The input file for the circuit is given in Table 16.20 in which, initially, we define the subcircuit. The definition commences with a '.SUBCKT' line, and ends with a '.ENDS' line. The first statement in the '.SUBCKT' line gives the *name* of the subcircuit, together with a list of node numbers which are to be transferred to the main circuit. When the subcircuit is *called* by the main circuit, the number of nodes in the '.SUBCKT' line must be equal to the number of nodes in the subcircuit calling line (also see later). The four resistors $R1$, $R2$, $R3$ and $R4$ in the subcircuit are defined in the usual way using the nodes in Figure 16.10(a).

Next, the main circuit calls the subcircuit three times, using an 'X' line. In this case, the calling routine contains the appropriate nodes used in the main circuit, to which the nodes listed in the '.SUBCKT' are transferred. That is, in the X1 line, node 100 is transferred to node 1, and node 300 is transferred to node 2; in the X2 line, node 100 is transferred to node 2, and node 300 is transferred to node 3, etc. It is important to note that *node 0 must not be included in the list of nodes transferred to the main circuit*, since this is reserved for the global 'ground' node.

TABLE 16.21 Worked Example 16.9: output file

```
* * *  SMALL SIGNAL BIAS SOLUTION        TEMPERATURE = 27.000 DEG C

NODE VOLTAGE  NODE VOLTAGE  NODE VOLTAGE  NODE VOLTAGE
(    1)  100.0000  (    2)   18.7120  (    3)   3.5418  (    4)   .8854

(X1.200)  42.3050  (X2.200)   7.9336  (X3.200)  1.5938

  VOLTAGE SOURCE CURRENTS
  NAME      CURRENT

    V1       -1.577E+00

  TOTAL POWER DISSIPATION     1.58E+02   WATTS
```

Since we have not called for any specific type of analysis to be performed in this case, SPICE merely performs a SMALL SIGNAL BIAS SOLUTION on the circuit, which is listed in Table 16.21. This solution presents not only the voltage at each node in the main circuit, but also the voltage at each node within the subcircuit when it is connected in the main circuit. That is, the voltage at node 200 within X1 is given as the voltage at node (X1.200), the voltage at node 200 within X2 is given as the voltage at node (X2.200), etc.

16.11 Sources of SPICE-based software

SPICE-based software is available for all types of computer, ranging from portable computers to main-frame computers. The author uses an evaluation version of PSpice, which is more than adequate for most applications.

Versions for microcomputers usually have on-disc documentation and are available from the address below and through the pages of magazines dealing with *computer shareware*.

ARS Microsystems,
Herriard Business Centre,
Alton Road,
Basingstoke RG25 2PN

Full documentation and more comprehensive versions of PSpice are available from the above address.

Self-test questions

16.1 Write a SPICE input file for the following circuit. A 5.5 V battery is connected between node 0 and node 1 of a circuit (positive to node 0), in which a resistor of 6 Ω is connected between node 1 and node 2, a resistor of 8 Ω is connected between node 2 and node 0, a battery of 8 V is connected between node 3 and node 0 (node 3 to positive pole), and a resistor of 10 Ω is connected between node 3 and node 2. Determine the voltage of node 2 with respect to node 0, and the magnitude of the current in the 8 Ω resistor.

16.2 A series-connected *R*-*C* circuit containing a 1 kΩ resistor and a 1 μF capacitor, is suddenly connected to a 10 V d.c. supply. Write down a SPICE input file which will print out the voltage across *C* and the current in the circuit when (a) $t = 1$ ms, (b) $t = 3$ ms after the supply is connected.

16.3 A series a.c. circuit contains a 10 Ω resistor and a 16 μF capacitor, which is supplied at 100 V at a frequency of 1 kHz. Write down a SPICE input file which will print the magnitude, the phase angle, the real part and the imaginary part of the voltage across the capacitance, and the magnitude and phase angle of the current.

Summary of important facts

A range of software packages is available for the solution of electrical and electronic circuits, perhaps the most useful being **SPICE** (Simulation Program with Integrated Circuit Emphasis) or one of its derivatives.

Each circuit is described in an **input file** in terms of the circuit elements, the supply sources, etc., which is analysed by a **software analyser**, which checks the input file for errors. If no error exists, the circuit is solved, and the solution displayed on the computer screen and, if needed, printed out.

Many versions of SPICE have a **graphics post-processor**, which converts the system into a *software oscilloscope*, so that waveshapes can be displayed.

The software also contains a **library of subcircuits** which can be called into use, allowing the design of complex systems to be simplified.

Solutions

Chapter 1

1.1 (a) 2,2,3,3,3,3; (b) 5,7,7,11; (c) 2,5,9,13.
1.2 2100
1.3 10
1.4 (a) $\frac{3}{5}$; (b) $\frac{1}{8}$; (c) $\frac{5}{16}$
1.5 (a) $1\frac{17}{24}$; (b) $1\frac{1}{6}$; (c) $6\frac{11}{40}$
1.6 (a) $-\frac{1}{24}$; (b) $\frac{19}{30}$; (c) $-\frac{21}{40}$
1.7 46 A
1.8 2.44 mA
1.9 (a) $\frac{5}{9}$; (b) $\frac{5}{4}$; (c) $\frac{15}{72}$; (d) $\frac{4}{15}$
1.10 (a) $\frac{25}{64}$; (b) $\frac{1}{6}$; (c) $\frac{125}{256}$; (d) $\frac{41}{72}$
1.11 (a) 1.0101×10^5; (b) 1.0101×10^{-3}; (c) 1.0101×10^2
1.12 (a) 2.56 M; (b) 0.67 T; (c) 1.03 m; (d) 79 p
1.13 (a) 1.414×10^2; (b) 2.857

Chapter 2

2.1 (a) 5798; (b) 1500; (c) 105; (d) 111; (e) 2396; (f) 1806.36; (g) 11.25; (h) 115.9375
2.2 (a) 1010010010100; (b) 10111.11; (c) 0.000000110011
2.3 (a) 1494; (b) 17.c; (c) 0.03
2.4 (a) 0.0001; (b) 0.111; (c) 0.101010...; (d) 0.10001
2.5 (a) 1735; (b) 3220; (c) 12001; (d) 1021112
2.6 (a) 3124; (b) 464; (c) 2022
2.7 1110 1111 1100
2.8 (a) 1011; (b) 100100; (c) 11110.01; (d) 111.1011; (e) 10010.101
2.9 (a) 11; (b) 1010; (c) 1111 (to 4 bits); (d) 10; (e) 1.11
2.10 (a) 10010; (b) 100011; (c) 11100.001; (d) 1.0001; (e) 11110100 (to 8 bits)
2.11 (a) 10; (b) 11; (c) 0.0011; (d) 110.1

Chapter 3

3.1 (a) 0.7574; (b) 1.8675; (c) 2.9587; (d) $\bar{1}.7574$ or -0.2426; (e) $\bar{3}.0899$ or -2.9101
3.2 (a) 6.1518; (b) 28.58; (c) 2 089 300; (d) 0.0575
3.3 (a) 1.744; (b) 4.3; (c) 6.8126; (d) $\bar{1}.4414$ or -0.5516; (e) $\bar{7}.2993$ or -6.7007
3.4 (a) 2.2034; (b) 10.591; (c) 0.194; (d) 330.3; (e) 0.3012
3.5 (a) 1.6132; (b) 0.1484; (c) 2.1383; (d) -1.5339 or $\bar{2}.4661$, (e) 0.7468

3.6 (a) 50.34 V; (b) 63.31 V; 80.47 s
3.7 (a) 0.069 s; (b) 0.19 s
3.8 (a) 38.06 dB; (b) 4.382 N
3.9 (a) 1.1133; (b) −1.161 or $\bar{2}.839$; (c) 0.6309

Chapter 4

4.1 (a) $17x + y$; (b) $18a$; (c) $-3x + 16b$
4.2 (a) $(x + y)^2$; (b) $(a - b)(a^2 + 3ab + b^2)$
4.3 (a) $(2/y) - (3/x) + 5$; (b) $y[x^2 + y^2(2 - w) + 4wx]/w$; (c) $a + 2b$
4.4 (a) HL/N; (b) $I\mu_O/(2\pi B)$; (c) $\surd(2\mu_O F/a)$; (d) $re^{L\pi/\mu}$; (e) $(3I_{R2} - I_R - a^2 I_Y)/a$; (f) $-\tau \ln(Ri/E)$; (g) $1/(Lw_O{}^2 - (1/C_1))$
4.5 (a) $2(x - 2.5)(x + 3)$; (b) $(2x + 6)(x - 1)$
4.6 $\dfrac{1}{2x + 6}\left[\dfrac{1}{x - 2.5} + \dfrac{1}{x + 1}\right]$
4.7 (a) $x = 1$ or -1; (b) $x = 3$ or -1.5; (c) $x = -2$
4.8 (a) −1.55 or −6.45; (b) −1.84 or −8.16; (c) −0.342 or −3.658
4.9 $10I^2 + 40I - 120 = 0$; 2 A or −6 A (the latter is not allowable because the power consumed is greater than 120 W!)
4.10 8 Ω and 12 Ω (the other possibility is 3 Ω and 17 Ω, which does not give the correct parallel resistance)

Chapter 5

5.1 $x = -0.357$; $y = 2.143$
5.2 $x = 1.992$; $y = -0.338$
5.3 The equations depend on the loops chosen, and the following are typical

$$-10 = 3I_1 - 2I_2$$
$$-10 = -2I_1 + 5I_2$$

Current in E_1 = 6.36 A; current in E_2 = 1.81 A; current in E_3 = 4.55 A; V_{40} = 106.4 V
5.4 95.9 V
5.5 $x = 1.1$; $y = -2$; $z = 3$
5.6 Current in E_1 = 3.36 A; Current in E_2 = 6.46 A; Current in E_3 = 9.82 A (charging)
5.7 $I_1 = 0.647$ A; $I_2 = 4.764$ A; $I_B = 5.411$ A

Chapter 6

6.1 (a) 0.7145; (b) 0.637; (c) −0.62; (d) −0.7738; (e) 0.509; (f) 0.4921; (g) −0.9763; (h) −0.9367; (i) −4.1022
6.2 (a) 60° or 120°; (b) 80° or −80°; (c) 10° or 190° or −170°; (d) −12° or 192° or −168°
6.3 (a) 20 ms, 50 Hz, 2.1 V; (b) 10.5 ms, 95.5 Hz, 2.71 A

6.4 (a) v_2 leads v_1 by $2\pi/3$ rad or 120°; (b) i_2 leads i_1 by 40°;
(c) v_2 lags v_1 by $3\pi/4$ rad or 135°; (d) v_1 lags i_1 by $\pi/3$ rad or 60°
6.5 203.6° or −156.4°; −0.9164; 0.4369
6.6 94.59° and 265.41°
6.7 (a) 0; (b) 0.2588

Chapter 7

7.1 (a) $a = 4.88$, $\angle B = 57.47°$, $\angle C = 62.53°$; (b) $\angle A = 71.6°$, $\angle B = 48.4°$, $a = 24.1$;
(c) $b = 5.59$, $c = 7.88$, $\angle C = 56°$; (d) $c = 40.92$, $\angle A = 65.3°$, $\angle B = 36.7°$;
(e) $b = 24.7$, $\angle A = 72.53°$, $\angle C = 47.47°$
7.2 (a) 0.866; (b) −0.342; (c) 0.5; (d) 0.94; (e) 1.732; (f) −0.364
7.4 (a) $10\sin(\omega t + 53.1°)$; (b) $7.21\sin(\omega t + 146.3°)$; (c) $51.6\sin(\omega t + 54.5°)$
7.5 0.39; 0.199
7.7 60°, 120°, 240°, 300°

Chapter 8

8.1 $3\sqrt{3}w$
8.2 8.84 rev/s
8.3 3.41 rev/s
8.4 79.54 m^2
8.5 2.6 cm^2
8.6 cylinder:sphere:cone = 3:2:1
8.7 (a) 1147 cm^2; (b) 2396 cm^3
8.8 60.67; 6.067
8.9 15.83 A
8.10 62.5 Hz; 104.25 A

Chapter 9

9.1 $y = 2x$
9.2 $y = x + 3$, 3; $y = x - 1$, −1
9.3 (a) $m = 0.2$, $c = 0.6$; (b) $m = 0.25$, $c = -1.75$
9.4 $N = 5$ V; (a) 6.67 rev/s; (b) 20.83 rev/s
9.5 $E = 10$ V; $R = 0.1\,\Omega$
9.6 $x = 9$, $y = 24$
9.7 (a) $x = 0.667$ or -2.5; (b) $x = 2$ or -0.6; (c) $x = -3$ or 8;
(d) $x = 2.59$ or -0.26
9.8 $x = -2.4$, $y = 6$ and $x = 6.3$, $y = 41$
9.10 $y = 6x - 2$; x values are 1.5 and 5, y values are −8, −2 and 16
9.11 100; 0.75
9.12 $k_1 = 0.1$; $k_2 = 0.005$
9.13 $C = 520$; $n = 1.4$
9.14 40 mA
9.15 (a) 7 s; (b) 10 s; (c) 30 s

Chapter 10

10.1 (a) horizontal force = −2.14 kN, vertical (downwards) force = 10.68 kN; (b) 10.89 kN at an angle of −101.3°
10.2 33.92 kN at −72.2°
10.3 $35.36 \sin 139.6t$; (a) 22.73 A; (b) 30.62 A; (c) −12.09 A; (d) −22.73 A
10.4 8.33 Hz; 0.12 s
10.5 $12.1 \sin(\omega t - 0.096\,\text{rad})$
10.6 109 V; 23.5°
10.7 $43.77 \sin(\omega t - 1.107\,\text{rad})$
10.8 $72.73 \sin(100\pi t + 9.9°)$
10.9 $13.33 \sin(\omega t + 36.9°)$; 7.07 A, 3.54 A, 5.66 A, 9.43 A
10.10 $150 \sin(\omega t - 60°)$ V

Chapter 11

11.2 (a) $10.63\angle -131.2°$; (b) $8.06\angle 29.74°$; (c) $8.06\angle -60.26°$; (d) $5\angle 143.1°$
11.3 (a) $-6.13 - j5.14$; (b) $-3 + j5.2$; (c) $0.623 - j2.93$; (d) $0.544 + j6.48$
11.4 (a) $5 + j13$, $13.92\angle 68.96°$; (b) $-0.05 + j10.95$, $10.95\angle 90.26°$; (c) $8.49 - j0.29$, $8.49\angle -1.98°$
11.5 (a) $-1 - j3$, $3.16\angle -108.4°$; (b) $-9.95 + j1.05$, $10\angle 174°$; (c) $17.5 + j15.3$, $23.23\angle 41.17°$
11.6 (a) $300\angle 65.84°$, $122.8 + j273.7$; (b) $29.57\angle -9.11°$, $29.2 - j4.68$; (c) $39.05\angle -76.67°$, $9 - j38$
11.7 (a) $0.333\angle -25.84°$, $0.3 - j0.15$; (b) $0.44\angle 121.7°$, $-0.23 + j0.374$; (c) $0.64\angle -177°$, $-0.639 - j0.03$
11.8 $2.75\angle -70.6°$ A, $0.92 - j2.6$ A
11.9 (a) $50\angle 45°$ V; (b) $14.142\angle -45°\,\Omega$; (c) $3.536\angle 90°$ A
11.10 (a) $15.22\angle 14.93°\,\Omega$; (b) $7.09\angle 30.07°$ A; (c) $\mathbf{V}_1 = 47.55\angle 93.5°$ V, $\mathbf{V}_2 = 28.36\angle 30.07°$ V, $\mathbf{V}_3 = 58.46\angle 16.03°$ V

Chapter 12

12.2 (a) 5; (b) $24t^3 + 3t^2$; (c) $8t - 3$; (d) $-2/x^3$
12.3 (a) $12x^2 - 6$; (b) $2.5/\sqrt{x}$; (c) $20m^3 + 12m - 3$; (d) $12.32x^{1.2} - 8x^{-2} - 2.5/\sqrt{x}$; (e) $1.44x^{1.4}$
12.4 Two stationary points; a minimum point occurs at $x = 2$, and a maximum occurs at $x = 3$
12.5 $x_1, y_1 = 2, 128$; (b) $x_2, y_2 = 6, 0$
12.6 The curve has a maximum at $x, y = 2.5, -0.75$; (a) gradient = 2, $y = -1.75$; (b) gradient = 0, $y = -0.75$; (c) gradient = −2, $y = -1.75$
12.7 0 or −1
12.8 (a) $4x \cos x + 4 \sin x$; (b) $2e^{-x} - e^{-x} \ln x^2$; (c) $\cos 2x$

Chapter 13

13.1 (a) $-2x^3 + x^2 - 3x + K$; (b) $2x^3 - \frac{1}{2}x^2 - 2x + K$; (c) $-1/(3x^3) + K$;
(d) $-(16/x) - 40 \ln x + 25x + K$; (e) $2x^{7/2}/7 + K$;
(f) $m^3x^4/4 + km^2x^3 + 3k^2mx^2/2 + k^3x + K$; (g) $e^{4x}/4 + K$;
(h) $e^x - e^{2x} + e^{3x}/3 + K$; (i) $3(x + [\sin 2x]/2) + K$

13.2 (a) 16; (b) $ab/2$; (c) 36; (d) 25.33; (e) $\pi + 2$

13.3 (a) $56\pi/3$; (b) 625π; (c) $416\pi/3$; (d) 14π; (e) $3\pi^2/2$

13.4 $V_{av} = 33.3$ V; $V_{eff} = 57.7$ V

13.5 2.89 V

13.6 $V_{av} = 31.8$ V; $V_{eff} = 50$ V

Chapter 14

14.1 23 s

14.2 (a) 6.93 s; (b) 10 s; (c) 29.9 s

14.3 73.5 ms

14.4 (a) 0.75 s; (b) 133.3 V/s; (c) 86.46 V; (d) 0.01 A; (e) 1.04 s

14.5 126.38 V

14.6 $0.135I_M$

14.7 38.8 A

14.8 (a) 400 A/s; (b) 147 A/s; (c) 10 A

14.9 (a) 1.04 kV; (b) 80 Ω

Chapter 15

15.1 (a) AND; (b) OR

15.2 A logic '1' appears for $A.\bar{B}.\bar{C}.\bar{D}$, $A.\bar{B}.\bar{C}.D$, $A.\bar{B}.C.\bar{D}$, $A.\bar{B}.C.D$, $A.B.\bar{C}.\bar{D}$, $A.B.\bar{C}.D$, $A.B.C.\bar{D}$ and $A.B.C.D$; the expression can be minimised to $f = A$

15.3 $f = A.\bar{B} + \bar{A}.B$

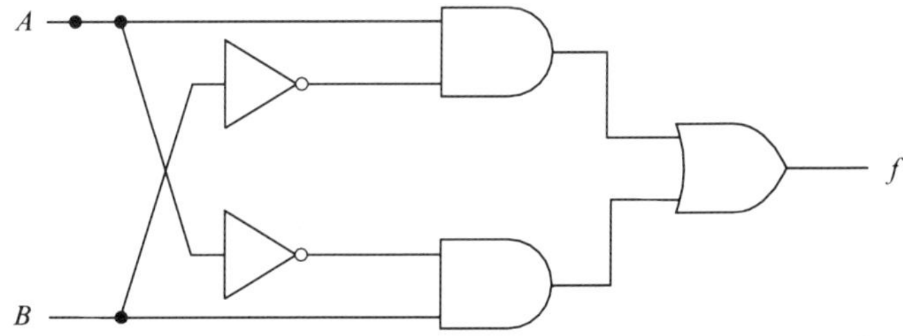

Solution to self-test question 15.3

15.10 Both $A.B$ and $B.C$

15.11 (b)

Chapter 16

16.1 Note: an 'ammeter' has been connected in series with the 8 Ω resistor (node 4 has been inserted)

```
V1    0    1    dc    5.5V
V2    3    0    dc    8V
R1    1    2    6ohm
R2    4    0    8ohm
R3    2    3    10ohm
Vam   2    4    0V
.OPTIONS NOPAGE
.END
```

−0.2979 V; 37.23 mA

16.2

```
Vs    1    0    PULSE(0V 10V 0S 1Ns 1Ns 1s 1.1s)
Vam   1    2    0V
R     2    3    1Kohm
C     3    0    1UF
.TRAN      1Ms  10Ms
.PRINT     TRAN  V(3)    I(Vam)
.OPTIONS NOPAGE
.END
```

6.316 V, 3.684 mA; 9.506 V, 0.494 mA

16.3

```
Vs    1    0    AC    100V
Vam   1    2    0V
R     2    3    10ohm
C     3    0    16UF
.AC   LIN  1    1KHz 1KHz
.PRINT     AC    VM(3)    VP(3)    VR(3)    VI(3)
.PRINT     AC    IM(Vam)  IP(Vam)
.OPTIONS NOPAGE
.END
```

$70.52\angle -45.15^\circ$ V $= 49.74 - j50$ V; $7.09\angle 44.85^\circ$ A.

Index